Applicable Mathematics
and
Mathematical Methods
Volume 2

Second Edition

A Pearson Custom Publication

Applicable Mathematics
and
Mathematical Methods
Volume 2

Second Edition

Dr Derek W. Arthur

PEARSON

Custom
Publishing

Pearson Education Limited
Edinburgh Gate
Harlow
Essex CM20 2JE

And associated companies throughout the world

Visit us on the World Wide Web at:
www.pearsoned.co.uk

First published 2006

This Custom Book Edition © University of Edinburgh 2007

ISBN 10   1 84658 625 9
ISBN 13   978 1 84658 625 5

Printed and bound in Great Britain by 4edge, Hockley, www.4edge.co.uk

Introduction

The content of this textbook is closely based on the lectures that have been delivered in the two courses *Applicable Mathematics 2* and *Mathematical Methods 2* at the *University of Edinburgh*, from 2002. These courses are taught in parallel, in alternate lectures. Although the two parts in this book are largely independent, there are points of contact between them.

A possible timetable is set out overleaf.

How the text is structured

This is similar to *Volume 1*, the *Introduction* to which provides more detail. Most of the text, printed in this font size, is aimed at presenting a coherent 'storyline' as succinctly as possible, backed up by a generous selection of examples. Each of these is numbered and presented with a full solution, terminated by a ■ character.

Three other elements are woven throughout the text.

> **Frame X.xx**   *Key formula*
> These boxes contain the most important and heavily used of the formulae in the text. They are individually numbered to aid cross-reference and are presented in this way so they are easily found.

The remaining two are asides from the main story, but often contain useful ideas. They are presented in this way to avoid interrupting the flow of the main story.

Notation
Such entries make comments about notation and nomenclature.

Think about it like this
Such entries draw parallels between mathematical results or methods, and ideas encountered in elementary science, or even everyday life.

How to use this book

Try to read through the pages devoted to each lecture, as shown in the table overleaf, *before* attending the lecture. Make a note of parts that you find difficult so that you can concentrate on those when they are covered. If you still have problems with them, this record will help when you seek further assistance. The text has generous margins to allow students to add notes or comments.

The worked examples show how the material can be put into practice. There are exercises for you to try on your own, many of which are similar in style to the examples. They are generally located at the end of the section in which the relevant material has been introduced. There are further exercises at the end of each chapter. The majority of these are examination questions set in previous sessions.

A valuable resource in any textbook is the **index**. The index in this volume has been constructed with an emphasis on the description of a method or the definition of a term. Minor references, which are likely to be a distraction, are generally not given. There are exceptions, where earlier references provide a reason for the inclusion of the item later in the text.

This **second edition** is largely identical to the first, except for the addition of exercises (and answers), as well as an interchange of order within Chapter 5 of *Mathematical Methods*.

D.W.A.

May 2006

Outline Lecture Programme

The table below gives a possible way in which the text in this book could be distributed across a timetable consisting of 43 lectures of 50 minutes each. Each part would occupy 21–22 lectures, as shown in the table. Some items, marked "Optional", may not be covered; they are included for reference.

Lecture	AM2 Sections	MM2 Sections
1	1.1–1.3	1.1–1.3
2	1.4–1.6	1.4–1.6
3	1.7–1.9	2.1
4	2.1–2.3	2.2–2.3
5	2.4–2.5	2.3–2.4
6	2.6–2.7	3.1–3.3
7	2.8–2.9	4.1–4.2
8	2.10–2.12	4.3
9	3.1–3.3	4.4
10	4.1–4.3	5.1–5.2
11	4.4–5.1	5.3–5.5
12	5.2–5.6	6.1–6.2
13	6.1–6.3	6.3–6.4
14	6.4–6.6	7.1–7.2
15	7.1–7.3	7.3–7.4
16	7.4–7.6	7.5
17	7.7–8.2	8.1–8.4
18	8.3–8.6	8.5–9.2
19	9.1–9.3	9.3–10.2
20	9.4–9.5	10.2–10.3
21	9.6–9.9	10.4
22	(None)	10.5–10.6

Contents

Applicable Mathematics

Mathematical Methods

The Greek Alphabet

Upper	Lower	Name	Upper	Lower	Name
A	α	alpha	N	ν	nu
B	β	beta	Ξ	ξ	xi
Γ	γ	gamma	O	o	omicron
Δ	δ	delta	Π	π	pi
E	ϵ	epsilon	R	ρ	rho
Z	ζ	zeta	Σ	σ	sigma
H	η	eta	T	τ	tau
Θ	θ	theta	Υ	υ	upsilon
I	ι	iota	Φ	ϕ	phi
K	κ	kappa	X	χ	chi
Λ	λ	lambda	Ψ	ψ	psi
M	μ	mu	Ω	ω	omega

Notes

APPLICABLE

MATHEMATICS

2

1 POWER SERIES

For **arithmetic** and **geometric series**, there are expressions for the sum of any specified number of terms. But, in the geometric case, we can also find the **sum to infinity**, under certain circumstances. It is this aspect that we now pursue, since forming an infinite sum can deliver functions of a quite different type from those that are being added up.

We shall concentrate on infinite series that can be built up using **powers** x^k, which means that their **partial sums** are **polynomials**. The advantages are that polynomials

- are easy to evaluate;

- have simple calculus rules;

- are easy to graph;

- are well-behaved.

Such series are called **power series**, since they are generated by 'powers' x^k. The key applications of these involve 'truncating' the series after some point, thereby obtaining a polynomial. If the series is well-behaved, this will deliver a good *approximation* to its overall sum, in the form of a very convenient function.

Although dealing with sums of terms is normally in the domain of *Algebra*, the ideas of limits and convergence required for an infinite sum properly belong to *Analysis*, a subject closely related to *Calculus*. Indeed, we shall find calculus a helpful tool in this chapter.

1.1 Introduction

A **power series** is an infinite sum of the following form.

Frame 1.1   *Definition of a power series*

$$S(x) = a_0 + a_1 x + a_2 x^2 + \cdots + a_k x^k + \cdots$$

$$= \sum_{r=0}^{\infty} a_k x^k$$

The **constant** a_k is the kth **coefficient**, irrespective of whether we start counting at 0 or 1. The nth **partial sum**

$$S_n(x) = a_0 + a_1 x + a_2 x^2 + \cdots + a_n x^n \tag{1.1}$$

is seen to be a **polynomial**.

It is our hope that, at least for some values of x, $S_n(x)$ approaches a well-defined value (or **limit**) $S(x)$ as $n \to \infty$. Then the series is **convergent** and $S(x)$ is the **sum to infinity**. When this does not occur, the series is **divergent**.

1.2   Geometric and Binomial Series

Before embarking on a general approach to constructing power series, there are two particularly important cases available from basic algebra.

It is a basic result that the sum of a (finite) **geometric series** is

$$S_n(x) = 1 + x + x^2 + \cdots + x^n = \frac{1 - x^{n+1}}{1 - x}.$$

If we let $n \to \infty$ and assume that $|x| < 1$, then $x^{n+1} \to 0$ and hence $S_n(x) \to S(x) = \dfrac{1}{1 - x}$.

Frame 1.2   *Geometric series, common ratio x*

$$1 + x + x^2 + \cdots + x^k + \cdots = \frac{1}{1 - x} \qquad (|x| < 1) \qquad (1.2)$$

Think about it like this

The most striking thing about this result is that the series is constructed using multiplication and addition, while the sum involves the different operation of division. Thus, (1.2) could be used by a calculating machine that is unable to divide, in order to 'perform' the division $\frac{1}{1-x}$. This would give only an approximate answer since we cannot carry out the infinite number of calculations implied by the left-hand side of (1.2).

This reveals the key use: a complicated function can be expressed as a sum of simple functions, a truncated version of which can deliver good approximations.

Example 1.1   Consider the case $x = 0.1$. The sum to infinity is

$$\frac{1}{1 - 0.1} = \frac{10}{9} = 1.11111\,11111\,\ldots.$$

The partial sums are

$$S_0 = 1, \quad S_1 = 1 + 0.1 = 1.1, \quad S_2 = 1 + 0.1 + 0.1^2 = 1.11,$$
$$S_3 = 1.111, \quad S_4 = 1.1111, \quad \text{etc.}$$

This shows very clearly the effect of truncating the series: the values we find are reasonably near the sum to infinity and the more terms we take, the closer we get.   ■

The second case appears, at first, to be merely the **Binomial Theorem**.

Frame 1.3   *Binomial series*

$$(1+x)^n = 1 + \binom{n}{1}x + \binom{n}{2}x^2 + \cdots + \binom{n}{k}x^k + \cdots \qquad (|x| < 1),$$

$$\tag{1.3}$$

$$\binom{n}{k} = \frac{n(n-1)\cdots(n-k+1)}{k!} \tag{1.4}$$

When n is a positive whole number this is indeed the Binomial Theorem, with no restriction on x and a *finite* number of terms on the right of (1.3). The result, however, remains true as an *infinite* (power) series for all other values of n, provided $|x| < 1$, which is why it is called the **binomial series**.

Evaluation of the **binomial coefficients** $\binom{n}{r}$, for such n, requires the form in (1.4). The alternative, using three factorials, cannot be used since we have no method of evaluating $\frac{1}{2}!$ or $(-1)!$, for example.

Example 1.2   Consider the case $n = -1$:

$$\binom{n}{1} = n = -1, \qquad \binom{n}{2} = \frac{n(n-1)}{2!} = \frac{(-1)\times(-2)}{2} = 1,$$

$$\binom{n}{3} = \frac{n(n-1)(n-2)}{3!} = \frac{(-1)\times(-2)\times(-3)}{6} = -1,$$

which suggests a pattern: $\binom{n}{k} = (-1)^k$, leading to

$$(1+x)^{-1} = \frac{1}{1+x} = 1 - x + x^2 - x^3 + \cdots.$$

This is precisely the geometric series from Frame 1.2, with x replaced by $-x$, since $(-x)^k = (-1)^k x^k$. This lends credibility to the calculation, and shows the result to be valid for $|x| < 1$. ∎

Example 1.3   Consider the case $n = \frac{1}{2}$:

$$\binom{n}{1} = n = \frac{1}{2}, \qquad \binom{n}{2} = \frac{n(n-1)}{2!} = \frac{\frac{1}{2}\times(-\frac{1}{2})}{2} = -\frac{1}{8},$$

$$\binom{n}{3} = \frac{n(n-1)(n-2)}{3!} = \frac{\frac{1}{2}\times(-\frac{1}{2})\times(-\frac{3}{2})}{6} = \frac{1}{16}, \quad \text{etc.,}$$

which gives

$$(1+x)^{1/2} = \sqrt{1+x} = 1 + \frac{1}{2}x - \frac{1}{8}x^2 + \frac{1}{16}x^3 - \cdots.$$

Note the unusual signs at the start: $+\ +\ -\ +\ -\ +\ \cdots$, with alternation eventually setting in. This is never the case in the standard Binomial Theorem, where signs are either all positive or alternate from the start. ∎

The change from x to $-x$ noted in Example 1.2 is an illustration of the very powerful **substitution** technique. This allows us to extend a small set of 'standard' power series, such as may be found in a textbook or reference source, to more complicated situations where direct calculation by the general method in §1.5, would be prohibitively time-consuming.

Example 1.4 Substitute x^4 and $(-0.1x)$ for x in the geometric series (1.2):

$$\frac{1}{1-x^4} = 1 + x^4 + (x^4)^2 + (x^4)^3 + \cdots$$
$$= 1 + x^4 + x^8 + x^{12} + \cdots,$$
$$\frac{1}{10+x} = \frac{1}{10}\left[\frac{1}{1+0.1x}\right]$$
$$= \frac{1}{10}\left[1 + (-0.1x) + (-0.1x)^2 + (-0.1x)^3 + \cdots\right]$$
$$= \frac{1}{10}\left[1 - 0.1x + 0.01x^2 - 0.001x^3 + \cdots\right].$$

Note how, in the second case, we had to manipulate the given function to achieve the "$1 + \cdots$" form used in the standard result (1.2). ∎

A final example of the binomial series has a direct application, interpreting a well-known formula in Physics.

Example 1.5 Consider the case $n = -\frac{1}{2}$:

$$\binom{n}{1} = n = -\frac{1}{2}, \qquad \binom{n}{2} = \frac{n(n-1)}{2!} = \frac{-\frac{1}{2} \times (-\frac{3}{2})}{2} = \frac{3}{8},$$
$$\binom{n}{3} = \frac{n(n-1)(n-2)}{3!} = \frac{-\frac{1}{2} \times (-\frac{3}{2}) \times (-\frac{5}{2})}{6} = -\frac{5}{16}, \quad \text{etc.,}$$

which gives

$$(1+x)^{-1/2} = \frac{1}{\sqrt{1+x}} = 1 - \frac{1}{2}x + \frac{3}{8}x^2 - \frac{5}{16}x^3 + \cdots.$$

Now substitute $-v^2/c^2$ for x:

$$\frac{1}{\sqrt{1-\frac{v^2}{c^2}}} = 1 + \frac{1}{2}\frac{v^2}{c^2} + \frac{3}{8}\frac{v^4}{c^4} + \cdots,$$

and apply the result to Einstein's famous formula

$$E = mc^2 = \frac{m_0 c^2}{\sqrt{1-\frac{v^2}{c^2}}}$$
$$= m_0 c^2 + \frac{1}{2}m_0 v^2 + \frac{3}{8}m_0\frac{v^4}{c^2} + \cdots.$$

This shows the energy of a moving body to be its rest energy $m_0 c^2$, plus the well-known Newtonian kinetic energy ($\frac{1}{2}m_0 v^2$), with the **principal correction term** $\frac{3}{8}m_0 v^4/c^2$. This last quantity allows us to estimate the size of the error in using Newtonian calculations for a fast-moving body. ∎

Ex 1.1

(a) Sum the geometric series: $1 - \frac{1}{2}x + \frac{1}{4}x^2 - \frac{1}{8}x^3 + \frac{1}{16}x^4 - \cdots$.

(b) Use the binomial series

$$(1 + x)^{1/2} = 1 + \frac{1}{2}x - \frac{1}{8}x^2 + \frac{1}{16}x^3 - \cdots$$

to find the start of the power series for $\sqrt{1 - 2y^3}$.

Ex 1.2 Find the value of r such that

$$(1 + x)^r = 1 + \frac{1}{3}x - \frac{1}{9}x^2 + \frac{5}{81}x^3 - \frac{10}{243}x^4 + \cdots, \qquad |x| < 1.$$

Find the coefficient of x^5.

Ex 1.3 Consider the series $S(x) = 1 + 2x + 3x^2 + 4x^3 + \cdots$, which converges for $|x| < 1$.

(a) Find $S(x) - xS(x)$ and hence find a formula for $S(x)$. Note that the result agrees with the binomial series, with $n = -2$.

(b) Use the result above, with $x = 1 - T$, to calculate the following, which occurs in an analysis of α-particle decay: $\displaystyle\sum_{k=1}^{\infty} kT(1 - T)^{k-1}$.

1.3 Radius of Convergence

Both the standard series in the previous section require $|x| < 1$, equivalent to $-1 < x < 1$, for convergence. This is a general type of condition, shared by all power series:

$$S_n(x) \to S(x) \text{ as } n \to \infty \quad \text{if} \quad -R < x < R, \tag{1.5}$$

where R is the **radius of convergence**. Also, $-R < x < R$ is the **interval of convergence**.

There are some points to note about this result.

- The series will definitely **diverge** for all $|x| > R$.

- The situation at $x = R$ and $x = -R$ is unpredictable: the series may converge or diverge at either. We shall ignore this fine detail, since one should never apply a power series at the limit of convergence, if only because the rate of convergence is very slow near there.

- R can be ∞ (or even zero).

- Although we shall not make use of it, this topic extends to *complex x*, where it is standard to use z. The condition $|z| < R$ then defines a *disc* in the Argand Diagram, which explains the use of the word *radius*.

Think about it like this

> Clearly, it is entirely invalid to use a power series outside its interval of convergence. But the series will converge very slowly inside that interval and close to its boundary. Hence there would be little point in using the geometric series for $x = 0.9$, say, let alone worrying about the cases $x = 1$ and $x = -1$. In fact, in both cases, the geometric series diverges. You should always bear in mind that there are limits on permissible x and, *in theoretical calculations*, care is needed not to exceed them else the final result may be invalid.

There are methods for finding R, if we know a formula for a_k, but there is none guaranteed always to work. It is easier to use the following 'Rule'.

> R is the distance from the point $x = 0$ to the nearest point (*in the Argand Diagram*) at which $S(x)$ 'misbehaves'.

Example 1.6   The following explain some of the values of R seen earlier.

$$\frac{1}{1-x} \quad \text{is undefined at } x = 1 \quad : \ R = 1,$$

$$\sqrt{1+x} \ \text{ is undefined for } x < -1 \ : \ R = 1,$$

$$\frac{1}{1+x^2} \quad \text{is undefined at } x = \pm i \quad : \ R = 1.$$

In the second case the *derivative* $\frac{1}{2}(1+x)^{-1/2}$ is undefined at $x = -1$, which also makes $x = -1$ a 'bad' point.

Note the need to look for complex number behaviour in the last case, in spite of the function and all its derivatives being well-behaved on the whole of the real line. This result will be confirmed in the next example.   ■

When using the powerful substitution method described in the previous section, one must also substitute for the radius of convergence.

Example 1.7   We can obtain the series for the last function in the previous example by substituting $-x^2$ for x in the geometric series:

$$\frac{1}{1+x^2} = \frac{1}{1-(-x^2)} = 1 + (-x^2) + (-x^2)^2 + (-x^2)^3 + \cdots$$
$$= 1 - x^2 + x^4 - x^6 + \cdots .$$

But we also need to make that substitution in the condition $|x| < 1$ to obtain $|-x^2| < 1$, i.e., $0 \leqslant x^2 < 1$, which also gives $|x| < 1$. This confirms the claim made in Example 1.6.   ■

Example 1.8   In Example 1.4 we substituted $-0.1x$ in the geometric series to find a series for $1/(10+x)$. This requires

$$|-0.1x| < 1 \quad \Rightarrow \quad |0.1x| < 1 \quad \Rightarrow \quad |x| < 10,$$

so the radius of convergence is $R = 10$.   ■

Example 1.9 In Example 1.5 we substituted $-v^2/c^2$ in the binomial series. This requires

$$\left|-\frac{v^2}{c^2}\right| < 1 \quad \Rightarrow \quad |v^2| < |c^2| \quad \Rightarrow \quad |v| < c,$$

which is physically sensible, noting the well-known feature of Einstein's special theory of relativity: objects cannot be accelerated to travel faster than the speed of light. ■

Convergence is likely to be slow near $x = \pm R$ and, conversely, very fast when x is near 0. In modelling physical phenomena, however, it is often useful to know the behaviour of a quantity for *large* values of $|x|$, e.g., how does the magnetic field behave as we move further from a magnet?

Such questions can be answered by seeking a power series using *negative powers*, which is equivalent to a series in $1/x$ rather than x:

$$T(x) = a_0 + a_1 x^{-1} + a_2 x^{-2} + \cdots = a_0 + \frac{a_1}{x} + \frac{a_2}{x^2} + \cdots .$$

The argument is that if $|x|$ is large, i.e., it is close to ∞, then $1/x$ is small and so the series may converge quickly.

Again, we can develop such series using **substitution**; the range of x values guaranteeing convergence can be found at the same time, now in the form $|x| > R$.

Example 1.10 Expand $1/(x-1)$ in powers of $1/x$, i.e., for large $|x|$.

Use the geometric series (1.2):

$$\frac{1}{x-1} = \frac{1}{x}\left[\frac{1}{1-\frac{1}{x}}\right]$$

$$= \frac{1}{x}\left[1 + \frac{1}{x} + \left(\frac{1}{x}\right)^2 + \cdots\right]$$

$$= \frac{1}{x} + \frac{1}{x^2} + \frac{1}{x^3} + \cdots .$$

For convergence, we require $\left|\frac{1}{x}\right| < 1$, i.e., $|x| > 1$. ■

For a further example, see Example 1.12, in the next section.

Ex 1.4 What is the radius of convergence for the series in Exercise 1.1?

Ex 1.5 A power series for $\sqrt[3]{1 + y^2/2}$ can be found by substitution in the binomial series for $(1+x)^r$. What is the radius of convergence of the result?

Ex 1.6 Use the geometric series to find series for the functions below, after making appropriate rearrangements. In each case find the range of x values giving convergence.

$$(\text{Using } x^n): \quad \frac{1}{1+2x^2}, \quad \frac{1}{x-4}; \quad (\text{using } x^{-n}): \quad \frac{1}{x^2-x}, \quad \frac{1}{2+x}.$$

1.4 Calculus for Power Series

It is permissible to differentiate and integrate power series, on one condition: the calculations are valid only within the interval of convergence. This is a useful technique and easy to apply, since the power series resembles a polynomial, the easiest of all functions on which to perform calculus.

The general results are as follows.

Frame 1.4   *Calculus for power series*

$$S(x) = a_0 + a_1 x + a_2 x^2 + a_3 x^3 + \cdots$$
$$S'(x) = a_1 + 2a_2 x + 3a_3 x^2 + \cdots \qquad (1.6)$$

$$\int S(x)\, dx = C + a_0 x + \tfrac{1}{2}a_1 x^2 + \tfrac{1}{3}a_2 x^3 + \tfrac{1}{4}a_3 x^4 + \cdots \qquad (1.7)$$

Example 1.11   Differentiate the geometric series (1.2):

$$\frac{d}{dx}\left[\frac{1}{1-x}\right] = -\frac{1}{(1-x)^2} \times (-1) = \frac{1}{(1-x)^2}$$
$$= \frac{d}{dx}\left[1 + x + x^2 + x^3 + x^4 + \cdots\right] = 1 + 2x + 3x^2 + 4x^3 + \cdots.$$

This should also be the binomial series for $(1-x)^{-2}$. Set $n = -2$ and replace x by $-x$ in (1.3). We require:

$$\binom{-2}{1} = -2, \quad \binom{-2}{2} = \frac{-2(-3)}{2} = 3, \quad \binom{-2}{3} = \frac{-2(-3)(-4)}{6} = -4,$$

and so on, with an obvious pattern: $\binom{-2}{k} = (-1)^k (k+1)$.

This delivers the series:

$$(1-x)^{-2} = 1 - 2(-x) + 3(-x)^2 - 4(-x)^3 + \cdots$$
$$= 1 + 2x + 3x^2 + 4x^3 + \cdots$$

as before.

The calculus condition requires $|x| < 1$, which agrees with what we know from the general binomial series, and from the observation that the function misbehaves at $x = 1$. ∎

> *Think about it like this*
>
> As can be seen in this example, the calculus involved in the power series part is very straightforward. The right-hand sides are little more than polynomials in standard form, except that they don't have a final highest degree term. The calculations can be done simply by treating them as such.

We can extend the result in Example 1.11, to find another version that will prove useful in §1.9.

Example 1.12   Expand $(a + x)^{-2}$ in powers of x^{-1}, assuming $a > 0$.

Use the series found in Example 1.11, substituting $-\frac{a}{x}$ for x:

$$\frac{1}{(a+x)^2} = \frac{1}{x^2} \frac{1}{\left(1 + \frac{a}{x}\right)^2}$$

$$= \frac{1}{x^2}\left[1 - 2\frac{a}{x} + 3\left(\frac{a}{x}\right)^2 - \cdots\right]$$

$$= \frac{1}{x^2} - \frac{2a}{x^3} + \frac{3a^2}{x^4} - \cdots,$$

provided $\left|\frac{a}{x}\right| < 1$, i.e., $|x| > a$.

We shall use this series later, to derive a result in electromagnetism. ∎

Example 1.13   Integrate the geometric series (with $-x$ in place of x).

$$\ln(1+x) = \int \frac{dx}{1+x}$$

$$= \int \left[1 - x + x^2 - \cdots\right] dx = C + x - \frac{1}{2}x^2 + \frac{1}{3}x^3 - \cdots.$$

Set $x = 0$: $\ln 1 = C + 0 - 0 + 0 - \cdots \Rightarrow C = 0$. This gives

$$\ln(1+x) = x - \frac{1}{2}x^2 + \frac{1}{3}x^3 - \cdots + \frac{(-1)^{k+1}}{k}x^k + \cdots, \qquad (1.8)$$

which is the **logarithmic series**. It has radius of convergence 1. (Note that $\ln(1 + x)$ is undefined at $x = -1$, at distance 1 from $x = 0$.)

This series allows approximate calculation of logarithms within the interval of convergence, using simple arithmetic. Convergence is slow, however, except for very small x. ∎

Ex 1.7   Use the substitution $-x^2$ in place of x in the geometric series, to find a series for $\dfrac{1}{1 + x^2}$.

By integrating the result, find a series for $\tan^{-1} x$.

Using $x = 1$, find a series for $\pi/4$.

Ex 1.8   Recall that

$$(1+x)^{-1/2} = 1 - \frac{1}{2}x + \frac{3}{8}x^2 - \frac{5}{16}x^3 + \cdots, \qquad |x| < 1.$$

Hence find the start of a series for $1/\sqrt{1 - x^2}$, and integrate to find that for $\sin^{-1} x$.

What is the radius of convergence of the latter series? How does this relate to the properties of $\sin^{-1} x$?

1.5 Maclaurin Series

The differentiation used in the previous section, applied to a *general* function, provides a guaranteed method for finding a power series for any such function, subject to one condition: it must be **infinitely differentiable** at the origin, i.e., $f^{(n)}(0)$ must exist for all n. By this, we mean that the values are properly defined, avoiding the sort of 'infinite' value that occurs for derivatives of $f(x) = \sqrt{x}$; it does not require that we are able to calculate all the values.

Suppose, then, that we seek the coefficients in

$$f(x) = a_0 + a_1 x + a_2 x^2 + a_3 x^3 + \cdots \qquad (|x| < R). \qquad (1.9)$$

Let $x = 0$, which gives $f(0) = a_0$. Hence we immediately determine one coefficient. Now, differentiate (1.9):

$$f'(x) = a_1 + 2a_2 x + 3a_3 x^2 + \cdots,$$

and so (setting $x = 0$) $f'(0) = a_1$, providing the next one. Repeat this:

$$f''(x) = 2a_2 + 6a_3 x + \cdots,$$

and so (setting $x = 0$) $f''(0) = 2a_2$, providing the next one. This method can continue for ever, relating a_k and $f^{(k)}(0)$, the only strange feature being the numbers 2, 6, 24, etc., which are clearly factorials. (This is confirmed by examining the way they build up.)

Hence we conclude that

$$f^{(k)}(0) = k! a_k \quad \Rightarrow \quad a_k = \frac{1}{k!} f^{(k)}(0), \qquad (1.10)$$

which allows us to construct the **Maclaurin series**.

Frame 1.5   *The Maclaurin series for function $f(x)$*

$$f(x) = f(0) + f'(0)x + \frac{1}{2!} f''(0)x^2 + \frac{1}{3!} f'''(0)x^3 + \cdots \qquad (1.11)$$

Notation

The coefficients for the first two terms could also include $\frac{1}{0!}$ and $\frac{1}{1!}$, to maintain the pattern, but these are both 1 and needlessly complicate the result.

The one thing this method does not do is deliver a value for the radius of convergence. There are various methods for finding this, but the easiest is simply to look for the nearest 'bad' value of x, as recommended in §1.3.

Think about it like this

The Maclaurin series may appear intimidating, but its structure is actually quite straightforward. Simply differentiate the given function several times, set $x = 0$ in these derivatives and feed the numbers into the template in (1.11): $f^{(k)}(0)$ is the coefficient of $x^k/k!$. The only really hard part is carrying out the differentiations, which can quickly become very complicated.

Example 1.14 Find the Maclaurin series for $1/(1-x)$.

$$f(x) = \frac{1}{1-x} \qquad\qquad f(0) = 1,$$

$$f'(x) = -\frac{1}{(1-x)^2} \times (-1) \qquad\qquad f'(0) = 1,$$

$$f''(x) = \frac{2}{(1-x)^3} \qquad\qquad f''(0) = 2,$$

and so on, building up

$$f(x) = 1 + x + \frac{2}{2!}x^2 + \frac{6}{3!}x^3 + \cdots$$

$$= 1 + x + x^2 + x^3 + \cdots .$$

This is the **geometric series** (1.2), which is no surprise, since a function has just one power series (if it has one at all).

As noted before, the nearest 'bad' point to $x = 0$ is $x = 1$, so $R = 1$. ■

Think about it like this

There is no fundamental difference between a 'special' series, such as the geometric series, and the Maclaurin series for its sum function. If a function has a power series, it is unique, in the sense that the coefficient of each x^n is unique and is determined solely by the properties of the function. **Hence, a given function has only one power series.** The name *Maclaurin series* tends to be used merely to signal that it has been constructed using its derivatives. Alternative constructions, if they can be found, are often much easier to carry out. It is easier to find a series for $\frac{1}{1-x}$ using the geometric series than by differentiation, although the same answer is found.

Example 1.15 Find the Maclaurin series for $(1+x)^{-1/2}$.

$$f(x) = (1+x)^{-1/2} \qquad\qquad f(0) = 1,$$

$$f'(x) = -\tfrac{1}{2}(1+x)^{-3/2} \qquad\qquad f'(0) = -\tfrac{1}{2},$$

$$f''(x) = -\tfrac{1}{2}\left(-\tfrac{3}{2}\right)(1+x)^{-5/2} \qquad\qquad f''(0) = \tfrac{3}{4},$$

$$f'''(x) = -\tfrac{1}{2}\left(-\tfrac{3}{2}\right)\left(-\tfrac{5}{2}\right)(1+x)^{-7/2} \qquad\qquad f'''(0) = -\tfrac{15}{8},$$

and so on, building up

$$f(x) = 1 - \frac{1}{2}x + \frac{1}{2!}\cdot\frac{3}{4}x^2 - \frac{1}{3!}\cdot\frac{15}{8}x^3 + \cdots$$

$$= 1 - \frac{1}{2}x + \frac{3}{8}x^2 - \frac{5}{16}x^3 + \cdots ,$$

as we found using the **binomial series** in Example 1.5.

Again, the radius of convergence is 1, the distance from 0 to -1. ■

Ex 1.9 Calculate the first four terms of the Maclaurin series for $(1+x)^{7/2}$.

1.6   Exponential and Trigonometric Series

The Maclaurin series, as set out in Frame 1.5, enables us to derive three key series, those for e^x, $\cos x$ and $\sin x$.

1.6.1   The Exponential Series

$$f(x) = e^x, \qquad f'(x) = e^x, \qquad f''(x) = e^x, \qquad \text{etc.,}$$
$$f(0) = 1, \qquad f'(0) = 1, \qquad f''(0) = 1, \qquad \text{etc.,}$$

which values produce the **exponential series**.

Frame 1.6   *The exponential series*

$$e^x = 1 + x + \frac{1}{2!}x^2 + \frac{1}{3!}x^3 + \cdots + \frac{1}{k!}x^k + \cdots \qquad (1.12)$$

1.6.2   The Cosine Series

$$f(x) = \cos x, \qquad f'(x) = -\sin x, \qquad f''(x) = -\cos x, \qquad \text{etc.,}$$
$$f(0) = 1, \qquad f'(0) = 0, \qquad f''(0) = -1, \qquad \text{etc.,}$$

building up the following sequence, generated by repeating four terms:

$$\boxed{1,\ 0,\ -1,\ 0,}\ 1,\ 0,\ -1,\ 0,\ \ldots.$$

These values produce the **cosine series**.

Frame 1.7   *The cosine series*

$$\cos x = 1 - \frac{1}{2!}x^2 + \frac{1}{4!}x^4 - \cdots + \frac{(-1)^k}{(2k)!}x^{2k} + \cdots \qquad (1.13)$$

1.6.3   The Sine Series

$$f(x) = \sin x, \qquad f'(x) = \cos x, \qquad f''(x) = -\sin x, \qquad \text{etc.,}$$
$$f(0) = 0, \qquad f'(0) = 1, \qquad f''(0) = 0, \qquad \text{etc.,}$$

building up the following sequence, generated by repeating four terms:

$$\boxed{0,\ 1,\ 0,\ -1,}\ 0,\ 1,\ 0,\ -1,\ \ldots.$$

These values produce the **sine series**.

Frame 1.8   *The sine series*

$$\sin x = x - \frac{1}{3!}x^3 + \frac{1}{5!}x^5 - \cdots + \frac{(-1)^k}{(2k+1)!}x^{2k+1} + \cdots \qquad (1.14)$$

There are several points to note about these series.

1. Each of these three functions has no 'bad' points; they and their derivatives are defined with finite values everywhere. The series therefore converge for all values of x, i.e., $R = \infty$. (They do not, however, deliver *speedy* convergence for large $|x|$ values.)

2. The cosine series is built up using **even** powers of x, which reflects the fact that $\cos x$ is an even function. Similarly, the sine series is built up using **odd** powers.

3. Substitution, as always, is a powerful tool for extending these series. For example, changing x to $-x$, x^2 and $2x$, respectively, produces

$$e^{-x} = 1 - x + \frac{1}{2!}x^2 - \frac{1}{3!}x^3 + \cdots,$$

$$e^{x^2} = 1 + x^2 + \frac{1}{2!}x^4 + \frac{1}{3!}x^6 + \cdots,$$

$$\cos 2x = 1 - \frac{2^2}{2!}x^2 + \frac{2^4}{4!}x^4 - \cdots,$$

more quickly than using derivatives, especially in the second example.

4. These series continue to make sense when x is a **complex** number. In particular, recalling that $i^2 = -1$, $i^3 = -i$, $i^4 = 1$, etc.:

$$e^{ix} = 1 + ix + \frac{i^2}{2!}x^2 + \frac{i^3}{3!}x^3 + \frac{i^4}{4!}x^4 + \cdots$$

$$= \left[1 - \frac{x^2}{2!} + \frac{x^4}{4!} - \cdots \right] + i\left[x - \frac{x^3}{3!} + \frac{x^5}{5!} - \cdots \right]$$

$$= \cos x + i \sin x,$$

the well-known **Euler formula**.

Ex 1.10 Write down the first three non-zero terms of the Maclaurin series for:

$$\sin 3x, \quad e^{-x/2}, \quad \cos \pi x.$$

1.7 Algebra of Power Series

Hitherto we have been adding and subtracting power series without comment. This is indeed permitted, provided we remain within the radius of convergence of *both* series.

This permission extends to multiplication of series, which proves to be particularly powerful. The mechanism is straightforward: multiply the series as if they are polynomials, i.e., temporarily ignore the "$+\cdots$". It is strongly recommended that the calculation is performed systematically. The following is one method:

> To find $P(x)Q(x)$, multiply all of $Q(x)$ by each term in $P(x)$, using a separate row in each case, offset to align equal powers.

Example 1.16 Find the power series for $e^{-x}/(1+x)$. Thus would be a difficult task by a direct differentiation method, requiring ever more complicated applications of the quotient rule. Instead, multiply the well-known series for e^{-x} (exponential) and $1/(1+x)$ (geometric).

$$
\begin{aligned}
\frac{e^{-x}}{1+x} &= \left[1 - x + x^2 - x^3 + \cdots\right]\left[1 - x + \tfrac{1}{2}x^2 - \tfrac{1}{6}x^3 + \cdots\right] \\
&= 1 - x + \tfrac{1}{2}x^2 - \tfrac{1}{6}x^3 + \cdots && \left[\times 1\right] \\
&\quad - x + x^2 - \tfrac{1}{2}x^3 + \cdots && \left[\times(-x)\right] \\
&\quad\quad + x^2 - x^3 + \cdots && \left[\times x^2\right] \\
&\quad\quad\quad - x^3 + \cdots && \left[\times(-x^3)\right] \\
&= 1 - 2x + \tfrac{5}{2}x^2 - \tfrac{8}{3}x^3 + \cdots && \left[\text{ADD}\right]
\end{aligned}
$$

■

Example 1.17 Find the power series for $e^x \cos x$. This is better done in the order $\cos x\, e^x$. Multiply the exponential series by the first three terms of the cosine series:

$$
\begin{aligned}
\cos x\, e^x &= \left[1 - \tfrac{1}{2}x^2 + \tfrac{1}{24}x^4 - \cdots\right]\left[1 + x + \tfrac{1}{2}x^2 + \tfrac{1}{6}x^3 + \tfrac{1}{24}x^4 + \cdots\right] \\
&= 1 + x + \tfrac{1}{2}x^2 + \tfrac{1}{6}x^3 + \tfrac{1}{24}x^4 + \cdots \\
&\quad\quad - \tfrac{1}{2}x^2 - \tfrac{1}{2}x^3 - \tfrac{1}{4}x^4 - \cdots \\
&\quad\quad\quad\quad + \tfrac{1}{24}x^4 + \cdots \\
&= 1 + x \quad\quad\quad - \tfrac{1}{3}x^3 - \tfrac{1}{6}x^4 + \cdots
\end{aligned}
$$

This series can also be found, as a Maclaurin series, by differentiation, then using trigonometry to reveal a pattern:

$$
\begin{aligned}
f(x) &= e^x \cos x \\
f'(x) &= -e^x \sin x + e^x \cos x = \sqrt{2}e^x \cos\left(x + \tfrac{\pi}{4}\right) \\
f''(x) &= -2e^x \sin x = 2e^x \cos\left(x + \tfrac{\pi}{2}\right)
\end{aligned}
$$

and so on. Each differentiation multiplies the previous answer by $\sqrt{2}$ and adds $\frac{\pi}{4}$ to the angle. Hence

$$f^{(n)}(x) = \left(\sqrt{2}\right)^n e^x \cos\left(x + \frac{n\pi}{4}\right),$$

which produces the values

$$f(0) = 1, \quad f'(0) = 1, \quad f''(0) = 0, \quad f'''(0) = -2, \quad f^{iv}(0) = -4,$$

and leads to the same series.

There is also a method based on complex numbers, writing $\cos x$ as $\mathrm{Re}\left(e^{ix}\right)$ and using de Moivre's Theorem. The details of those calculations have strong similarities to the trigonometry used above. ∎

Ex 1.11 An important function in electronics is $\mathrm{sinc}(t) = \dfrac{\sin t}{t}$.

Write down a Maclaurin series for this function. Suggest a value for $\mathrm{sinc}(0)$.

Ex 1.12

(a) Find a series for $\sin x \cos x$, noting its link to $\sin 2x$.

(b) Division of power series must be performed by indirect means. Find c_1 and c_3 such that

$$x - \frac{1}{6}x^3 + \cdots = \left[1 - \frac{1}{2}x^2 + \cdots\right]\left[c_1 x + c_3 x^3 + \cdots\right].$$

This represents $\sin x = \cos x \tan x$, so these are the first two coefficients for $\tan x$.

What do you expect the radius of convergence to be?

(c) Compose $\ln(1+x) = x - \frac{1}{2}x^2 + \frac{1}{3}x^3 - \cdots$ and $\sin x = x - \frac{1}{6}x^3 + \cdots$ to find the terms up to and including that in x^3 for $\ln(1 + \sin x)$.

1.8 Taylor Series

The Maclaurin series, apparently able to deliver a power series whenever one exists, has one major drawback: it is strongly tied to $x = 0$. This means that its precision falls away as we move from that point. But there is an even more fundamental problem, as we see in the next example.

Think about it like this

This is not unexpected. The Maclaurin series is constructed from data obtained only at the single point $x = 0$. Hence we would expect its effectiveness to deteriorate as we move away from that point, further 'into the unknown'.

Example 1.18 Find a power series for $\ln x$.

This fails at the very start: $\ln 0$ is not defined. Nor, indeed, are any of the derivatives, at $x = 0$.

The solution is to move the 'origin' to a better point; in this case $x = 1$ is a good choice. Let $y = x - 1$, so that $y = 0$ at $x = 1$ and the origin should be acceptable for constructing a series if we use the variable y. Noting that $x = 1 + y$, our function is $\ln(1 + y)$ for which we already have the power series (1.8):

$$\ln(1 + y) = y - \tfrac{1}{2}y^2 + \tfrac{1}{3}y^3 - \cdots. \tag{1.15}$$

We can readily convert this to an x-formula:

$$\ln x = (x - 1) - \tfrac{1}{2}(x - 1)^2 + \tfrac{1}{3}(x - 1)^3 - \cdots. \tag{1.16}$$

∎

The series (1.16) is the **Taylor series** for $\ln x$ **about** $x = 1$. The form (1.15) contains precisely the same information and so is equivalent to it. Both versions are used in practice, for different purposes. The form (1.15), with y replaced by h, is often used for computational purposes; recall the use of h (assumed small) in the definition of a derivative. Applications will be illustrated in §1.9.

Think about it like this

A Taylor series about $x = a$ uses terms containing $(x - a)^n$. The Maclaurin series is therefore just a Taylor series **about** $x = 0$. But this is such a key value of x that the Maclaurin series retains its separate identity. We now use it as an indicator for how to derive Taylor series more directly than the method used in Example 1.18.

The direct method for finding a Taylor series for $f(x)$ about $x = a$ involves repeated differentiation, followed by setting $x = a$. This picks off the coefficients of the terms $(x - a)^n$, one at a time, resulting in the following.

Frame 1.9   *The Taylor series for $f(x)$ about $x=a$*

$$f(x) = f(a) + (x - a)f'(a) + \frac{1}{2!}(x - a)^2 f''(a) + \cdots$$

$$\cdots + \frac{1}{k!}(x - a)^k f^{(k)}(a) + \cdots \tag{1.17}$$

$$= \sum_{k=0}^{\infty} \frac{1}{k!}(x - a)^k f^{(k)}(a)$$

Setting $x = a + h$ gives the alternative form.

Frame 1.10   *The Taylor series for $f(a+h)$ in terms of h*

$$f(a + h) = f(a) + hf'(a) + \frac{1}{2!}h^2 f''(a) + \cdots + \frac{1}{k!}h^k f^{(k)}(a) + \cdots \tag{1.18}$$

Think about it like this

> The Taylor series looks more complicated than the Maclaurin one, but the easiest way to view it is as a Maclaurin series shifted along the axis, i.e., the point $x = 0$ has become $x = a$. Recall that such a shift is equivalent to replacing x by $x - a$.

> Constructing the Taylor series is straightforward except, perhaps, for the differentiation. Find the derivatives, set $x = a$ and feed the numbers into the template in (1.17): $f^{(k)}(a)$ is the coefficient of $(x - a)^k / k!$.

The second form gives a hint of what sort of convergence condition we expect to find. It will produce a radius of convergence requirement $|h| < R$, which translates into

$$|x - a| < R, \quad \text{i.e., } x \text{ is in the interval } (a - R, a + R).$$

To find a suitable value of R we can again look for the nearest bad point.

Example 1.19 For the case of $\ln x$ about $x = 1$, the nearest bad point is $x = 0$, at distance 1 from $x = 1$, so the convergence condition is

$$|x - 1| < 1, \quad \text{i.e., } x \text{ is in } (0, 2).$$

■

Example 1.20 Find the Taylor series for $f(x) = 4 + 3x + x^2$ about $x = 2$.

$$f'(x) = 3 + 2x, \quad f''(x) = 2, \quad f'''(x) = 0, \quad \text{etc.,}$$
$$f(2) = 14, \quad f'(2) = 7, \qquad f''(2) = 2, \quad f'''(2) = 0, \quad \text{etc.,}$$

Hence the Taylor series is finite:

$$f(x) = 14 + 7(x - 2) + \frac{2}{2!}(x - 2)^2 = 14 + 7(x - 2) + (x - 2)^2.$$

If the bracketed terms are expanded we regain the original form. Although this suggests that we have achieved nothing significant, the new form is much more useful for any work we carry out in the vicinity of $x = 2$. ■

Example 1.21 Find the Taylor series for $f(x) = 1 + x + x^2 + x^3$ about $x = -1$.

$$f'(x) = 1 + 2x + 3x^2, \quad f''(x) = 2 + 6x, \quad f'''(x) = 6,$$
$$f(-1) = 0, \quad f'(-1) = 2, \qquad f''(-1) = -4, \qquad f'''(-1) = 6.$$

Hence the Taylor series is again finite:

$$f(x) = 0 + 2\big(x - (-1)\big) - \frac{4}{2!}\big(x - (-1)\big)^2 + \frac{6}{3!}\big(x - (-1)\big)^3$$
$$= 2(x + 1) - 2(x + 1)^2 + (x + 1)^3.$$

Again, expansion of the bracketed terms delivers the original form. ■

Example 1.22   Find the Taylor series for $f(x) = \sin x$ about $x = \frac{\pi}{4}$.

$$f(x) = \sin x \qquad\qquad f\left(\frac{\pi}{4}\right) = \frac{1}{\sqrt{2}},$$
$$f'(x) = \cos x \qquad\qquad f'\left(\frac{\pi}{4}\right) = \frac{1}{\sqrt{2}},$$
$$f''(x) = -\sin x \qquad\qquad f''\left(\frac{\pi}{4}\right) = -\frac{1}{\sqrt{2}},$$
$$f'''(x) = -\cos x \qquad\qquad f'''\left(\frac{\pi}{4}\right) = -\frac{1}{\sqrt{2}},$$

and so on. These values generate the two forms:

$$\sin x = \frac{1}{\sqrt{2}} + \frac{1}{\sqrt{2}}\left(x - \frac{\pi}{4}\right) - \frac{1}{2\sqrt{2}}\left(x - \frac{\pi}{4}\right)^2 - \frac{1}{6\sqrt{2}}\left(x - \frac{\pi}{4}\right)^3 + \cdots,$$

$$\tag{1.19}$$

$$\sin\left(\frac{\pi}{4} + h\right) = \frac{1}{\sqrt{2}}\left[1 + h - \tfrac{1}{2}h^2 - \tfrac{1}{6}h^3 + \cdots\right]. \tag{1.20}$$

Both converge everywhere, since $\sin x$ has no 'bad' points.   ■

Think about it like this

All the series in this section have been derived under the assumption that they actually exist. There is a result, known as *Taylor's Theorem*, that provides conditions on $f(x)$ under which we may safely assume existence. We shall not pursue this except to note the following feature.

Construction of the Maclaurin and Taylor series requires knowledge of derivatives *of all orders* at the point in question. Some functions do not have a full set of derivatives and so a full construction of the series would not be possible. Nevertheless, the part that can be constructed *may* deliver some useful information, although great care is needed in such circumstances.

Ex 1.13   Find the Taylor series for $-3x^2 + 2x + 1$ about $x = 2$.

Ex 1.14   Find the first **three** terms (zero or non-zero) in the Taylor series for the following. First find the $f(x)$ form, then write down the $f(a + h)$ form.

(a) $\sqrt[3]{x}$ about $x = 1$.

(b) $\sin x$ about $x = \frac{\pi}{2}$.

(c) $1 + x + x^2 + x^3 + x^4$ about $x = -1$.

(d) $1/x^2$ about $x = a$.

1.9   Applications

There are two principal applications of Taylor and Maclaurin series. One is computational: the series can be stopped early and the first few terms used to approximate values of the function involved.

First, however, we examine the other application: we investigate the behaviour of a function near some point, or perhaps distant from some point, which is tantamount to being near 'infinity' as we saw in §1.3.

Example 1.23 Consider a charged circular disc, radius R, with electric charge per unit area σ [lower case *sigma*]. The electric field at distance z along its axis has a complicated form. We can simplify it by using a series. Since the aim is to consider large values of z, we expand in powers of $1/z$.

$$E(z) = \frac{\sigma}{2\epsilon_0}\left[1 - \frac{z}{(z^2 + R^2)^{1/2}}\right]$$

$$= \frac{\sigma}{2\epsilon_0}\left[1 - \frac{1}{\left[1 + \left(\frac{R}{z}\right)^2\right]^{1/2}}\right]$$

$$= \frac{\sigma}{2\epsilon_0}\left[1 - \left\{1 - \frac{1}{2}\frac{R^2}{z^2} + \frac{3}{8}\frac{R^4}{z^4} - \cdots\right\}\right]$$

(thinking of R^2/z^2 as a quantity x, which allows Example 1.5 to be used).

$$E(z) = \frac{\sigma}{4\epsilon_0}\frac{R^2}{z^2} - \frac{3\sigma}{16\epsilon_0}\frac{R^4}{z^4} + \cdots$$

$$= \frac{q}{4\pi\epsilon_0}\frac{1}{z^2} - \frac{3q}{16\pi\epsilon_0}\frac{R^2}{z^4} + \cdots,$$

where $q = \sigma(\pi R^2)$ is the total charge on the disc (charge per unit area times area).

We now recognise the first term as the field due to having a **point charge** q at $z = 0$. Hence, as we might expect, at a large distance from the disc the field is largely what it would be if the charge were concentrated at its centre. But now we have a **principal correction term** – the second term in the series – which allows us to estimate the error in treating the disc in that way, and which shows this 'error' dies away as we get further from the disc. ■

Example 1.24 The field strength of a thin bar magnet, length $2L$, at a point on its axis at distance x from its centre is

$$H = \frac{K}{2L}\left[\frac{1}{(x - L)^2} - \frac{1}{(x + L)^2}\right],$$

where K is a constant.

Use the series for $(a + x)^{-2}$ found in Example 1.12. We use $a = L$ and in one case rewrite $(x - L)^2$ as $(L - x)^2$.

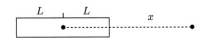

$$H = \frac{K}{2L}\left[\frac{1}{x^2} + \frac{2L}{x^3} + \frac{3L^2}{x^4} + \frac{4L^3}{x^5} + \cdots\right.$$

$$\left. - \frac{1}{x^2} + \frac{2L}{x^3} - \frac{3L^2}{x^4} + \frac{4L^3}{x^5} - \cdots\right]$$

$$= \frac{K}{2L}\left[\frac{4L}{x^3} + \frac{8L^3}{x^5} + \cdots\right] = \frac{2K}{x^3} + \frac{4L^2K}{x^5} + \cdots.$$

This shows that the field is approximately proportional to $1/x^3$ for large $|x|$; it also delivers a 'correction' term. ∎

The z-**transform** is a device used in digital electronics, for calculations with a signal **sampled** at intervals of T, such as the signal that is used to store music on a CD.

Suppose the values sampled at times 0, T, $2T$, ... are a_0, a_1, a_2, ... Then we define the z-transform as the function

$$X(z) = a_0 + \frac{a_1}{z} + \frac{a_2}{z^2} + \cdots . \tag{1.21}$$

Example 1.25 Find the z-transform for a constant signal, and then for an exponentially decaying signal.

For the constant signal we have $a_k \equiv 1$, so

$$X(z) = 1 + \frac{1}{z} + \frac{1}{z^2} + \frac{1}{z^3} + \cdots = \frac{1}{1 - \frac{1}{z}} = \frac{z}{z-1},$$

on summing the geometric series.

Suppose the decaying signal is sampled from e^{-at}, at times $t = kT$, so $a_k = \exp(-akT)$. Then

$$X(z) = 1 + \frac{e^{-aT}}{z} + \frac{e^{-2aT}}{z^2} + \cdots$$
$$= \frac{1}{1 - \frac{e^{-aT}}{z}} = \frac{z}{z - e^{-aT}},$$

again summing a geometric series, this time with common ratio e^{-aT}/z. ∎

An important calculation associated with this is deducing the signal when the transform is known. This requires expanding a given $X(z)$ as a power series in $1/z$.

Example 1.26 Find the signal associated with $X(z) = \dfrac{z}{z^2 - 1}$.

$$X(z) = \frac{1}{z}\left[\frac{1}{1 - \frac{1}{z^2}}\right] = \frac{1}{z}\left[1 + \frac{1}{z^2} + \frac{1}{z^4} + \cdots\right],$$

on using the geometric series with x replaced by $1/z^2$.

Removing the brackets and reading off the coefficients of the powers of z (starting with z^0), we deduce the signal 0, 1, 0, 1, 0, 1, ... ∎

The other type of application is to compute values for functions, which cannot be evaluated by simple arithmetic. The approach is to find a power series, preferably one with speedy convergence, then calculate sufficient terms to deliver the accuracy wished. We aim to **truncate** the series after the term in $(x-a)^n$ for some n, i.e., we use the **partial sum** $S_n(x)$ to approximate the **sum to infinity** $S(x)$. Recall that $S_n(x)$ is a **polynomial**, which is easily evaluated.

Example 1.27 Estimate $\sqrt{1.1}$.

Use three terms of the power series from Example 1.3 with $x = 0.1$:

$$(1+x)^{1/2} = 1 + \tfrac{1}{2}x - \tfrac{1}{8}x^2 + \tfrac{1}{16}x^3 - \cdots$$
$$S_2(0.1) = 1 + \tfrac{1}{2}0.1 - \tfrac{1}{8}0.01 = 1.048\,750.$$

The correct answer, to 6 dp, is $1.048\,809$. ■

Example 1.28 Estimate $e^{0.2}$.

Use four terms of the exponential series, (1.12), with $x = 0.2$:

$$S_3(0.2) = 1 + 0.2 + \frac{0.04}{2} + \frac{0.008}{6} = 1.221\,333,$$

and the correct answer, to 6 dp, is $1.221\,403$. ■

Since we usually do not know the correct answer, an immediate question is: how accurate are these answers? The usual procedure is to calculate an **error estimate**, which is simply the next term in the series.

Example 1.29 For $\sqrt{1.1}$, the next term is $\tfrac{1}{16} \times (0.1)^3 = 0.000\,063$, while the actual error is $\left|\sqrt{1.1} - S_2(0.1)\right| = 0.000\,059$.

For $e^{0.2}$, the next term is $\tfrac{1}{24} \times (0.2)^4 = 0.000\,067$, while the actual error $\left|e^{0.2} - S_3(0.2)\right| = 0.000\,069$ is slightly larger. ■

Think about it like this

There is a method for obtaining a precise **error bound**, by carrying out a more detailed analysis of the derivative contained in this 'next' term. For Example 1.28, this delivers the error bound $0.000\,081$, which is on the *correct* side of the actual error, but further away than the error estimate.

In cases where the series alternates (eventually), as in Example 1.27, the estimate is guaranteed to be a bound. This is verified by the calculation in Example 1.29.

Example 1.30 Estimate $\sin 46°$.

Rather than use the sine series, it is better to use the series in Example 1.22, since $46°$ is much nearer $\pi/4$ than 0. To find a suitable x, write $46 = 45 + 1$, but convert to **radians**: use $\tfrac{\pi}{4} + \tfrac{\pi}{180}$. Set $h = \tfrac{\pi}{180}$ in (1.20):

$$\sin 46° \simeq \frac{1}{\sqrt{2}}\left[1 + \frac{\pi}{180} - \frac{1}{2}\left(\frac{\pi}{180}\right)^2 - \frac{1}{6}\left(\frac{\pi}{180}\right)^3\right]$$
$$= 0.719\,34,$$

which is correct to all 5 decimal places.

If we stop two terms earlier, we obtain $0.719\,45$, which is in error by $0.000\,11$. The error estimate, from $\frac{1}{2\sqrt{2}}\left(\frac{\pi}{180}\right)^2$, is also $0.000\,11$. ■

Ex 1.15

(a) Use the last of the three series in Exercise 1.10 to estimate $\cos(\pi/4)$.

(b) Find the first three terms of the Taylor series for $\sqrt{x}$ about $x = 9$.

(c) Use the first two terms in the result in (b) to estimate $\sqrt{9.1}$. Estimate the error in the answer, using the third term.

Ex 1.16 An important function in modelling heat conduction is the **error function**:

$$\operatorname{erf}(x) = \frac{2}{\sqrt{\pi}} \int_0^x e^{-t^2}\, dt.$$

Find its power series and deduce its behaviour for small values of x.

Ex 1.17 We wish to approximate $f(x) = \ln x$ in the neighbourhood of $x = 10$. Write down the first four derivatives of $\ln x$ and their values at $x = 10$. Use your calculator to obtain $\ln 10$ to 6 dp.

Write down the first five terms for the Taylor series. Evaluate the first four terms at $x = 11$ and use the fifth to estimate the error in the result.

1.10 Revision Exercises

Ex 1.18 Write down the first **four** non-zero terms in the power series for:

$$\frac{1}{1 + 3x}, \qquad e^{-x^2/2}.$$

Ex 1.19

(a) Write down the first three non-zero terms in the power series for:

$$\frac{1}{1 - 3x^2}, \qquad \cos\frac{x}{2}.$$

(b) Find the sum of the series

$$1 - x^2 + \frac{1}{2!}x^4 - \frac{1}{3!}x^6 + \cdots + \frac{(-1)^r}{r!}x^{2r} + \cdots.$$

Ex 1.20 Using calculus, construct the Taylor series for

$$f(x) = 3x^3 - 2x^2 + x - 1$$

about $x = 2$.

Ex 1.21 Find the first four terms in the Maclaurin series for $(4 + x)^{1/2}$.

Use the first three terms to find an approximation to $\sqrt{4.2}$. **Estimate** the error in this approximation.

2 MATRICES

A **matrix** is a rectangular array or grid of **elements**, normally numbers or symbols representing numbers, where the position of each element is strictly defined.

We can define various 'arithmetic' operations for the matrices as whole entities, using their elements to specify the results. In this sense, matrices are a convenient way of systematising large-scale computations. But we shall find this shorthand leads us to discover properties, formulae and applications that otherwise may be overlooked.

2.1 Definitions and Notation

If the rectangular array defining a **matrix** has m **rows** and n **columns**, the matrix has **order** $m \times n$ (read as "m by n"). It therefore contains mn elements. The case where $m = n$ is particularly important and such matrices are called **square**.

There is then an implied *coordinate system* or *grid reference system*, allowing us to specify the position of each element: we state the row number followed by the column number, as subscripts. Thus, the element in row i and column j, the (i, j)-element, is written a_{ij}.

The matrix as a single entity is notated here using upper case italic letters, such as A. When a link to a specific (lower case) letter for the elements is more useful, we write $[a_{ij}]$. This notation reflects the full notation for an $m \times n$ matrix:

$$A = \begin{bmatrix} a_{11} & a_{12} & a_{13} & \cdots & a_{1n} \\ a_{21} & a_{22} & a_{23} & \cdots & a_{2n} \\ \vdots & \vdots & \vdots & \ddots & \vdots \\ a_{m1} & a_{m2} & a_{m3} & \cdots & a_{mn} \end{bmatrix}. \tag{2.1}$$

This notation can act in reverse, writing a_{ij} as $[A]_{ij}$.

Notation
Some authors use **A**, A, *A* or other font types. There are also other bracketing conventions, and the use of () is perhaps more common. But for our purposes it is sensible to avoid using the same notation as that for geometrical vectors.

Think about it like this
The 'coordinate' system above is similar to two other well-known systems:

- an **array** such as A[i,j] in computing;
- a **cell** in a **spreadsheet**, but here the order is usually the opposite: B5 is in the position of a_{52}.

Example 2.1 The following matrices are 2×4, 3×2 and 2×3, respectively:

$$\begin{bmatrix} a_{11} & a_{12} & a_{13} & a_{14} \\ a_{21} & a_{22} & a_{23} & a_{24} \end{bmatrix}, \quad \begin{bmatrix} 0 & 0 \\ 1/2 & 1/3 \\ 1 & 2/3 \end{bmatrix}, \quad \begin{bmatrix} 0 & 1 & 2 \\ 1 & 0 & 1 \end{bmatrix}.$$

■

In some circumstances we have a *formula* for the matrix elements.

Example 2.2   For the second and third matrices in the previous example,

$$a_{ij} = \frac{i-1}{j+1}, \qquad a_{ij} = |i-j|,$$

respectively.   ■

The elements for which $i = j$, i.e., those of the form a_{ii}, are the **diagonal** elements and are of great importance; see §2.3. They lie in the 'NW–SE' diagonal of the array, which is called the **main diagonal**.

There is an important special type of matrix, where we normally use a different notation. When the order is $m \times 1$, the matrix resembles a **vector** written vertically:

$$A = \begin{bmatrix} a_{11} \\ a_{21} \\ \vdots \\ a_{m1} \end{bmatrix} \quad \text{or} \quad \mathbf{a} = \begin{bmatrix} a_1 \\ a_2 \\ \vdots \\ a_m \end{bmatrix}.$$

Thus, consistent with some of the principal applications of matrices, we shall regard such a matrix as a vector – it is often called a **column vector** – and use the standard vector notation, **a**.

Example 2.3   The vector $(1, -1, 2)$, or $\mathbf{i} - \mathbf{j} + 2\mathbf{k}$, is analogous to the matrix

$$\begin{bmatrix} 1 \\ -1 \\ 2 \end{bmatrix}.$$

■

One drawback to this is the space taken up by writing in columns. This is often bypassed by using the $(\ldots)$ notation (except in calculations) or an idea associated with matrices, covered in §2.3.

Ex 2.1   Construct matrices A as follows:

(a) 3×2, $a_{ij} = i^2 j$;

(b) 3×3, $a_{ij} = 1/(i+j-1)$;

(c) 4×4, $a_{ij} = (-1)^{i+j}$.

2.2   Basic Matrix Operations

Matrices will provide little more than a systematised method of storage unless we can define ways to combine them, e.g., arithmetic operations. Once that has been achieved, we can generate equations connecting them, which raises the fundamental question: when are two matrices equal?

Frame 2.1   *Equality of matrices*

$A = B$ if their orders agree, and $a_{ij} = b_{ij}$ for all i, j.

This is analogous to the idea of equality of two vectors, and we can extend some of the vector ideas further, effectively treating the matrix as a vector with mn elements, written in a compactified manner. (This is helpful in this section, but fails to deliver some of our later requirements.)

Thus, there is a **zero matrix** for any given order, written O and having all its elements zero, as in

$$\begin{bmatrix} 0 & 0 & 0 \\ 0 & 0 & 0 \end{bmatrix}.$$

We can add, subtract and multiply matrices by scalars, as if they were compactified vectors.

Frame 2.2   *Basic matrix operations*

$$[A + B]_{ij} = [A]_{ij} + [B]_{ij} \tag{2.2}$$
$$[A - B]_{ij} = [A]_{ij} - [B]_{ij} \tag{2.3}$$
$$[\lambda A]_{ij} = \lambda [A]_{ij} \tag{2.4}$$

(assuming that A and B have the same order)

Here, λ [*lambda*] is a **scalar**; for our purposes that is a *real* or *complex* number.

Example 2.4 The following exemplify addition and subtraction.

$$\begin{bmatrix} 3 & 1 \\ 2 & 7 \\ 4 & 9 \end{bmatrix} + \begin{bmatrix} 1 & 2 \\ 3 & 3 \\ 1 & 4 \end{bmatrix} = \begin{bmatrix} 4 & 3 \\ 5 & 10 \\ 5 & 13 \end{bmatrix}$$

$$\begin{bmatrix} 1 \\ -1 \end{bmatrix} - \begin{bmatrix} -2 \\ 1 \end{bmatrix} = \begin{bmatrix} 3 \\ -2 \end{bmatrix}$$

equivalent to: $(1, -1) - (-2, 1) = (3, -2)$

$$\begin{bmatrix} 2 & 1 \end{bmatrix} + \begin{bmatrix} 1 \\ 2 \end{bmatrix} \quad \text{cannot be done}$$

$$\begin{bmatrix} 1 & 0 \\ 1 & -1 \end{bmatrix} + \begin{bmatrix} -1 & 0 \\ -1 & 1 \end{bmatrix} = \begin{bmatrix} 0 & 0 \\ 0 & 0 \end{bmatrix} = O$$

■

Example 2.5   Scalar multiplication is exemplified by

$$2 \begin{bmatrix} 1 & 2 & 3 \\ 4 & 5 & 6 \end{bmatrix} = \begin{bmatrix} 2 & 4 & 6 \\ 8 & 10 & 12 \end{bmatrix}, \quad -3 \begin{bmatrix} 1 \\ -1 \end{bmatrix} = \begin{bmatrix} -3 \\ 3 \end{bmatrix}.$$

The second example is equivalent to $-3(1, -1) = (-3, 3)$.   ■

Also like vectors, there are two ways to define $-A$ and they are the same: $A + (-A) = O$ and $-A = (-1) \times A$. This is exemplified by the last case in Example 2.4:

$$\begin{bmatrix} -1 & 0 \\ -1 & 1 \end{bmatrix} = - \begin{bmatrix} 1 & 0 \\ 1 & -1 \end{bmatrix}.$$

The three basic operations in Frame 2.2 satisfy the normal rules for number-based arithmetic, such as $A + B = B + A$.

Example 2.6   Monthly production (in units of 1000) from factories F_1 and F_2, of articles A, B, C and D, is given by tables such as:

January Production				
	A	B	C	D
Factory F_1	10	8	0	6
Factory F_2	3	4	12	7

This data can be stored in a 2×4 matrix, with rows (invisibly) labelled F_1, F_2 and columns A–D. Thus, in units of 1000, the production for January and February is given by:

$$J = \begin{bmatrix} 10 & 8 & 0 & 6 \\ 3 & 4 & 12 & 7 \end{bmatrix}, \quad F = \begin{bmatrix} 8 & 7 & 2 & 7 \\ 4 & 4 & 10 & 6 \end{bmatrix}.$$

Over two months, we have:

$$J + F = \begin{bmatrix} 18 & 15 & 2 & 13 \\ 7 & 8 & 22 & 13 \end{bmatrix}.$$

The estimated production for a full year is then:

$$6(J + F) = \begin{bmatrix} 108 & 90 & 12 & 78 \\ 42 & 48 & 132 & 78 \end{bmatrix}.$$

If, however, we prefer to choose an article and read how many are produced from each factory, we would use a 4×2 matrix, e.g.,

$$J' = \begin{bmatrix} 10 & 3 \\ 8 & 4 \\ 0 & 12 \\ 6 & 7 \end{bmatrix}.$$

where the rows are labelled A–D and the columns F_1, F_2.   ■

2.3 Special Matrix Forms

The matrix J' in Example 2.6 has a name and notation, to link it with J. It is called the **transpose** of J, written J^T (or sometimes J^t or J', as above).

Frame 2.3   *The transpose A^T of the matrix A*

Write the columns of A as the rows of A^T,

or write the rows of A as the columns of A^T,

in the same order.

$$\left[A^T\right]_{ij} = [A]_{ji}$$

Think about it like this

> This last version is very useful in writing computer programs. It is sometimes read as 'reflecting' A about its main diagonal, but this is dangerous, unless $m = n$. For hand calculation it is much safer (and easier) to write column 1 as row 1, etc.

One simple property is

$$A \, : \, m \times n \quad \Rightarrow \quad A^T \, : \, n \times m.$$

This provides a useful way to write vectors. When converting $(x_1, x_2, \ldots, x_m)$ to a matrix-type vector, instead of writing it explicitly in a vertical format, we can write

$$\mathbf{x}^T = \begin{bmatrix} x_1 & x_2 & \cdots & x_m \end{bmatrix} \quad \text{or} \quad \mathbf{x} = \begin{bmatrix} x_1 & x_2 & \cdots & x_m \end{bmatrix}^T.$$

Transposition also obeys simple rules such as $(A + B)^T = A^T + B^T$ and $(\lambda A)^T = \lambda A^T$. One that is especially noteworthy is

$$(A^T)^T = A, \tag{2.5}$$

since transposing twice will take column 1 to row 1 and back to column 1, etc.

Matrices often represent 'linkage' between objects, e.g., factory F_2 and article C are linked using $[J]_{23}$. We could use a matrix G to store the gravitational pull on planet i due to planet j in g_{ij}.

In many cases, such as the gravitational one, the two sets of objects linked by the matrix are the same. Then we must have $m = n$ and the matrix is **square**.

In *some* of these square cases the ij and ji linkages are the same, e.g., planets i and j exert the same pull on each other. When this occurs we have $a_{ij} = a_{ji}$ and hence $A = A^T$.

> **Frame 2.4**   *Definition of a symmetric matrix*
>
> The matrix A is **symmetric** if $A = A^T$

Example 2.7   Consider the following:

$\begin{bmatrix} 1 & 2 \\ 2 & 3 \end{bmatrix}$: symmetric.

$\begin{bmatrix} 1 & -1 \\ 1 & -1 \end{bmatrix}^T = \begin{bmatrix} 1 & 1 \\ -1 & -1 \end{bmatrix}$: not symmetric ($a_{12} = -1$, $a_{21} = +1$).

The general 3×3 symmetric matrix has the pattern $\begin{bmatrix} a & b & c \\ b & d & e \\ c & e & f \end{bmatrix}$, where $a, \dots, f$ represent general elements. ■

Although it is often possible to check for symmetry just by looking at the matrix, as in this last example, there are situations where the definition in Frame 2.4 is more useful.

Example 2.8   Show that, for any square matrix A, the matrix $\frac{1}{2}\left(A + A^T\right)$ is symmetric.

$$\left[\tfrac{1}{2}\left(A + A^T\right)\right]^T = \tfrac{1}{2}\left[A^T + (A^T)^T\right] = \tfrac{1}{2}\left(A^T + A\right),$$

so transposing does not change the matrix. Note that A must be square else we cannot add A and A^T. ■

A matrix is said to be **skew-symmetric** if $A^T = -A$, i.e., $a_{ij} = -a_{ji}$ for all i and j.

Example 2.9   The following are skew-symmetric:

$$\begin{bmatrix} 0 & -1 \\ 1 & 0 \end{bmatrix}, \quad \begin{bmatrix} 0 & 0 \\ 0 & 0 \end{bmatrix}, \quad \begin{bmatrix} 0 & a & b \\ -a & 0 & c \\ -b & -c & 0 \end{bmatrix}.$$

Note that the zero matrix is the only matrix that is both symmetric and skew-symmetric. ■

The fact that the elements in the main diagonal are zero in these skew-symmetric matrices is no accident and is easily proved.

It is possible to write any square matrix as the sum of a symmetric and a skew-symmetric matrix:

$$A = \tfrac{1}{2}\left(A + A^T\right) + \tfrac{1}{2}\left(A - A^T\right). \tag{2.6}$$

We showed that the first is symmetric in Example 2.8 and the skew-symmetric property of the second is shown similarly.

There is no restriction that matrix elements must be numbers or represent numbers, although that is the most usual situation in practical applications.

But it is quite common for these numbers to be **complex**, especially in quantum mechanics.

Example 2.10   The **Pauli spin matrices are**:

$$P_x = \begin{bmatrix} 0 & 1 \\ 1 & 0 \end{bmatrix}, \qquad P_y = \begin{bmatrix} 0 & -i \\ i & 0 \end{bmatrix}, \qquad P_z = \begin{bmatrix} 1 & 0 \\ 0 & -1 \end{bmatrix}.$$

∎

When complex numbers are involved, the transpose is not normally as useful as a matrix involving **complex conjugates**, in addition to transposition. Write $\overline{A}$ for the matrix with all its elements replaced by their complex conjugates: $\overline{x + iy} = x - iy$.

Frame 2.5   *The hermitian conjugate of a matrix*

The **hermitian conjugate** of A is $A^* = (\overline{A})^T$

If $A = A^*$ then A is **hermitian**

Notation

Some people write A^H for A^*. Our notation also explains why some write z^* for $\overline{z}$: a single number z can be thought of as a 1×1 matrix, whose hermitian conjugate will be the 1×1 matrix containing $\overline{z}$.

Note that if A is entirely real then $A^* = A^T$ and there is no distinction between the two matrices.

Example 2.11   Consider the Pauli spin matrix P_y:

$$P_y^T = \begin{bmatrix} 0 & i \\ -i & 0 \end{bmatrix}, \qquad \overline{P_y} = \begin{bmatrix} 0 & i \\ -i & 0 \end{bmatrix}, \qquad P_y^* = \overline{P_y}^T = \begin{bmatrix} 0 & -i \\ i & 0 \end{bmatrix},$$

so P_y is hermitian but not symmetric. Its companions are also hermitian, through being real and symmetric. ∎

Returning to the idea of 'linkage', if there is no link between different objects we have $a_{ij} = 0$ for $i \neq j$. The matrix has non-zero elements only in its main diagonal, e.g.,

$$\begin{bmatrix} a & 0 & 0 \\ 0 & b & 0 \\ 0 & 0 & c \end{bmatrix}.$$

Such a matrix is called **diagonal**.

The sum, difference and scalar multiples of diagonal matrices (of the same order) are also diagonal.

Think about it like this

> Obtaining a diagonal matrix is an objective of many matrix calculations:
> physical interpretations are then much simplified. If all the off-diagonal
> elements are zero, the components are 'uncoupled', which means that each
> can be analysed independently of the others. For example, a clever choice of
> coordinate system can reduce a complicated 3-D problem to three separate
> 1-D problems.

One particular diagonal matrix is the most important matrix of all; its
importance is only evident when we introduce multiplication, in the next
section. This is the **identity matrix**.

Frame 2.6   *The identity matrix I_n*

I_n is the $n \times n$ diagonal matrix with diagonal elements 1;

its elements are notated $[I]_{ij} = \delta_{ij}$

Example 2.12   Simple cases are:

$$I_2 = \begin{bmatrix} 1 & 0 \\ 0 & 1 \end{bmatrix}, \qquad I_3 = \begin{bmatrix} 1 & 0 & 0 \\ 0 & 1 & 0 \\ 0 & 0 & 1 \end{bmatrix}.$$

∎

It is most common to write simply I, unless there is a danger of ambiguity.
The quantity

$$\delta_{ij} = \begin{cases} 1 & \text{if } i = j, \\ 0 & \text{if } i \neq j. \end{cases} \tag{2.7}$$

is called the **Kronecker delta**. It is commonly used in Physics, as part of a
neat computational notation we shall mention in the next section.

Notation

> The δ_{ij} notation is used for I because the natural notation, i_{ij}, would be
> nonsensical, with its clashing uses of i.

Example 2.13   If we write the usual orthonormal 3-D basis vectors as
$\mathbf{i} = \mathbf{e}_1$, $\mathbf{j} = \mathbf{e}_2$, $\mathbf{k} = \mathbf{e}_3$, we can sum up their **orthonormal** property by:

$$\mathbf{e}_i \bullet \mathbf{e}_j = \delta_{ij}.$$

∎

Ex 2.2 Let $P = \begin{bmatrix} 2 & 1 \\ -2 & 0 \end{bmatrix}$, $Q = \begin{bmatrix} -5 & 1 & 2 \\ -3 & 3 & 1 \end{bmatrix}$, $R = \begin{bmatrix} 1 & 1 \\ 3 & 4 \end{bmatrix}$, $S = \begin{bmatrix} 3 & 0 \\ -1 & -1 \\ 0 & 2 \end{bmatrix}.$

Calculate, if they are defined, the matrices

$$P^T, \quad P+Q, \quad P+R, \quad 2Q, \quad 2R-P, \quad R-S, \quad Q+S^T.$$

Ex 2.3 For each of the following matrices, find A^T and A^* (if different). State whether the matrix is symmetric, skew-symmetric, hermitian or none of these.

$$\begin{bmatrix} 0 & 1 & -1 \\ -1 & 0 & 1 \\ 1 & -1 & 0 \end{bmatrix}, \begin{bmatrix} i & -1 & 1+i \\ -1 & 0 & 2-i \\ 1-i & 2+i & 2 \end{bmatrix}, \begin{bmatrix} 9 & 8 & 7 \\ 8 & 7 & 6 \\ 7 & 6 & 5 \end{bmatrix}, \begin{bmatrix} 1 & i & -1 \\ -i & 2 & 3+2i \\ -1 & 3-2i & 0 \end{bmatrix}.$$

Ex 2.4

(a) Let A be a **hermitian matrix**, i.e., $A^* = A$. Show that its diagonal is real.

(b) Write each of $\begin{bmatrix} 1 & 2 \\ -4 & 3 \end{bmatrix}$ and $\begin{bmatrix} -1 & 3 \\ 3 & 2 \end{bmatrix}$ as the sum of a symmetric and a skew-symmetric matrix.

(c) A complex matrix Z can be written as $X + iY$, with X and Y being real. Show that Z is hermitian if X is symmetric and Y is skew-symmetric.

Ex 2.5 Diagonal matrices are often given a special notation: diag (a_{11}, a_{22}, a_{33}) for the 3×3 diagonal matrix with a_{11}, a_{22}, a_{33} on its diagonal. Calculate $3A - 2B$, where $A = \text{diag}(2, 0, -1)$, $B = \text{diag}(1, -1, 3)$.

Ex 2.6

(a) Show that any 2×2 matrix can be written in the form $aA + bB + cC + dD$, where

$$A = \begin{bmatrix} 1 & 0 \\ 0 & 0 \end{bmatrix}, \quad B = \begin{bmatrix} 0 & 1 \\ 0 & 0 \end{bmatrix}, \quad C = \begin{bmatrix} 0 & 0 \\ 1 & 0 \end{bmatrix}, \quad D = \begin{bmatrix} 0 & 0 \\ 0 & 1 \end{bmatrix}.$$

(b) Find a suitable set of matrices guaranteed to build up all **symmetric** 2×2 matrices (and no others), in this way. Repeat for **diagonal** matrices.

(c) How many matrices would be required in (a) and (b) for the 3×3 case?

(d) The three **Pauli spin matrices** can build up all 2×2 hermitian matrices, provided we add one more matrix to the set. Suggest an appropriate fourth matrix.

Ex 2.7 Construct a 3×4 matrix with $a_{ij} = \delta_{ij}$ (the Kronecker delta).

2.4 Matrix Multiplication

In contrast to the simple and 'obvious' method for adding matrices, the method for multiplying them seems complicated and strange. Yet it turns out to be the natural method for almost every context in which matrices are used. The answer to this riddle is that the process is not really multiplication – in spite of the notation and terminology used – but is more akin to *function composition*, as we shall see much later.

We begin by extending the idea in Example 2.6.

Example 2.14 Suppose that each of the manufactured articles A–D requires components P, Q and R:

Component List			
	P	Q	R
Article A	3	7	1
Article B	2	0	5
Article C	6	1	2
Article D	8	3	0

This data can be stored in the matrix $X = \begin{bmatrix} 3 & 7 & 1 \\ 2 & 0 & 5 \\ 6 & 1 & 2 \\ 8 & 3 & 0 \end{bmatrix}$.

Suppose we ask how many of Q are needed in the factory F_1 in January. Using data from Example 2.6, the calculation is a natural one:

$$\underset{(A)}{10} \times 7 + \underset{(B)}{8} \times 0 + \underset{(C)}{0} \times 1 + \underset{(D)}{6} \times 3 = \mathbf{88}.$$

Similarly, if asked how many of P are required in F_2:

$$3 \times 3 + 4 \times 2 + 12 \times 6 + 7 \times 8 = \mathbf{145}.$$

This is the basis for calculating a matrix product, written:

$$JX = \begin{bmatrix} 10 & 8 & 0 & 6 \\ 3 & 4 & 12 & 7 \end{bmatrix} \begin{bmatrix} 3 & 7 & 1 \\ 2 & 0 & 5 \\ 6 & 1 & 2 \\ 8 & 3 & 0 \end{bmatrix}$$

$$= \begin{bmatrix} 94 & \mathbf{88} & 50 \\ \mathbf{145} & 54 & 47 \end{bmatrix},$$

in which the results of the two calculations above are emboldened. This result can then produce a table:

January Components			
	P	Q	R
Factory F_1	94	88	50
Factory F_2	145	54	47

Note that the articles have completely disappeared from view. They were the common link between J and X and their number (4), which appears in the orders of both J and X, has disappeared from the order of the result, which is 2×3, the number of factories $\times$ the number of components. ■

This is the basis for the definition of matrix multiplication, which uses a systematic arrangement of **dot products**:

Frame 2.7   *Matrix multiplication*

AB is defined only if A is $m \times n$, B is $n \times p$,

i.e., number of columns in A equals number of rows in B

$$[AB]_{ij} = [\text{row } i \text{ of } A] \bullet [\text{col } j \text{ of } B]$$

$$= a_{i1}b_{1j} + a_{i2}b_{2j} + \cdots + a_{in}b_{nj}$$

$$= \sum_{k=1}^{n} a_{ik}b_{kj}$$

For 'hand' calculation, we use our hands (literally, or in our minds) to underline the ith row of A and to sideline the jth column of B, to produce the (i, j)-element of AB. Thus, the $(2, 1)$-element below is found as the dot product of the highlighted 'vectors':

$$\begin{bmatrix} a_{11} & a_{12} & a_{13} \\ a_{21} & a_{22} & a_{23} \\ a_{31} & a_{32} & a_{33} \end{bmatrix} \begin{bmatrix} b_{11} & b_{12} \\ b_{21} & b_{22} \\ b_{31} & b_{32} \end{bmatrix},$$

$$[AB]_{21} = a_{21}b_{11} + a_{22}b_{21} + a_{23}b_{31}.$$

It is essential to be systematic in applying this, if the entire product is required. For example, use the order:

$$\text{row 1 of } A \bullet [\text{col 1 of } B, \text{ col 2 of } B, \ldots]$$
$$\text{row 2 of } A \bullet [\text{col 1 of } B, \text{ col 2 of } B, \ldots]$$
$$\text{and so on}$$

There is a simple way to check that the orders are suitable (A and B are **conformable** for multiplication). Write down their orders, A then B, and if the numbers in the middle agree, the multiplication can be performed and the result has order given by deleting the middle numbers:

$$m \times \boxed{n, \ n} \times p \quad \text{produces} \quad m \times p. \tag{2.8}$$

Example 2.15   The four calculations required for

$$\begin{bmatrix} 1 & 2 & 3 \\ 4 & 5 & 6 \end{bmatrix} \begin{bmatrix} 0 & 1 \\ 1 & -2 \\ 3 & 9 \end{bmatrix} = \begin{bmatrix} 11 & 24 \\ 23 & 48 \end{bmatrix}$$

are:

$$1 \cdot 0 + 2 \cdot 1 + 3 \cdot 3 = 11,$$
$$1 \cdot 1 + 2 \cdot (-2) + 3 \cdot 9 = 24,$$
$$4 \cdot 0 + 5 \cdot 1 + 6 \cdot 3 = 23,$$
$$4 \cdot 1 + 5 \cdot (-2) + 6 \cdot 9 = 48.$$

The orders are connected by:

$$2 \times \boxed{3, \ 3} \times 2 \quad \text{produces} \quad 2 \times 2.$$

∎

Multiplication satisfies natural rules, such as $A(B+C) = AB + AC$, *with one important exception.* When AB is defined, there is no guarantee about the existence or value of BA. Thus:

$$AB \text{ defined: orders must be } \quad m \times \boxed{n, \ n} \times p;$$

$$BA \text{ defined: } \quad n \times \boxed{p, \ m} \times n \quad \Rightarrow \quad p = m;$$

$$AB: \ m \times m, \quad BA: \ n \times n, \quad \text{both square.}$$

Hence, in general, even if both are simultaneously defined, they may have different orders.

Example 2.16   The matrices in the previous example, when multiplied in the opposite order, give

$$\begin{bmatrix} 0 & 1 \\ 1 & -2 \\ 3 & 9 \end{bmatrix} \begin{bmatrix} 1 & 2 & 3 \\ 4 & 5 & 6 \end{bmatrix} = \begin{bmatrix} 4 & 5 & 6 \\ -7 & -8 & -9 \\ 39 & 51 & 63 \end{bmatrix}.$$

∎

We can now ask when AB and BA can have the same order. The analysis above shows that this requires $m = n$, so both A and B must be square and of the same order.

Example 2.17   Consider a 2×2 case:

$$\begin{bmatrix} 1 & 2 \\ 3 & 4 \end{bmatrix} \begin{bmatrix} 1 & 1 \\ 1 & 1 \end{bmatrix} = \begin{bmatrix} 3 & 3 \\ 7 & 7 \end{bmatrix},$$

$$\begin{bmatrix} 1 & 1 \\ 1 & 1 \end{bmatrix} \begin{bmatrix} 1 & 2 \\ 3 & 4 \end{bmatrix} = \begin{bmatrix} 4 & 6 \\ 4 & 6 \end{bmatrix}.$$

∎

Hence we must conclude that, in general, $AB \neq BA$ even if both are defined and have the same order: matrices fail to **commute** when multiplied. The order of multiplication is important and, in AB, we say that A **premultiplies** B, while B **postmultiplies** A.

Think about it like this

> This failure reflects the fact that the 'multiplication' process is really a function composition, as we shall see later, and it is well-known that $f \circ g(x) \neq g \circ f(x)$ in general. It is not a major obstacle for matrix work, merely requiring care when writing down products.

It would be more catastrophic if **associativity** were missing, but it isn't:

$$(AB)C = A(BC) \quad \text{for all matrices where the products are defined.} \quad (2.9)$$

In some cases this allows us to order calculations to reduce the workload.

Example 2.18 Return to the January production data in Examples 2.6 and 2.14. Suppose we know the costs of each component: each P costs 3, each Q costs 4 and each R costs 2, in some monetary unit. This data can be put into a matrix:

$$Z = \begin{bmatrix} 3 \\ 4 \\ 2 \end{bmatrix}.$$

The total cost for each factory in January can be found by multiplying component requirements – calculated in Example 2.14 – by costs:

$$(JX)Z = \begin{bmatrix} 94 & 88 & 50 \\ 145 & 54 & 47 \end{bmatrix} \begin{bmatrix} 3 \\ 4 \\ 2 \end{bmatrix} = \begin{bmatrix} 734 \\ 745 \end{bmatrix}.$$

i.e., the F_1 cost is 734 and the F_2 cost is 745.

We would get the same answer by starting with a matrix giving the total cost of the components needed to make one of each article:

$$XZ = \begin{bmatrix} 3 & 7 & 1 \\ 2 & 0 & 5 \\ 6 & 1 & 2 \\ 8 & 3 & 0 \end{bmatrix} \begin{bmatrix} 3 \\ 4 \\ 2 \end{bmatrix} = \begin{bmatrix} 39 \\ 16 \\ 26 \\ 36 \end{bmatrix},$$

so the components to make an article A cost 39, etc. Now calculating $J(XZ)$ not only produces the same result, as promised by (2.9), but does so with fewer calculations. ∎

A further strange-looking result concerns transposition:

$$(AB)^T = B^T A^T. \quad (2.10)$$

Example 2.19 Multiply to find AB and $B^T A^T$ for two 2×2 matrices:

$$AB = \begin{bmatrix} 1 & 0 \\ 1 & 1 \end{bmatrix} \begin{bmatrix} 1 & 2 \\ 3 & 4 \end{bmatrix} = \begin{bmatrix} 1 & 2 \\ 4 & 6 \end{bmatrix},$$

$$B^T A^T = \begin{bmatrix} 1 & 3 \\ 2 & 4 \end{bmatrix} \begin{bmatrix} 1 & 1 \\ 0 & 1 \end{bmatrix} = \begin{bmatrix} 1 & 4 \\ 2 & 6 \end{bmatrix}.$$

We see that $B^T A^T$ is indeed the transpose of AB. ∎

Investigating the orders in the non-square situation shows that this is the only possible simple result:

$$AB: \; m \times \boxed{n, \; n} \times p \quad \leftrightarrow \quad B^T A^T: \; p \times \boxed{n, \; n} \times m.$$

Example 2.22 gives a general proof of this. Also, the context of Example 2.14 supports this result, as the next example shows.

Example 2.20   Suppose that we work with 'tables' J^T (articles/factories) and X^T (components/articles). Then the only sensible calculations are related to $X^T J^T$ (so that 'articles' is the common factor in the middle). In Example 2.14 we used JX, again with 'articles' as the common factor.   ■

Ex 2.8 Let $A = \begin{bmatrix} 1 & 0 & 2 \\ -1 & 3 & 1 \end{bmatrix}$, $B = \begin{bmatrix} -3 & 4 \\ 2 & 0 \end{bmatrix}$, $C = \begin{bmatrix} 1 & 2 \\ 3 & 4 \\ 0 & -2 \end{bmatrix}$, $D = \begin{bmatrix} 5 \\ 2 \end{bmatrix}$.

Find, if possible, the following: BD, AB, D^2, CB, AD, B^2.

What are the orders of AC and CA (if they are defined)?

Ex 2.9 A builder produces three types of house: villas, semis and bungalows. The basic materials required and their unit costs (in appropriate units) are shown as follows:

	semi	bung	villa
bricks	12	8	15
timber	10	14	14
glass	6	4	8
paint	5	4	7
labour	13	12	14

	bricks	timber	glass	paint	labour
cost	5	6	4	4	10

It is proposed to build on three sites:

(a) 12 semis, 7 bungalows, 5 villas; (b) 12 bungalows, 10 villas; (c) 6 of each type.

Indicate how to use matrices to draw up tables of site against materials, house type against cost, site against cost.

Ex 2.10

(a) For the matrices in Exercise 2.8, find (if it exists) each of:

$$A^T C^T, \quad A^T B, \quad B^T A, \quad C D^T, \quad B^T D, \quad C^T A^T B^T D.$$

(b) Find non-zero matrices A and B such that $AB = O$.

(c) Suppose that $\begin{bmatrix} a & b \\ c & d \end{bmatrix}$ commutes with both $\begin{bmatrix} 1 & 0 \\ 0 & 0 \end{bmatrix}$ and $\begin{bmatrix} 0 & 1 \\ 0 & 0 \end{bmatrix}$. Show that it must be a multiple of I. (Hence only multiples of I commute with every possible matrix.)

(d) For the Pauli spin matrices, calculate $P_y P_x$ and compare the answer with $P_x P_y$. Investigate the other possible products of P_x, P_y and P_z.

Ex 2.11 Show that $A^T A$ and $A A^T$ are symmetric. (Hint: calculate $(A^T A)^T$.) Are they the same matrix?

2.5 Special Matrices

The calculation in Example 2.16 produced the following outline result:

$$\begin{bmatrix} 0 & 1 \\ . & . \end{bmatrix} \begin{bmatrix} . & . & . \\ 4 & 5 & 6 \end{bmatrix} = \begin{bmatrix} 4 & 5 & 6 \\ . & . & . \end{bmatrix},$$

i.e., the row $\begin{bmatrix} 0 & 1 \end{bmatrix}$ moved row 2 of the second matrix to the position of row 1. This is true in general: **premultiplying** A by a such a row:

$$\begin{bmatrix} 0 & 0 & \cdots & 1 & \cdots & 0 \end{bmatrix} A$$

$$\uparrow k^{\text{th}} \text{ position}$$

delivers row k of A.

A matrix P, composed of rows of the identity matrix I, permuted in some order, is a **permutation matrix**. Then PA is A with its rows permuted in the same order as the rows of I occur in P.

Permuting the rows of I automatically permutes its columns, but not necessarily in the same order. But, **postmultiplying** A by P permutes the columns of A to match that column order.

Example 2.21 Permuting the rows of I_3 in order $[3, 1, 2]$ is the same as permuting the columns in the order $[2, 3, 1]$. The multiplication effects are as follows:

$$\begin{bmatrix} 0 & 0 & 1 \\ 1 & 0 & 0 \\ 0 & 1 & 0 \end{bmatrix} \begin{bmatrix} 11 & 12 & 13 \\ 21 & 22 & 23 \\ 31 & 32 & 33 \end{bmatrix} = \begin{bmatrix} 31 & 32 & 33 \\ 11 & 12 & 13 \\ 21 & 22 & 23 \end{bmatrix}$$

$$\begin{bmatrix} 11 & 12 & 13 \\ 21 & 22 & 23 \\ 31 & 32 & 33 \end{bmatrix} \begin{bmatrix} 0 & 0 & 1 \\ 1 & 0 & 0 \\ 0 & 1 & 0 \end{bmatrix} = \begin{bmatrix} 12 & 13 & 11 \\ 22 & 23 & 21 \\ 32 & 33 & 31 \end{bmatrix}$$

∎

A special case of this, of huge importance, is the **identity** matrix itself. Since its rows are not jumbled, it leaves the rows (and columns) of A unaffected. This explains its name.

Frame 2.8   *The identity matrix in multiplication*

$$AI = IA = A$$

The identity matrix is an example of a **diagonal** matrix. These also have simple multiplication properties: if they have the same (square) order, we need only multiply corresponding diagonal terms. This means they commute. For example (suppressing the zero elements for the sake of clarity):

$$\begin{bmatrix} a_1 & & \\ & a_2 & \\ & & a_3 \end{bmatrix} \begin{bmatrix} b_1 & & \\ & b_2 & \\ & & b_3 \end{bmatrix} = \begin{bmatrix} a_1 b_1 & & \\ & a_2 b_2 & \\ & & a_3 b_3 \end{bmatrix}. \qquad (2.11)$$

The summation version in Frame 2.7, for $C = AB$:

$$c_{ij} = \sum_{k=1}^{n} a_{ik}b_{kj}$$

is particularly useful for programming, since it can easily be implemented in a 'for' loop. It is also the basis for a neat convention invented by Einstein, popular with physicists, who call it the **summation convention**.

We drop the sigma sign and simply write $c_{ij} = a_{ik}b_{kj}$, with the understanding that the **repeated subscript** k (appearing exactly twice) implies that the expression should be 'summed' over all values of k:

$$c_{ij} = a_{i1}b_{1j} + a_{i2}b_{2j} + \cdots + a_{1n}b_{nj},$$

with k starting at 1 and ending at the final value for which a_{ik} (and b_{kj}) is defined.

Typical of its use is the calculation of AI. Since I is represented by the Kronecker delta, we have $c_{ij} = a_{ik}\delta_{kj} = a_{ij} \times 1$, since δ_{kj} has a non-zero value only when $k = j$. Hence $C = AI = A$, as we found earlier.

Example 2.22 Use the summation convention to find $(AB)^T$.

First of all, transposition is carried out by swapping subscripts: $[C^T]_{ij} = [C]_{ji}$. We have $[AB]_{ij} = a_{ik}b_{kj}$ and so

$$[(AB)^T]_{ij} = [AB]_{ji} = a_{jk}b_{ki} = b_{ki}a_{jk} = [B^T]_{ik}[A^T]_{kj} = [B^T A^T]_{ij},$$

proving (2.10). ∎

Ex 2.12 *Write down* the products: $\begin{bmatrix} 1 & 2 & 3 \\ 4 & 5 & 6 \\ 7 & 8 & 9 \end{bmatrix} \begin{bmatrix} 0 & 0 & 1 \\ 1 & 0 & 0 \\ 0 & 1 & 0 \end{bmatrix}, \begin{bmatrix} 0 & 0 & 1 \\ 1 & 0 & 0 \\ 1 & 0 & 0 \end{bmatrix} \begin{bmatrix} 1 & 2 & 3 \\ 4 & 5 & 6 \\ 7 & 8 & 9 \end{bmatrix}.$

Ex 2.13 Let $A = \mathrm{diag}(1, -1, 0)$, $B = \mathrm{diag}(2, -3, 1)$, $C = \mathrm{diag}(i, -i)$.
Calculate AB, BA, C^*C, C^6.

Ex 2.14 A square matrix L is **lower triangular** if $l_{ij} = 0$ when $i < j$.

(a) Write down general 2×2 and 3×3 lower triangular matrices.

(b) Formulate a definition for an **upper triangular** matrix U.

(c) Are any matrices both lower and upper triangular?

(d) Show that any matrix can be written as $A = L + U$ for some L, U. Is this unique?

(e) Explain why the product of two $n \times n$ lower triangular matrices is lower triangular.

2.6   The Inverse Matrix

Having found a way of multiplying matrices, it is inviting to ask if there is a **division** method. There is, indeed, a procedure that one can think of as division, but the analogy must not be pushed too far.

To see how we could define this, start with the concept of division by numbers:

$$px = q \quad \Rightarrow \quad x = \frac{q}{p}.$$

Let us see if we can rewrite the definition in a more suggestive way:

$$\frac{1}{p}(px) = \frac{1}{p}q \quad \Rightarrow \quad \left(\frac{1}{p} \times p\right)x = 1x = \frac{1}{p}q \quad \Rightarrow \quad x = \frac{1}{p}q.$$

In other words we **divide** by p through **multiplication** by $\frac{1}{p}$ or p^{-1}.

In matrix terms, then, we try to extract X from $AX = B$ as $X = A^{-1}B$, where A^{-1} is a matrix such that $A^{-1}A = I$, the equivalent of $\frac{1}{p} \times p = 1$.

This is indeed the method we seek, but there is the complication of non-commutativity to deal with. For a **square** matrix A, if we can find such an A^{-1}, it works on the other side of A as well. It is the **inverse matrix**.

Frame 2.9   *Definition of A^{-1}, the inverse of A*

$$A^{-1}A = AA^{-1} = I \tag{2.12}$$

Most square matrices have inverses and are then called **non-singular**. A matrix with no inverse is **singular**; we shall investigate one idea related to the singular case in §2.11.

Care is needed to write A^{-1} on the correct side. For example:

$$AX = B \quad \Rightarrow \quad A^{-1}AX = A^{-1}B \quad \Rightarrow \quad IX = A^{-1}B \quad \Rightarrow \quad X = A^{-1}B,$$

although most people will skip the intermediate equations. This result differs from

$$XA = B \quad \Rightarrow \quad XAA^{-1} = BA^{-1} \quad \Rightarrow \quad XI = BA^{-1} \quad \Rightarrow \quad X = BA^{-1},$$

and so we require both equations in Frame 2.9.

Notation

This is why, although we may wish to *think* of the inverse as $\frac{I}{A}$, we must never write it like that. Purists would point out that, since matrix multiplication is really 'composition', we must use the notation of the **inverse 'function'**. This is one of the few contexts where the two uses of the notation $^{-1}$ (inversion and division) are consistent.

Example 2.23   Consider the following multiplications:

$$\begin{bmatrix} -1 & -1 \\ -3 & -2 \end{bmatrix} \begin{bmatrix} 2 & -1 \\ -3 & 1 \end{bmatrix} = \begin{bmatrix} 1 & 0 \\ 0 & 1 \end{bmatrix} = \begin{bmatrix} 2 & -1 \\ -3 & 1 \end{bmatrix} \begin{bmatrix} -1 & -1 \\ -3 & -2 \end{bmatrix}.$$

This shows that $\begin{bmatrix} -1 & -1 \\ -3 & -2 \end{bmatrix}$ is the inverse of $\begin{bmatrix} 2 & -1 \\ -3 & 1 \end{bmatrix}$. Or, does it show that $\begin{bmatrix} 2 & -1 \\ -3 & 1 \end{bmatrix}$ is the inverse of $\begin{bmatrix} -1 & -1 \\ -3 & -2 \end{bmatrix}$? In fact, it shows both.

We can use this to solve matrix equations, e.g.,

$$\begin{bmatrix} 2 & -1 \\ -3 & 1 \end{bmatrix} X = \begin{bmatrix} 1 & -1 \\ -2 & 0 \end{bmatrix} \quad \Rightarrow \quad X = \begin{bmatrix} -1 & -1 \\ -3 & -2 \end{bmatrix} \begin{bmatrix} 1 & -1 \\ -2 & 0 \end{bmatrix} = \begin{bmatrix} 1 & 1 \\ 1 & 3 \end{bmatrix}.$$

∎

This example illustrates:

$$(A^{-1})^{-1} = A,$$

i.e., the inverse of the inverse is the original matrix; (2.12) can be read both ways.

An obvious question is: how can we calculate the inverse matrix?

- If the matrix is 2×2, see below.

- If the matrix is 3×3, see §2.10 and §3.3.

- If the matrix has one of certain special forms, e.g., diagonal or orthogonal (see below), there is little calculation needed.

- If we have some partial information about the inverse we may be able to fill in the rest, straight from the definition; see Example 2.24.

- Otherwise, leave it to a computer. In fact, the number of calculations ($+$, $\times$, etc.) required is the same as for finding A^2, but their organisation is much more complicated, although readily programmable.

Example 2.24   Given that the inverse of $\begin{bmatrix} 1 & 1 & 1 \\ 1 & 2 & 2 \\ 1 & 2 & 3 \end{bmatrix}$ is $\begin{bmatrix} 2 & -1 & 0 \\ -1 & 2 & -1 \\ a & b & c \end{bmatrix}$ for some choice of a, b and c, multiplying these two matrices produces for the first row, which must match that of I:

$$\begin{bmatrix} 1+a & 1+b & -1+c \end{bmatrix} = \begin{bmatrix} 1 & 0 & 0 \end{bmatrix}.$$

This shows $a = 0$, $b = -1$, $c = 1$, which completes the inverse.

In such circumstances, one should proceed to calculate the second and third rows, to confirm that they also match I: the original information may have been faulty.

Note that this matrix and its inverse are both symmetric. We shall see later that this is no accident.   ∎

This example gives a hint of how complex the relationship between A and A^{-1} is. But for 2×2 matrices there is a formula that is easily memorised.

Frame 2.10 *Inverse of a 2×2 matrix*

$$\begin{bmatrix} a & b \\ c & d \end{bmatrix}^{-1} = \frac{1}{ad - bc} \begin{bmatrix} d & -b \\ -c & a \end{bmatrix} \qquad (2.13)$$

provided that $ad - bc \neq 0$ (2.14)

The quantity $ad - bc$ is the **determinant** of A, written as either $\det A$ or $|A|$. (We prefer the former, to avoid confusion with the notation for the absolute value.) Determinants have a chapter to themselves, but the key property for this context is contained in (2.14):

$$\text{a matrix } A \text{ is non-singular if and only if } \det A \neq 0. \qquad (2.15)$$

This condition applies to all square matrices, although its application to matrices of large order is not easy.

Think about it like this

When the matrix is non-singular, in addition to dividing by the determinant: *swap the main diagonal elements; change the sign of the others.*

Example 2.25 $\begin{bmatrix} 2 & 3 \\ 3 & 6 \end{bmatrix}$ has determinant $2 \times 6 - 3 \times 3 = 3$. The inverse is

$$\frac{1}{3} \begin{bmatrix} 6 & -3 \\ -3 & 2 \end{bmatrix} = \begin{bmatrix} 2 & -1 \\ -1 & 2/3 \end{bmatrix}.$$

This is another example of symmetry being preserved. ∎

Example 2.26 $\begin{bmatrix} 1 & -1 \\ -2 & 2 \end{bmatrix}$ has determinant $2 \times 2 - (-1) \times (-2) = 0$ and so is singular. ∎

There are several formulae related to inverses that are useful in practice. The first of these has already been noted.

Frame 2.11 *Properties of the inverse matrix*

$$(A^{-1})^{-1} = A \qquad (2.16)$$
$$(A^T)^{-1} = (A^{-1})^T \qquad (2.17)$$
$$(\lambda A)^{-1} = \frac{1}{\lambda} A^{-1} \text{ if } \lambda \neq 0 \qquad (2.18)$$
$$(AB)^{-1} = B^{-1} A^{-1} \qquad (2.19)$$

Example 2.27   The following inverses can be calculated using (2.13):

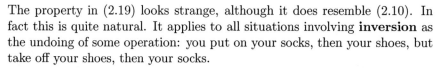

$$A = \begin{bmatrix} 2 & -1 \\ -1 & 1 \end{bmatrix}, \qquad A^{-1} = \frac{1}{2-1}\begin{bmatrix} 1 & 1 \\ 1 & 2 \end{bmatrix} = \begin{bmatrix} 1 & 1 \\ 1 & 2 \end{bmatrix}$$

$$B = \begin{bmatrix} -4 & 2 \\ 2 & -2 \end{bmatrix}, \qquad B^{-1} = \frac{1}{8-4}\begin{bmatrix} -2 & -2 \\ -2 & -4 \end{bmatrix} = \begin{bmatrix} -1/2 & -1/2 \\ -1/2 & -1 \end{bmatrix}.$$

Note that $B = -2A$ and $B^{-1} = -\frac{1}{2}A^{-1}$. Since inversion has some of the features of division, using the inverse of $-2A$ is equivalent to using the inverse of A **and** dividing by -2.   ∎

Example 2.28   Show that the inverse of a symmetric matrix is symmetric. If A is symmetric then, by definition, $A = A^T$. Use (2.17):

$$(A^{-1})^T = (A^T)^{-1} = A^{-1},$$

so A^{-1} is also symmetric, on using the same definition.   ∎

Think about it like this

> The property in (2.19) looks strange, although it does resemble (2.10). In fact this is quite natural. It applies to all situations involving **inversion** as the undoing of some operation: you put on your socks, then your shoes, but take off your shoes, then your socks.

Finally, there are some types of matrix for which inversion is straightforward. (2.11) shows that the inverse of a **diagonal** matrix with diagonal $[a_1, a_2, a_3, \ldots]$ must also be diagonal, with elements $[1/a_1, 1/a_2, 1/a_3, \ldots]$, provided all the a_k are non-zero.

There are two other important types of matrix, heavily used in applications:

Frame 2.12   *Definition of orthogonal and unitary matrices*

$$Q \text{ is \textbf{orthogonal} if } Q^{-1} = Q^T \qquad (2.20)$$
$$U \text{ is \textbf{unitary} if } U^{-1} = U^* \qquad (2.21)$$

We shall see the 'physical' importance of these in the next section. But the computational importance is clear: transposition is a trivial task, while inversion is complicated. If a matrix is known to be orthogonal or unitary its inverse is easy to find.

Think about it like this

> If an orthogonal matrix is real it is also unitary, but this is not the case if it is complex. The rule is simple: if working in a 'real' environment, use orthogonal; if working with complex numbers, use unitary.

Noting the following:

- $Q^{-1} = Q^T$ is equivalent to $Q^T Q = I$;

- a row of Q^T is a column of Q;

- an element in AB is the dot product of a row of A and a column of B;

- the general element of I is δ_{ij};

we can argue that:

$$\text{col } i \text{ of } Q \bullet \text{col } j \text{ of } Q = \delta_{ij},$$

and so the columns are unit in length and mutually orthogonal.

Example 2.29   The following matrix is orthogonal.

$$\begin{bmatrix} \frac{1}{\sqrt{2}} & \frac{1}{\sqrt{2}} \\ -\frac{1}{\sqrt{2}} & \frac{1}{\sqrt{2}} \end{bmatrix} : \qquad \begin{bmatrix} \frac{1}{\sqrt{2}} & -\frac{1}{\sqrt{2}} \\ \frac{1}{\sqrt{2}} & \frac{1}{\sqrt{2}} \end{bmatrix} \begin{bmatrix} \frac{1}{\sqrt{2}} & \frac{1}{\sqrt{2}} \\ -\frac{1}{\sqrt{2}} & \frac{1}{\sqrt{2}} \end{bmatrix} = I.$$

Also,

$$\left(\frac{1}{\sqrt{2}}, -\frac{1}{\sqrt{2}} \right) \bullet \left(\frac{1}{\sqrt{2}}, \frac{1}{\sqrt{2}} \right) = 0,$$

and these vectors each have length $\sqrt{\frac{1}{2} + \frac{1}{2}} = 1$.   ∎

Ex 2.15

(a) Evaluate the determinants and, if possible, the inverses for:

$$A = \begin{bmatrix} 3 & -1 \\ -5 & 2 \end{bmatrix}, \quad B = \begin{bmatrix} 4 & -2 \\ -6 & 3 \end{bmatrix}, \quad C = \begin{bmatrix} 4 & 2 \\ 3 & -1 \end{bmatrix}, \quad D = \begin{bmatrix} i & -2 \\ 1 & i \end{bmatrix}.$$

(b) Find a, b, c such that $\begin{bmatrix} a & 2 & -1 \\ 0 & b & -1 \\ 1 & -1 & c \end{bmatrix}$ is the inverse of $\begin{bmatrix} 0 & 1 & 1 \\ 1 & 1 & 2 \\ 1 & 0 & 2 \end{bmatrix}$.

Ex 2.16

(a) Given a matrix $A = \begin{bmatrix} 1/2 & 1/3 \\ 1/3 & 1/4 \end{bmatrix}$, find a number k such that kA contains only whole numbers. Invert kA and hence write down the inverse of A.

(b) Find values of k for which $W = \begin{bmatrix} 7-k & 8 \\ 4 & 21-k \end{bmatrix}$ has no inverse.

(c) Let $A = \begin{bmatrix} 1 & 1 \\ -2 & 4 \end{bmatrix}$ and $B = \begin{bmatrix} 1 & 1 \\ 1 & 2 \end{bmatrix}$. Verify that $B^{-1}AB$ is a diagonal matrix.

Calculate $\left(B^{-1}AB \right)^4$ and hence calculate A^4. (Hint: Write out $\left(B^{-1}AB \right)^4$ as a repeated product, then simplify.) What would be the best way to calculate A^{100}?

Ex 2.17 Find k, l, m so that $\begin{bmatrix} k & l & m \\ -k & l & -m \\ k & 0 & -2m \end{bmatrix}$ is **orthogonal**.

2.7   Matrix-Vector Multiplication

We chose, in §2.1, to continue to write column **vectors** ($n \times 1$ **matrices**) using the notation of geometrical vectors, e.g., **x**.

We noted, in §2.2, that matrices offer a fruitful way to represent 'linkages' between objects and many models take advantage of this in elaborate ways. But, ultimately, such models must address the question of what the 'state' of the process is before or after processing the linkages. This is where a vector comes in: it provides the initial data to drive the model or the final data to be extracted from it, e.g., population distribution at a certain time, or data measured by an observer at one point in space.

In this section, we shall pursue how matrices and vectors interact. We start with simple vectors. We can multiply two vectors **x** and **y**, of the same length, in two ways. The simpler, and more useful, is $\mathbf{x}^T\mathbf{y}$: the orders being $1 \times \boxed{n,\, n} \times 1$, this produces an answer that is 1×1, i.e., a number.

$$\mathbf{x}^T\mathbf{y} = \begin{bmatrix} x_1 & x_2 & \cdots & x_n \end{bmatrix} \begin{bmatrix} y_1 \\ y_2 \\ \vdots \\ y_n \end{bmatrix} = x_1 y_1 + x_2 y_2 + \cdots + x_n y_n, \qquad (2.22)$$

which is simply the **dot product**. This should be no surprise, since we noted in §2.4 that full matrix multiplication consists of a collection of dot products.

The special case where $\mathbf{x} = \mathbf{y}$ is important:

$$\mathbf{x}^T\mathbf{x} = x_1^2 + x_2^2 + \cdots + x_n^2 = |\mathbf{x}|^2,$$

where the magnitude notation refers to the geometrical vector $(x_1, \ldots, x_n)$, although it is often used for the column vector **x** as well.

Note, however, that this works only if **x** is a *real* vector. If x_1, say, is complex, then x_1^2 will not be real, preventing a real measure for the magnitude. The key here is the **hermitian conjugate**:

$$\mathbf{x}^*\mathbf{x} = \overline{x_1}x_1 + \overline{x_2}x_2 + \cdots + \overline{x_n}x_n = |x_1|^2 + |x_2|^2 + \cdots + |x_n|^2,$$

which is real, allowing the square root to be taken to give the magnitude.

Example 2.30   Find the magnitudes of $\mathbf{x} = \begin{bmatrix} 3 \\ -4 \end{bmatrix}$ and $\mathbf{y} = \begin{bmatrix} 1-i \\ 2+i \end{bmatrix}$.

$$|\mathbf{x}|^2 = \mathbf{x}^T\mathbf{x} = 3^2 + (-4)^2 = 25 \quad \Rightarrow \quad |\mathbf{x}| = 5,$$
$$|\mathbf{y}|^2 \neq \mathbf{y}^T\mathbf{y} = (1-i)^2 + (2+i)^2 = 1 - 2i - 1 + 4 + 4i - 1 = 3 + 2i,$$
$$|\mathbf{y}|^2 = \mathbf{y}^*\mathbf{y} = (1+i)(1-i) + (2-i)(2+i) = 2 + 5 = 7 \quad \Rightarrow \quad |\mathbf{y}| = \sqrt{7}.$$

∎

It is this observation, above all else, that explains why it is essential to use A^* and $\mathbf{x}^*$ in work with complex numbers.

Vectors can also be multiplied in the opposite order, i.e., $\mathbf{xy}^T$: the orders being $n \times \boxed{1, 1} \times n$, this produces an answer that is $n \times n$, i.e., a square matrix.

$$\mathbf{xy}^T = \begin{bmatrix} x_1 \\ x_2 \\ \vdots \\ x_n \end{bmatrix} \begin{bmatrix} y_1 & y_2 & \cdots & y_n \end{bmatrix} = \begin{bmatrix} x_1 y_1 & x_1 y_2 & \cdots & x_1 y_n \\ x_2 y_1 & x_2 y_2 & \cdots & x_2 y_n \\ \vdots & \vdots & \ddots & \vdots \\ x_n y_1 & x_n y_2 & \cdots & x_n y_n \end{bmatrix}, \qquad (2.23)$$

where the (i, j)-element is $x_i y_j$.

Example 2.31 Multiply $\begin{bmatrix} 1 & 2 \end{bmatrix}^T$ and $\begin{bmatrix} 3 & 4 \end{bmatrix}^T$.

$$\begin{bmatrix} 1 & 2 \end{bmatrix} \begin{bmatrix} 3 \\ 4 \end{bmatrix} = 1 \times 3 + 2 \times 4 = 11,$$

$$\begin{bmatrix} 1 \\ 2 \end{bmatrix} \begin{bmatrix} 3 & 4 \end{bmatrix} = \begin{bmatrix} 1 \times 3 & 1 \times 4 \\ 2 \times 3 & 2 \times 4 \end{bmatrix} = \begin{bmatrix} 3 & 4 \\ 6 & 8 \end{bmatrix}.$$

■

Now consider the **matrix-vector product** $A\mathbf{x}$, with A an $m \times n$ matrix. Here the orders are $m \times \boxed{n, n} \times 1$, producing an answer that is $m \times 1$, i.e., another vector, although of a different order, unless A is square.

Example 2.32 Consider a 3×2 matrix:

$$\begin{bmatrix} 2 & 3 \\ 1 & -1 \\ 0 & 2 \end{bmatrix} \begin{bmatrix} 2 \\ -1 \end{bmatrix} = \begin{bmatrix} 2 \cdot 2 + 3 \cdot (-1) \\ 1 \cdot 2 + (-1) \cdot (-1) \\ 0 \cdot 2 + 2 \cdot (-1) \end{bmatrix} = \begin{bmatrix} 1 \\ 3 \\ -2 \end{bmatrix}.$$

■

The equation $\mathbf{y} = A\mathbf{x}$ can be read as a **transformation** or **function**, with A operating on an input vector $\mathbf{x}$ to produce an output vector $\mathbf{y}$, much as in $y = f(x)$. This can be represented by the sort of 'black box' diagram used for functions, e.g., using two such operations consecutively is shown by:

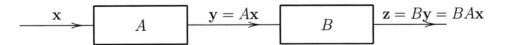

Here, the vector $\mathbf{x}$ is transformed into $\mathbf{z}$ via $\mathbf{y}$; the overall transformation is defined by BA.

Think about it like this

This is the link to (function) **composition** mentioned earlier. It explains why the multiplication method is universally used: it is a consequence of the natural matrix-vector multiplication illustrated in Example 2.32. It also explains non-commutativity – since function composition is not commutative in general – and how the inverse matrix works – as an inverse function.

The ideas of transformation and (vector) magnitude can be merged when we ask what effect multiplying $\mathbf{x}$ by a matrix has on its length. One special case is when the matrix (Q) is **orthogonal**; see Frame 2.12:

$$|\mathbf{y}|^2 = \mathbf{y}^T\mathbf{y} = (Q\mathbf{x})^T(Q\mathbf{x}) = \mathbf{x}^T Q^T Q\mathbf{x} = \mathbf{x}^T I\mathbf{x} = |\mathbf{x}|^2,$$

so the magnitude is unchanged.

It is this property that makes orthogonal (and unitary) matrices of great importance in physical applications – where sizes must not be changed – and in numerical computation – to avoid the growth of rounding error.

Finally, suppose that A is a (square) **symmetric** matrix. Then we can calculate $\mathbf{x}^T A\mathbf{x}$, as a **number**: $1 \times \boxed{n, n} \times \boxed{n, n} \times 1$ produces 1×1. This number has many applications. For example, suppose $\mathbf{x}$ is a vector of 'variables', $x_1, \ldots, x_n$.

Example 2.33　Find $\mathbf{x}^T A\mathbf{x}$ for $A = \begin{bmatrix} 1 & 2 \\ 2 & 3 \end{bmatrix}$.

$$\begin{bmatrix} x_1 & x_2 \end{bmatrix} \begin{bmatrix} 1 & 2 \\ 2 & 3 \end{bmatrix} \begin{bmatrix} x_1 \\ x_2 \end{bmatrix} = \begin{bmatrix} x_1 & x_2 \end{bmatrix} \begin{bmatrix} x_1 + 2x_2 \\ 2x_1 + 3x_2 \end{bmatrix}$$
$$= x_1^2 + 3x_2^2 + 4x_1 x_2.$$

∎

In general, the element a_{ij} produces the term $a_{ij}x_i x_j$. But the matrix is symmetric, so $a_{ij}x_i x_j = a_{ji}x_j x_i$ and the 'off-diagonal' terms pair up. The resulting expression, each of whose terms includes two x factors, is called a **quadratic form**.

Frame 2.13　　　*The general $n \times n$ quadratic form*

$$\mathbf{x}^T A\mathbf{x} = \sum_i a_{ii}x_i^2 + \sum_{i<j} 2a_{ij}x_i x_j \qquad (2.24)$$

Here, the sum $\sum_{i<j}$ means that only terms containing such a_{ij} are used: a_{12} is allowed, but not a_{21}.

This representation is easily reversed: the coefficients of the squares feed into the diagonal and the others are halved into symmetrically placed slots.

Example 2.34　Find the matrix to represent $2x_1^2 - 5x_3^2 + 4x_1 x_2 - 6x_2 x_3$.

The elements a_{22} and $a_{13} = a_{31}$ are zero, since there are no corresponding terms. Halve 4 and -6:

$$A = \begin{bmatrix} 2 & 2 & 0 \\ 2 & 0 & -3 \\ 0 & -3 & -5 \end{bmatrix}.$$

∎

Quadratic forms occur frequently as energy expressions for systems with several degrees of freedom, particularly when the system is near to equilibrium. For stability analysis, the general form in (2.24) is not easy to interpret. Suppose, however, that A is a **diagonal** matrix D. Then

$$\mathbf{x}^T D\mathbf{x} = d_{11}x_1^2 + d_{22}x_2^2 + \cdots + d_{nn}x_n^2,$$

which is called a **sum of squares**. It is now easy to see the effect of varying the x_k, since all of the variables are 'uncoupled'.

Example 2.35 Find $\mathbf{x}^T A\mathbf{x}$ for $A = \begin{bmatrix} 1 & 0 \\ 0 & 3 \end{bmatrix}$.

$$\begin{bmatrix} x_1 & x_2 \end{bmatrix} \begin{bmatrix} 1 & 0 \\ 0 & 3 \end{bmatrix} \begin{bmatrix} x_1 \\ x_2 \end{bmatrix} = \begin{bmatrix} x_1 & x_2 \end{bmatrix} \begin{bmatrix} x_1 \\ 3x_2 \end{bmatrix}$$
$$= x_1^2 + 3x_2^2.$$

∎

Ex 2.18

(a) Find $\mathbf{x}^T\mathbf{x}$ and $\mathbf{x}\mathbf{x}^T$, where $\mathbf{x} = [2 \ -1]^T$; find $\mathbf{y}^*\mathbf{y}$ and $\mathbf{y}\mathbf{y}^*$, where $\mathbf{y} = [i \ -1]^T$.

(b) Which of the following are defined, when A is 2×3, B is 3×2 and $\mathbf{x}$ is as in (c)?

$A^T\mathbf{x}, \quad A\mathbf{x}, \quad A\mathbf{x}^T, \quad \mathbf{x}^T A, \quad \mathbf{x}^T B^T, \quad AB\mathbf{x}.$

Ex 2.19 Show that $Q = I - 2\mathbf{u}\mathbf{u}^T$ is a symmetric orthogonal matrix, if $\mathbf{u}$ is a unit vector.

Ex 2.20 Let $A = \begin{bmatrix} 2 & 1 \\ 1 & 1 \end{bmatrix}$, $B = \begin{bmatrix} 1 & 0 \\ 1 & 1 \end{bmatrix}$ and $\mathbf{x} = \begin{bmatrix} x_1 \\ x_2 \end{bmatrix}$.

Evaluate $\mathbf{x}^T A\mathbf{x}$, verify that $B^T B = A$ and evaluate $\mathbf{x}^T B^T B\mathbf{x}$ after showing this can also be written $(B\mathbf{x})^T (B\mathbf{x})$. Reconcile the answers.

2.8 Matrix Design

Suppose we seek a matrix A to achieve some transformation $\mathbf{v} = A\mathbf{u}$, such as rotating a vector $\mathbf{u}$ through a given angle. There is a straightforward method for finding A, assuming that it exists. (There are, however, transformations that cannot be represented in this way.)

Consider the 3×3 case. Then any vector can be written:

$$\mathbf{u} = \begin{bmatrix} u_1 & u_2 & u_3 \end{bmatrix}^T = u_1\mathbf{e}_1 + u_2\mathbf{e}_2 + u_3\mathbf{e}_3,$$

where the $\mathbf{e}_i$ are column vector versions of those used in Example 2.13, as alternatives to $\mathbf{i}$, $\mathbf{j}$ and $\mathbf{k}$. Indeed, we shall relate $\mathbf{e}_1 = \begin{bmatrix} 1 & 0 & 0 \end{bmatrix}^T$ to $(1, 0, 0)$, etc., in what follows. Then

$$Au = u_1 A\mathbf{e}_1 + u_2 A\mathbf{e}_2 + u_3 A\mathbf{e}_3$$

$$= \begin{bmatrix} A\mathbf{e}_1 & A\mathbf{e}_2 & A\mathbf{e}_3 \end{bmatrix} \begin{bmatrix} u_1 \\ u_2 \\ u_3 \end{bmatrix}.$$

In other words, A is built up from columns specifying the effect of the transformation on each of the $\mathbf{e}_i$.

Example 2.36   Find a matrix that scales all vectors by a factor β.

We have $\mathbf{e}_1$ related to $(1, 0, 0)$, which is mapped to $(\beta, 0, 0)$, and similarly for $\mathbf{e}_2$ and $\mathbf{e}_3$. Feed $(\beta, 0, 0)$ into the first column of the matrix, and so on, to produce A. It is easily verified that

$$\begin{bmatrix} \beta & 0 & 0 \\ 0 & \beta & 0 \\ 0 & 0 & \beta \end{bmatrix} \begin{bmatrix} p \\ q \\ r \end{bmatrix} = \begin{bmatrix} \beta p \\ \beta q \\ \beta r \end{bmatrix},$$

which describes the required scaling.   ■

We shall now concentrate on the 2×2 case, where:

$$\mathbf{e}_1 = \begin{bmatrix} 1 \\ 0 \end{bmatrix} \text{ relates to } (1, 0), \qquad \mathbf{e}_2 = \begin{bmatrix} 0 \\ 1 \end{bmatrix} \text{ relates to } (0, 1).$$

We set out to find matrices to represent **rotation** about the origin and **reflection** in a line through the origin. Once we have these, the power of matrix multiplication comes into play, to allow investigation of sequences of these. These are fundamental transformations in *computer graphics*, in which matrices are a significant tool.

Firstly, we seek a matrix so that $R(\theta) \begin{bmatrix} x \\ y \end{bmatrix}$ gives the result of rotating (x, y) (written $\begin{bmatrix} x & y \end{bmatrix}^T$) about the origin, through angle θ. The following diagrams show the situation.

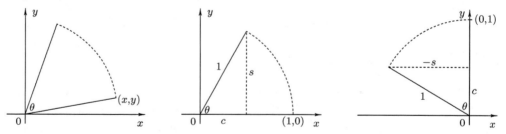

It would clearly be difficult to deal directly with the general situation on the left. But the cases of $(1, 0)$ and $(0, 1)$ are much easier. Noting that $c = \cos\theta$ and $s = \sin\theta$ in the diagrams,

$$(1, 0) \to (\cos\theta, \sin\theta), \qquad (0, 1) \to (-\sin\theta, \cos\theta).$$

Now feed these into the **columns** of $R(\theta)$.

Frame 2.14   *Formula for a rotation matrix*

$$R(\theta) = \begin{bmatrix} \cos\theta & -\sin\theta \\ \sin\theta & \cos\theta \end{bmatrix} \qquad (2.25)$$

There are two reassuring properties of this matrix:

$$\det R(\theta) = \cos^2\theta + \sin^2\theta = 1,$$

which illustrates a property of 2×2 determinants; they measure the factor by which area changes as a result of such a transformation. Rotations do not change areas. Also, using (2.13),

$$R(\theta)^{-1} = \begin{bmatrix} \cos\theta & \sin\theta \\ -\sin\theta & \cos\theta \end{bmatrix} = R(-\theta),$$

which is no surprise: a rotation through $-\theta$ will undo the effect of one through $+\theta$.

Notation

Some books appear to use our $R(-\theta)$ as the matrix for a rotation through θ, but close examination will reveal that the context is different; the point is being held fixed and it is the coordinate axes that are being rotated through θ, which is equivalent to rotating the point through $-\theta$.

The next calculation is to find the matrix $S(\phi)$ for a **reflection** in a line at angle ϕ to the x-axis, as shown in the diagram below. This can be analysed as above, but there is an informative 'trick' available. We rotate (x, y) through $-\phi$, which will also place the line on the x-axis, then reflect in the x-axis, which is easy to do – see the other diagram – finally rotating through $+\phi$ to return to the original scenario.

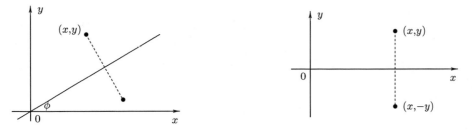

From the second diagram we see that the reflection in the x-axis (a line at angle $0°$) is described by $(x, y) \rightarrow (x, -y)$, and represented by

$$S(0) = \begin{bmatrix} 1 & 0 \\ 0 & -1 \end{bmatrix}.$$

The result of the original reflection is given by the product of the three matrices concerned, but in *right to left* order: $R(\phi)S(0)R(-\phi)$. That is an outcome of the composition mentioned in the previous section: the vector each matrix acts on is at the right and the first matrix to multiply it is $R(-\phi)$. Using the abbreviations $c = \cos\phi$, $s = \sin\phi$, we have the result:

$$S(\phi) = \begin{bmatrix} c & -s \\ s & c \end{bmatrix} \begin{bmatrix} 1 & 0 \\ 0 & -1 \end{bmatrix} \begin{bmatrix} c & s \\ -s & c \end{bmatrix}$$

$$= \begin{bmatrix} c & -s \\ s & c \end{bmatrix} \begin{bmatrix} c & s \\ s & -c \end{bmatrix} = \begin{bmatrix} c^2 - s^2 & 2sc \\ 2sc & -c^2 + s^2 \end{bmatrix}.$$

Using two simple trigonometric identities, this can be rewritten as follows.

Frame 2.15   *Formula for a reflection matrix*

$$S(\phi) = \begin{bmatrix} \cos 2\phi & \sin 2\phi \\ \sin 2\phi & -\cos 2\phi \end{bmatrix} \tag{2.26}$$

As we find for the rotation matrix, there are reassuring properties:

$$\det S(\phi) = -\cos^2 2\phi - \sin^2 2\phi = -1,$$

which reflects the fact that areas are not changed (in size). Also, using (2.13),

$$S(\phi)^{-1} = S(\phi).$$

This is no surprise: two identical reflections bring you back to the start.

The following example illustrates, probably better than any example to date, the power of the matrix representation.

Example 2.37   Find the result of a reflection in a line at 30° to the x-axis, *followed by* one at 60°. (The order does indeed matter here.)

Again using right to left order, the result we wish is described by

$$S(60)S(30) = \begin{bmatrix} -\frac{1}{2} & \frac{\sqrt{3}}{2} \\ \frac{\sqrt{3}}{2} & \frac{1}{2} \end{bmatrix} \begin{bmatrix} \frac{1}{2} & \frac{\sqrt{3}}{2} \\ \frac{\sqrt{3}}{2} & -\frac{1}{2} \end{bmatrix} = \begin{bmatrix} \frac{1}{2} & -\frac{\sqrt{3}}{2} \\ \frac{\sqrt{3}}{2} & \frac{1}{2} \end{bmatrix},$$

on working out the matrix multiplication as usual.

Careful inspection of the result reveals it to be $R(60)$, i.e., a rotation through 60°.   ∎

This result is no accident. The same method, working with general angles, reveals that

$$S(\phi)S(\theta) = R\left[2(\phi - \theta)\right].$$

Hence the product of two reflections is a rotation. This also confirms that the opposite order gives a different result: a rotation in the opposite direction.

A final observation about these matrices is that

$$R(\theta)^{-1} = R(\theta)^T, \qquad S(\phi)^{-1} = S(\phi)^T,$$

so both are **orthogonal** matrices. Lengths remain unchanged, as we would expect.

There are some very important results for 3×3 orthogonal matrices. They have determinant either $+1$ or -1. A matrix of the $+1$ variety represents a rotation about some axis in 3-D space; one of the -1 variety is the same, but with a reflection as well. The rotation can be broken down into the product of three rotations about the coordinate axes: *roll, pitch* and *yaw*.

Ex 2.21 **A shear transformation** leaves the vector $\mathbf{e}_1 = \begin{bmatrix} 1 \\ 0 \end{bmatrix}$ unchanged, but moves $\mathbf{e}_2 = \begin{bmatrix} 0 \\ 1 \end{bmatrix}$ to $\begin{bmatrix} a \\ 1 \end{bmatrix}$, where $a > 0$.

Find the 2×2 matrix P that achieves this. Calculate $P \begin{bmatrix} 1 \\ 1 \end{bmatrix}$ and draw a diagram to illustrate the effect of the transformation.

Ex 2.22 Construct matrices to represent reflections: $P = S(60°)$, $Q = S(30°)$. Calculate PQ and interpret the result.

Ex 2.23 Matrix methods are heavily used in *computer graphics*. One obstacle is that **translation**, where every point in a figure is displaced by the same vector, cannot be represented by a 2×2 matrix multiplication. This is solved by introducing an extra 'dimension', representing the point (x, y) by $\begin{bmatrix} x & y & 1 \end{bmatrix}^T$.

Verify that multiplying $\begin{bmatrix} x & y & 1 \end{bmatrix}^T$ by the matrices:

$$T = \begin{bmatrix} 1 & 0 & a \\ 0 & 1 & b \\ 0 & 0 & 1 \end{bmatrix}, \qquad R = \begin{bmatrix} \cos\theta & -\sin\theta & 0 \\ \sin\theta & \cos\theta & 0 \\ 0 & 0 & 1 \end{bmatrix}$$

delivers translation by the vector (a, b) and rotation through θ, respectively.

Find a matrix that will translate points through $(1, 0)$, **then** rotate through $90°$, verifying your answer geometrically, by examining the effect on $(1, 0)$ and $(0, 1)$.

2.9 Gaussian Elimination

We have described the key use of a matrix as a method for describing certain transformations or 'linkages' by

$$\mathbf{y} = A\mathbf{x}.$$

It is often the case that we can measure or deduce the **output** of such models and wish to calculate the corresponding **input**. In other words, changing to the more normal notation for this context, we wish to calculate $\mathbf{x}$ such that

$$A\mathbf{x} = \mathbf{b} \tag{2.27}$$

for a given $\mathbf{b}$.

This equation can involve a matrix of any size $m \times n$, although the usual situation is that there are infinitely many solutions when $m < n$, when there are fewer equations than unknowns, and no solutions when $m > n$, when there are more equations than unknowns. Hence, for almost all of what follows, we shall consider only the **square** case: $m = n$.

The matrix notation represents a set or **system** of **linear equations**.

Frame 2.16   Standard system of linear equations

$$a_{11}x_1 + a_{12}x_2 + \cdots + a_{1n}x_n = b_1$$
$$a_{21}x_1 + a_{22}x_2 + \cdots + a_{2n}x_n = b_2$$

$$\cdots$$

$$a_{n1}x_1 + a_{n2}x_2 + \cdots + a_{nn}x_n = b_n$$

Having the same number of equations and unknowns holds out hope that there may be a single well-defined solution, which is the usual situation. Our tasks are:

- to find a solution method;

- to use it to test whether there is a solution;

- to implement the method **safely**, **efficiently** and **accurately**.

This last objective is needed because, in practice, n can be very large, e.g., $n \simeq 10,000$ is not unknown. Hence we must minimise the number of calculations to save time and to reduce the effects of rounding errors.

The key process used is **elimination**, in which we can use two equations to 'eliminate' one of the variables. For example, giving the label E_k to the kth equation in Frame 2.16, and concentrating on the first two:

$$E_1: \quad a_{11}x_1 + a_{12}x_2 + \cdots + a_{1n}x_n = b_1$$
$$E_2: \quad a_{21}x_1 + a_{22}x_2 + \cdots + a_{2n}x_n = b_2.$$

$E_2 - \dfrac{a_{21}}{a_{11}}E_1$ gives a new equation in which x_1 does not feature: it has been 'eliminated'.

Example 2.38   Consider the system

$$2x_1 - 3x_2 = -4$$
$$-4x_1 + 5x_2 = 6.$$

We multiply the **first** equation by $-4/2 = -2$ to obtain $-4x_1 + 6x_2 = 8$ and **subtract** it from the **second** to find $-x_2 = -2$.

Thus our 2×2 system has generated an easier 1×1 system, with an obvious solution $x_2 = 2$. The original **first** equation, $2x_1 - 3x_2 = -4$, becomes $2x_1 - 3 \times 2 = -4$, i.e., $2x_1 = 2$ and so $x_1 = 1$. ∎

Applying elimination steps *in such a systematic way* produces a method known as **Gaussian Elimination**, which lies at the heart of most computer packages for solving linear equations.

The idea is to use E_1 with, in turn, E_2, E_3, ..., E_n, to eliminate x_1 and find a new system of $n-1$ equations in the $n-1$ unknowns x_2, ..., x_n. Our system of equations is now one degree smaller in size. Starting anew with this system produces one of size $n-2$ and so on. Eventually we should end up with **one** equation in **one** unknown (x_n).

This can be solved immediately, to commence a phase of the process known as **back-substitution**, in which we work backwards through the different systems, using their first equations to find x_{n-1}, x_{n-2}, ... and eventually x_1.

Think about it like this

There are several ways of organising the calculations that appear in books as *Gaussian Elimination*. For example, some recommend dividing the first equation by a_{11} before starting elimination. The alternatives are indeed equivalent in the amount of calculation required, but the method presented here preserves useful information that other methods lose; we will see in the next chapter how to *read off* the **determinant** from *our* results.

Before looking at further examples, we note a useful preliminary step. Example 2.38 reveals that only the coefficients and the constants on the right played a role in the calculation. We can erase the x_k, the $+$ and $=$ signs to make the problem easier to read. In the calculation we then rely on its position in the resulting tableau to tell us the status of each number. This is precisely what matrix notation delivers and this initial tableau is called the **augmented matrix**.

Frame 2.17   *The augmented matrix for A$\mathbf{x}$=$\mathbf{b}$*

$$\begin{bmatrix} a_{11} & a_{12} & \cdots & a_{1n} & | & b_1 \\ a_{21} & a_{22} & \cdots & a_{2n} & | & b_2 \\ \vdots & \vdots & \ddots & \vdots & | & \vdots \\ a_{n1} & a_{n2} & \cdots & a_{nn} & | & b_n \end{bmatrix}$$

The vertical division is optional, but does serve a purpose in making it clear to the reader that the matrix is an augmented one.

Example 2.39 The augmented matrix for the system in Example 2.38 is

$$\begin{bmatrix} 2 & -3 & | & -4 \\ -4 & 5 & | & 6 \end{bmatrix}.$$

■

Although this elimination method should be mastered by practising with numbers, rather than by memorising formulae, we shall preface the examples that follow with a typical solution lay-out for a 3×3 system. For such a system we can simplify the notation, using x, y, z for the unknowns and labels A, B, C for the rows. We typically have a **tableau**:

A	a_1	a_2	a_3	r_1	
B	b_1	b_2	b_3	r_2	
C	c_1	c_2	c_3	r_3	
B'	0	$\bar{b}_2$	$\bar{b}_3$	$\bar{r}_2$	$B - \alpha A$
C'	0	$\bar{c}_2$	$\bar{c}_3$	$\bar{r}_3$	$C - \beta A$
C''	0	0	$\hat{c}_3$	$\hat{r}_3$	$C' - \gamma B'$

Here the key **multipliers** are:

$$\alpha = \frac{b_1}{a_1}, \qquad \beta = \frac{c_1}{a_1}, \qquad \gamma = \frac{\bar{c}_2}{\bar{b}_2}.$$

From this tableau, we can complete the solution by **back-substitution**, finding:

$$z \text{ from } C'', \quad y \text{ from } B', \quad x \text{ from } A.$$

A look at this calculation shows the key role played by a_1, $\bar{b}_2$ and $\hat{c}_3$. These are called **pivots** and the rows they occur in are **pivotal rows**. For a reason associated with maintaining accuracy, the back-substitution phase of the process should *always* be carried out using the pivotal rows.

Example 2.40   Solve the system:

$$x - y + 2z = -1$$
$$2x - y + 2z = 1$$
$$-x + 3y - 3z = 4.$$

Set up the augmented matrix and complete the tableau:

A	1	-1	2	-1	
B	2	-1	2	1	
C	-1	3	-3	4	
B'	0	1	-2	3	$B - 2A$
C'	0	2	-1	3	$C + A$
C''	0	0	$\mathbf{3}$	-3	$C' - 2B'$

The pivots are shown in bold type. The solution is completed using back-substitution in the pivotal rows:

$$3z = -3 \qquad \Rightarrow \quad z = -1,$$
$$y - 2z = 3 \quad \Rightarrow \quad y + 2 = 3 \qquad \Rightarrow \quad y = 1,$$
$$x - y + 2z = -1 \quad \Rightarrow \quad x - 1 - 2 = -1 \quad \Rightarrow \quad x = 2,$$

and the final solution is $\mathbf{x} = \begin{bmatrix} 2 & 1 & -1 \end{bmatrix}^T$.   ∎

Note, particularly, that in every case the procedure has used:

new row = old row − multiple of pivotal row.

Deviations from this can destroy efficiency, accuracy and undermine the bonus of finding the determinant. This rule can lead to unpleasant arithmetic, but the calculations are usually carried out on computers, which are unperturbed by non-integers.

The only way in which the method can break down is if a pivot is zero, when the necessary division will fail. There are two cases to consider.

If any pivot, other than the final one, is zero it is usually possibly to work round the problem by swapping two rows. We look **below** the current zero pivot to see if there is a non-zero value in its column. If so, swap the two rows: changing the order of linear equations does not change the solution. (We cannot look above, since that will involve a previous pivotal row, which would bring back variables already eliminated.)

Example 2.41 Consider the tableau:

A	**−1**	2	3	1	
B	2	−4	−4	0	
C	1	−1	−1	1	
B'	0	0	2	2	$B+2A$
C'	0	1	2	2	$C+A$
C'	0	**1**	2	2	
B'	0	0	2	2	
B''	0	0	**2**	2	$B'-0C'$

From this, we complete the solution by:

$$(B'') \qquad\qquad\qquad 2z = 2 \qquad\qquad \Rightarrow \quad z = 1,$$
$$(C') \quad y + 2z = 2 \qquad \Rightarrow \quad y + 2 = 2 \qquad \Rightarrow \quad y = 0,$$
$$(A) \quad -x + 2y + 3z = 1 \quad \Rightarrow \quad -x + 0 + 3 = 1 \quad \Rightarrow \quad x = 2.$$

■

Think about it like this

This swapping process is called **pivoting**. In automatic computation, pivoting is always considered even when the natural pivot is non-zero. The computer chooses the largest possible pivot in the column, to protect against growth in rounding errors. This is rarely done in hand calculation using exact arithmetic, since it usually guarantees the occurrence of fractions.

The second case is when the final pivot is zero, in which case there are no further rows to consider for a swap. (This can also occur earlier, if all candidates for pivot are zero.) This case is described as **singular** and the system will have no solution or an infinite number of solutions. We shall not pursue this here – other than by a simple example – although we shall return to a special case in §2.11.

Example 2.42   Given the two vectors $\mathbf{u}_1 = (1, -2)$ and $\mathbf{u}_2 = (-2, 4)$, write each of the vectors $(3, -5)$ and $(3, -6)$ in the form $x\mathbf{u}_1 + y\mathbf{u}_2$.

This requires solution of $A\mathbf{x} = \mathbf{b}$, with

$$A = \begin{bmatrix} 1 & -2 \\ -2 & 4 \end{bmatrix}, \quad \mathbf{b}_1 = \begin{bmatrix} 3 \\ -5 \end{bmatrix}, \quad \mathbf{b}_2 = \begin{bmatrix} 3 \\ -6 \end{bmatrix}.$$

The two cases can be performed in one tableau, since all the decisions and multipliers in the elimination relate only to A.

A	**1**	-2	3	3	
B	-2	4	-5	-6	
B'	0	0	1	0	$B + 2A$

The final pivot is zero, which does not invalidate the elimination phase, but it prevents the back-substitution phase from starting. The system is singular.

In the first case, the final equation states $0 = 1$ and that is clearly impossible, so there is **no solution**.

In the second case, the final equation states $0 = 0$, which causes no problem, but means that we have only one equation for our two unknowns: the second equation is precisely -2 times the first. There is an **infinite number of solutions**: $x = 3 + 2k$, $y = k$ for any number k.

Geometrically, the vectors $\mathbf{u}_1$ and $\mathbf{u}_2$ are parallel, so they can generate only vectors in that single direction. $(3, -5)$ points in a different direction and so cannot be expressed in the desired form. $(3, -6)$, however, is also parallel to $\mathbf{u}_1$ and $\mathbf{u}_2$, which means it can be so expressed, but in many different ways.   ∎

The occurrence of a singular system is usually – but not always – a danger sign and requires careful investigation.

Ex 2.24

(a) Write the following set of equations in matrix form:

$$a + 3b - 7c = 0$$
$$3a - 2b \quad\quad = 7$$
$$-b + 4c = -2$$

(b) Use Gaussian elimination to solve:

$$2I_1 + I_2 = -4$$
$$3I_1 + 5I_2 = 1$$

(c) Use Gaussian elimination to solve:

$$-x + 2y + z = 2$$
$$y - 2z = -3$$
$$x + 4y - z = 4$$

Ex 2.25

(a) Solve the following system of equations using Gaussian elimination; do not change their order during the calculation.

$$2x + 3y + 5z = 10$$
$$3x + 7y + 4z = 3$$
$$x + 2y + 2z = 3$$

(b) Use appropriate pivoting to solve:

$$-y + z = -1$$
$$2z = -4$$
$$x + y - 2z = 4$$

Ex 2.26 Apply Gaussian elimination (without any change in the order of the equations) to the following system of equations, to find z:

$$0.900\,x + 0.120\,y + \qquad 0.936\,z = 1.200$$
$$0.450\,x - 0.780\,y + \qquad 0.708\,z = 0.000$$
$$0.150\,x - 0.820\,y + (0.376 + \alpha)z = -0.410 + \beta$$

Suppose that α and β represent errors in the last two numbers, with error bounds $|\alpha| \leqslant 0.001$ and $|\beta| \leqslant 0.001$. Find an interval inside which z must lie, whatever the values of α and β. Comment on its size.

Ex 2.27 Find the value of α for which the following system of equations has an infinite number of solutions:

$$2x + 3y = 6$$
$$6x + \alpha y = 18.$$

Ex 2.28 Investigate whether each of the following systems of equations has a solution:

(a) $x - 2y = 0$ (b) $x - y = 1$ (c) $x - y = -4$ (d) $2x - y = 2$
     $-2x + y = -3$ $-2x + 2y = -3$ $2x + 3y = 7$ $4x - 2y = 4$

2.10   Calculation of the Inverse

It may be thought that Gaussian Elimination could be avoided by using the **inverse matrix**:

$$A\mathbf{x} = \mathbf{b} \quad \Rightarrow \quad \mathbf{x} = A^{-1}\mathbf{b}.$$

This is indeed correct, but is only usable when we already know the inverse, e.g., when A is **orthogonal**.

The problem is that the most efficient way to calculate an inverse matrix in general is, in fact, to use **Gaussian Elimination**. Also, this calculation involves an 'overhead', with extra calculations that can never have their cost recouped, no matter how many times we use the inverse. If, however, we really do require the inverse, the following is a viable method.

First of all, we note that the matrix product AB can be viewed as a sequence of **matrix-vector** products:

$$A \begin{bmatrix} \mathbf{b}_1 & \mathbf{b}_2 & \cdots & \mathbf{b}_p \end{bmatrix} = \begin{bmatrix} A\mathbf{b}_1 & A\mathbf{b}_2 & \cdots & A\mathbf{b}_p \end{bmatrix},$$

where the $\mathbf{b}_k$ are the **columns** of B.

Suppose that A^{-1} has columns $\mathbf{x}_1, \ldots, \mathbf{x}_n$. We can rewrite $AA^{-1} = I$ as

$$\begin{bmatrix} A\mathbf{x}_1 & A\mathbf{x}_2 & \cdots & A\mathbf{x}_n \end{bmatrix} = \begin{bmatrix} \mathbf{e}_1 & \mathbf{e}_2 & \cdots & \mathbf{e}_n \end{bmatrix},$$

where the $\mathbf{e}_k$ are the columns of I, like those used in §2.8.

Thus, determination of A^{-1} is equivalent to solving the n systems of linear equations $A\mathbf{x}_k = \mathbf{e}_k$. Further, Example 2.42 showed that we can solve a collection of systems with the same matrix using a single tableau, with multiple augmentation on the right.

This is the required method:

1. Set up an augmented matrix of the form $[A \,|\, I]$.

2. Perform Gaussian Elimination, treating all columns of I simultaneously.

3. If an unavoidable zero pivot occurs, the matrix is singular and has no inverse.

4. Perform back-substitution, one column at a time, to find the columns of the inverse.

5. (An alternative to 4.) Perform an 'upside down' elimination, clearing non-diagonal terms in column n, then $n-1$, and so on, until a diagonal matrix appears on the left. Then divide each row by its diagonal element. This will leave the tableau in the form $[I \,|\, A^{-1}]$.

The alternative method is recommended for large systems, but the complexities of its description outweigh its benefits for small orders.

Example 2.43   Invert $\begin{bmatrix} 1 & -1 \\ -3 & 2 \end{bmatrix}$.

The tableau is:

A	**1**	-1	1	0
B	-3	2	0	1
B'	0	-1	3	1	$B+3A$

The back-substitutions give:

col 1: $-y = 3$, $y = -3$; $x - y = 1$, $x + 3 = 1$, $x = -2$;

col 2: $-y = 1$, $y = -1$; $x - y = 0$, $x + 1 = 0$, $x = -1$.

Hence the inverse is: $\begin{bmatrix} -2 & -1 \\ -3 & -1 \end{bmatrix}$. ∎

Row swaps are also allowed and will be used to overcome zero pivots in the non-singular case.

Example 2.44   Invert: $\begin{bmatrix} 1 & -1 & 0 \\ 2 & -2 & -2 \\ -2 & 1 & 2 \end{bmatrix}$.

A	**1**	−1	0	1	0	0	
B	2	−2	−2	0	1	0	
C	−2	1	2	0	0	1	
B'	0	0	−2	−2	1	0	$B-2A$
C'	0	−1	2	2	0	1	$C+2A$
C'	0	**−1**	2	2	0	1	
B'	0	0	**−2**	−2	1	0	

We ought to perform an elimination in the second column, but the $(3,2)$-element is already zero. Hence, proceed to back-substitution:

col 1: $-2z = -2$, $z = 1$; $-y + 2z = 2$, $y = 0$; $x - y = 1$, $x = 1$;

col 2: $-2z = 1$, $z = -1/2$; $-y + 2z = 0$, $y = -1$; $x - y = 0$, $x = -1$;

col 3: $-2z = 0$, $z = 0$; $-y + 2z = 1$, $y = -1$; $x - y = 0$, $x = -1$.

Hence the inverse is: $\begin{bmatrix} 1 & -1 & -1 \\ 0 & -1 & -1 \\ 1 & -1/2 & 0 \end{bmatrix}$. ∎

This method is particularly useful when only one element of the inverse is required. To find the (i, j)-element, use only $\mathbf{e}_j$ on the right and stop the back-substitution when the ith value has been found.

Think about it like this

Such a calculation is useful in *sensitivity analysis*. Suppose $A\mathbf{x} = \mathbf{y}$, where $B = A^{-1}$. If we change (only) x_j to $x_j + \Delta$, then y_i will change to $y_i + a_{ij}\Delta$.

If, however, we ask what the effect on x_i of a change Δ in y_j is, the answer is $b_{ij}\Delta$. In such a case this may be the only element in the inverse matrix that we need.

Ex 2.29 Use Gaussian Elimination to find the inverse of: $\begin{bmatrix} 1 & -1 \\ -2 & 3 \end{bmatrix}$.

Verify your answer using the formula for the inverse.

Ex 2.30

(a) Complete the calculation of the inverse of A from the table

$$A = \begin{bmatrix} 2 & 2 & -1 \\ -2 & -1 & 0 \\ 1 & 1 & -1 \end{bmatrix}$$

A	2	2	-1	$\mid$	1	0	0
B'	0	1	-1	$\mid$	1	1	0
C''	0	0	$-\frac{1}{2}$	$\mid$	$-\frac{1}{2}$	0	1

(b) Use Gaussian Elimination to find the inverse (if any) of:

$$\text{i.} \quad \begin{bmatrix} 1 & 0 & 1 \\ 0 & 0 & 1 \\ 1 & 1 & 0 \end{bmatrix}, \qquad \text{ii.} \quad \begin{bmatrix} 1 & 1 & -1 \\ 1 & 2 & 3 \\ 5 & 7 & 3 \end{bmatrix}.$$

2.11   Homogeneous Equations

One would be forgiven for thinking that **singularity** is a 'bad thing'. After all, our matrix has no inverse and any linear equations have no unique solution. There are, however, circumstances in which this is precisely what we require.

> *Frame 2.18*   *Definition of a system of homogeneous equations*
>
> $$A\mathbf{x} = \mathbf{0} \text{ is a } \textbf{homogeneous} \text{ system}$$

Suppose that A is non-singular in such a system. Then

$$A\mathbf{x} = \mathbf{0} \quad \Rightarrow \quad \mathbf{x} = A^{-1}\mathbf{0} = \mathbf{0},$$

which is called the **trivial solution**. Homogeneous equations always have $\mathbf{x} = \mathbf{0}$ as a solution; the problem with non-singular systems is that it is the *only* solution and is not of much interest.

Thus, for these systems we usually wish the system to be *singular*. Typical of the advantages is the fact that

$$A\mathbf{x} = \mathbf{0} \quad \Rightarrow \quad A(k\mathbf{x}) = k\mathbf{0} = \mathbf{0},$$

so that $k\mathbf{x}$ is also a solution. This allows us to choose k for some particular purpose, e.g., to make the solution a unit vector or to clear fractions from its elements.

The solution method is based on **Gaussian Elimination**. There is no need to use an augmented matrix since the last column starts as zero and remains zero. Assuming that we find a zero pivot only at the last step – we shall not investigate the more complicated situation when this happens earlier – we set the last variable to be k and use back-substitution to find all others in terms of k. In the following calculations we shall assume that $\mathbf{x}$ is the vector $\begin{bmatrix} x & y & z \end{bmatrix}^T$ rather than the more formally correct $\begin{bmatrix} x_1 & x_2 & x_3 \end{bmatrix}^T$, to avoid subscripts.

Example 2.45 Solve $\begin{bmatrix} 1 & -1 & 0 \\ -2 & 1 & 1 \\ 3 & -2 & -1 \end{bmatrix} \mathbf{x} = \mathbf{0}$.

A	**1**	-1	0	
B	-2	1	1	
C	3	-2	-1	
B'	0	-1	1	$B+2A$
C'	0	1	-1	$C-3A$
C''	0	0	0	$C'+B'$

The last row shows the matrix to be singular, and offers no information. Set $z = k$ and use back-substitution:

$$(B') \quad -y + z = 0 \quad \Rightarrow \quad y = k; \qquad (A) \quad x - y = 0 \quad \Rightarrow \quad x = k.$$

The general solution is $x = y = z = k$, i.e., $\mathbf{x} = k \begin{bmatrix} 1 & 1 & 1 \end{bmatrix}^T$. ∎

The following two examples illustrate the sort of context in which homogeneous systems arise and in which the lack of a unique solution is natural rather than problematic. The examples are small-scale, as is necessary for hand calculations, but could readily be scaled up for automatic computation.

Example 2.46 *Dimensional analysis* is a powerful technique in practical work. In this, combinations of physical variables are analysed in terms of their mass (M), length (L), time (T) and temperature (θ) content. One objective is to identify *dimensionless* combinations, which are potentially key physical parameters.

Suppose we have a model using:

$$\begin{array}{lll}
\text{heat transfer coefficient:} & h & MT^{-3}\theta^{-1}, \\
\text{heat conductivity:} & k & MLT^{-3}\theta^{-1}, \\
\text{viscosity:} & \mu & ML^{-1}T^{-1}, \\
\text{specific heat:} & C_p & L^2T^{-2}\theta^{-1}.
\end{array}$$

We seek a quantity $h^x k^y \mu^z C_p^w$ containing no M, L, T or θ. Then

$$\begin{array}{llll}
(M) & x + y + z & = 0 \\
(L) & y - z + 2w = 0 \\
(T) & -3x - 3y - z - 2w = 0 \\
(\theta) & -x - y \quad - w = 0
\end{array}$$

which is a homogeneous system. Set up a tableau and use Gaussian Elimination.

$$
\begin{array}{c|cccc|l}
A & \mathbf{1} & 1 & 1 & 0 & \\
B & 0 & 1 & -1 & 2 & \\
C & -3 & -3 & -1 & -2 & \\
D & -1 & -1 & 0 & -1 & \\
\hline
B' & 0 & \mathbf{1} & -1 & 2 & B \\
C' & 0 & 0 & 2 & -2 & C+3A \\
D' & 0 & 0 & 1 & -1 & D+A \\
\hline
C'' & 0 & 0 & \mathbf{2} & -2 & C' \\
D'' & 0 & 0 & 0 & 0 & D'-\frac{1}{2}C'
\end{array}
$$

The last row confirms that the system is singular, else there would be no solution of any interest. Let $w = \lambda$, since k is already in use. Back-substitution gives:

$$2z - 2w = 0, \ z = \lambda; \quad y - z + 2w = 0, \ y = -\lambda; \quad x + y + z = 0, \ x = 0.$$

Setting $\lambda = 1$, we have $x = 0$, $y = -1$, $z = 1$, $w = 1$ and the desired dimensionless combination is $\dfrac{C_p \mu}{k}$.

Other values of λ merely give powers of this quantity, which also must be dimensionless. For example, $\lambda = -1$ gives $\dfrac{k}{C_p \mu}$.   ■

The matrix involved in these homogeneous equations need not be square, as the following example shows.

Example 2.47 Find **integers** x, y, z, w to balance the chemical equation

$$x\mathrm{NH}_3 + y\mathrm{Cl}_2 \rightarrow z\mathrm{NCl}_3 + w\mathrm{NH}_4\mathrm{Cl}.$$

Equate the nitrogen, hydrogen and chlorine atoms on each side:

$$
\begin{aligned}
(\mathtt{N}) \quad & x \quad\quad\quad - z - w = 0 \\
(\mathtt{H}) \quad & 3x \quad\quad\quad\ \ - 4w = 0 \\
(\mathtt{Cl}) \quad & \quad\quad 2y - 3z - w = 0
\end{aligned}
$$

which is a homogeneous system. Set up a tableau and use Gaussian Elimination.

$$
\begin{array}{c|cccc|l}
A & \mathbf{1} & 0 & -1 & -1 & \\
B & 3 & 0 & 0 & -4 & \\
C & 0 & 2 & -3 & -1 & \\
\hline
B' & 0 & 0 & 3 & -1 & B-3A \\
C' & 0 & 2 & -3 & -1 & C \\
\hline
C' & 0 & \mathbf{2} & -3 & -1 & \\
B' & 0 & 0 & \mathbf{3} & -1 &
\end{array}
$$

Let $w = k$ and use back-substitution:

$$3z - w = 0, \ z = \tfrac{1}{3}k; \quad 2y - 3z - w = 0, \ y = k; \quad x - z - w = 0, \ x = \tfrac{4}{3}k.$$

Setting $k = 3$, which is the simplest choice that clears fractions, we have $x = 4$, $y = 3$, $z = 1$, $w = 3$ and the balanced equation is:

$$4\text{NH}_3 + 3\text{Cl}_2 \rightarrow \text{NCl}_3 + 3\text{NH}_4\text{Cl}.$$

∎

Ex 2.31 Solve the following homogeneous systems of equations:

$$\begin{bmatrix} 2 & -1 \\ 1 & 1 \end{bmatrix} \begin{bmatrix} x_1 \\ x_2 \end{bmatrix} = \begin{bmatrix} 0 \\ 0 \end{bmatrix}, \qquad \begin{bmatrix} -2 & 1 \\ 4 & -2 \end{bmatrix} \begin{bmatrix} x_1 \\ x_2 \end{bmatrix} = \begin{bmatrix} 0 \\ 0 \end{bmatrix}.$$

Ex 2.32 Use linear equations to balance the equation:

$$\text{Ca} + \text{H}_3\text{PO}_4 \rightarrow \text{Ca}_3\text{P}_2\text{O}_8 + \text{H}_2.$$

2.12 Method of Least Squares

A system of equations $A\mathbf{x} = \mathbf{b}$ where A is $m \times n$ with $m > n$ is unlikely to have a solution. There are more equations than the number of variables we have available and the system is **overconstrained**. Gaussian Elimination will run out of pivots after at most n steps, leaving $m - n$ zero rows for the matrix and the likelihood of some non-zero elements in the right-hand column, giving a contradiction of the type $0 = 1$.

Such systems do arise in practice, however, where the objective can only be to satisfy them 'as well as possible'.

Example 2.48 Fit a straight line $y = \alpha + \beta x$ to the measured data:

x_k	0	1	2	3	4
y_k	11	33	49	72	95

Forcing the data points to satisfy the equation produces five equations, in matrix form:

$$\begin{bmatrix} 1 & 0 \\ 1 & 1 \\ 1 & 2 \\ 1 & 3 \\ 1 & 4 \end{bmatrix} \begin{bmatrix} \alpha \\ \beta \end{bmatrix} = \begin{bmatrix} 11 \\ 33 \\ 49 \\ 72 \\ 95 \end{bmatrix}.$$

It is easily seen that there is no solution for these equations. ∎

The most popular approach to this problem is to seek a **least-squares** solution. Having chosen some set of x values, write the kth equation as

$$a_{k1}x_1 + a_{k2}x_2 + \cdots + a_{kn}x_n = y_k + \epsilon_k,$$

where ϵ_k is the 'error', judged by how much we have failed to satisfy the equation. The 'best' set of x values will

$$\textbf{minimise} : \epsilon_1^2 + \epsilon_2^2 + \cdots + \epsilon_m^2.$$

It can be shown (using detailed matrix calculations) that this occurs when $\mathbf{x}$ satisfies the **normal equations**.

Frame 2.19   *The normal equations for $A\mathbf{x}=\mathbf{b}$*

$$A^T A\mathbf{x} = A^T\mathbf{b} \qquad\qquad (2.28)$$

It is straightforward to show that $A^T A$ is square and symmetric.

Example 2.49   For the data in Example 2.48,

$$A^T A = \begin{bmatrix} 5 & 10 \\ 10 & 30 \end{bmatrix}, \qquad A^T\mathbf{b} = \begin{bmatrix} 260 \\ 727 \end{bmatrix},$$

and the normal equations become

$$5\alpha + 10\beta = 260$$
$$10\alpha + 30\beta = 727$$

These are easily solved by elimination to give α and β and the least-squares fit (to 3 sf)

$$y = 10.6 + 20.7x.$$

The following graph illustrates the quality of the result.

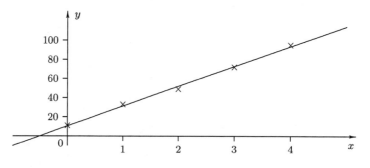

The general form of the normal equations for fitting straight lines is given in the following frame. It is programmed into many hand calculators, where it is usually called by the name favoured by statisticians: **regression**.

Frame 2.20   *Calculation of the regression line for m data pairs (x_k, y_k)*

$$\begin{bmatrix} m & \sum x_k \\ \sum x_k & \sum x_k^2 \end{bmatrix} \begin{bmatrix} \alpha \\ \beta \end{bmatrix} = \begin{bmatrix} \sum y_k \\ \sum x_k y_k \end{bmatrix}$$

Although this procedure is attractive, great care is needed when n is large, since the normal equations produce an $n \times n$ matrix that is almost singular. That makes it difficult to find *accurate* solutions, due to growth in any rounding errors in the calculation. The simple case in Frame 2.20, where $n = 2$, is perfectly safe.

Ex 2.33 The following (x, y) data values are to be 'best' fitted by the line $y = \alpha + \beta x$:

$$(2, 20), \ (3, 42), \ (4, 70).$$

Write down the three conditions for α and β. Rewrite them in the form $P\mathbf{z} \simeq \mathbf{q}$. Construct $P^T P \mathbf{z} = P^T \mathbf{q}$ and solve that system for $\mathbf{z} = \begin{bmatrix} \alpha & \beta \end{bmatrix}^T$.

Ex 2.34 Find a **best least squares** fit of the form $y = \alpha + \beta x$, for the following data set. You should do this by constructing and solving the **normal equations**. (It is sensible to ignore the '00' at the end of the y data and multiply the values of α and β by 100 at the end.)

x_i	10	20	30	40	50	60
y_i	5500	5000	4800	3700	2500	2800

2.13   Revision Exercises

Ex 2.35 Given the following values for matrices A, B and C

$$A = \begin{bmatrix} 2 & 1 \\ 0 & 1 \\ -1 & 2 \end{bmatrix}, \qquad B = \begin{bmatrix} 2 & 1 \\ -1 & 1 \end{bmatrix}, \qquad C = \begin{bmatrix} 3 & 0 & 1 \\ 2 & 2 & -1 \end{bmatrix},$$

determine which of the following exist, finding values for those that do.

(a) $A^T + 2C$,   (b) BA,   (c) AC^T,   (d) BC,   (e) $C^T B$.

Ex 2.36 Two products, A and B use components P, Q and R, as follows:

$$A: \ \ 3 \text{ of } P, \ \ 4 \text{ of } Q, \ \ 7 \text{ of } R; \qquad B: \ \ 6 \text{ of } P, \ \ 1 \text{ of } Q, \ \ 5 \text{ of } R.$$

Use a matrix formulation to answer the following:

(a) P cost £5 each, Q cost £4 each, R cost £8 each. Calculate the material costs for A and B separately.

(b) It is intended to make 100 of A and 50 of B. Calculate how many of each component must be obtained.

Ex 2.37 Let the matrices A, B, C and the column vectors $\mathbf{x}$, $\mathbf{y}$ be defined as

$$A = \begin{bmatrix} 2 & 1 \\ 1 & 0 \end{bmatrix}, \quad B = \begin{bmatrix} 1 & -1 & 1 \\ 2 & 0 & -1 \end{bmatrix}, \quad C = \begin{bmatrix} 1 & 2 \\ 2 & 1 \\ 0 & -1 \end{bmatrix}, \quad \mathbf{x} = \begin{bmatrix} 1 \\ -2 \end{bmatrix}, \quad \mathbf{y} = \begin{bmatrix} -1 \\ 0 \\ 1 \end{bmatrix}.$$

For each of the following, explain why the product is not defined or else calculate the product:

$$A^2, \quad C^T A, \quad \mathbf{x}^T A \mathbf{x}, \quad C^T \mathbf{y}, \quad \mathbf{y}^T B \mathbf{x}, \quad C^T B^T.$$

Ex 2.38 Calculate $A\mathbf{x}$ where $A = \begin{bmatrix} \frac{1}{\sqrt{2}} & -\frac{1}{\sqrt{2}} \\ \frac{1}{\sqrt{2}} & \frac{1}{\sqrt{2}} \end{bmatrix}$ and $\mathbf{x}$ is each of the column vectors representing the points $(1, 0)$ and $(0, 1)$ in the coordinate plane.

Plot the results of these calculations and hence describe geometrically the effect of the matrix A.

Without calculation, write down the value of A^4.

Ex 2.39 Find the inverse of the matrix $A = \begin{bmatrix} 2 & 1 \\ 4 & 3 \end{bmatrix}$ and hence solve, for X, the equation $XA = \begin{bmatrix} 2 & -3 \\ 4 & 0 \end{bmatrix}$.

Ex 2.40 Write the following equations in the form $A\mathbf{x} = \mathbf{0}$.

$$\begin{array}{rrrcl} -x_1 & -x_2 & +x_3 & = & 0 \\ x_1 & & -x_3 & = & 0 \\ 2x_1 & +x_2 & -2x_3 & = & 0 \end{array}$$

Use the substitution $\mathbf{x} = B\mathbf{y}$ with $B = \begin{bmatrix} 2 & 2 & 1 \\ -2 & -1 & 0 \\ 1 & 1 & 1 \end{bmatrix}$ to find a set of equations for $\mathbf{y}$.

Find the general solution for $\mathbf{y}$ and hence that for $\mathbf{x}$.

Ex 2.41 Use Gaussian elimination to show that the following system of equations has **no solution** for one particular value of θ. What is that value?

$$\begin{array}{rrrrrcr} x & + & y & + & z & = & 0 \\ 2x & - & 2y & + & z & = & -1 \\ -2x & + & 2y & + & \theta z & = & 2 \end{array}$$

Complete the solution for x, y and z, in the case $\theta = 0$.

Ex 2.42 Complete the following calculation, to find the inverse of:

$$M = \begin{bmatrix} 1 & -1 & 1 \\ 1 & -2 & 2 \\ -2 & 3 & -2 \end{bmatrix} \qquad \begin{array}{c} A \\ B' \\ C'' \end{array} \left[\begin{array}{rrr|rrr} 1 & -1 & 1 & 1 & 0 & 0 \\ 0 & -1 & 1 & -1 & 1 & 0 \\ 0 & 0 & 1 & 1 & 1 & 1 \end{array} \right]$$

3 DETERMINANTS

Like a matrix, a **determinant** is an array or grid of **elements**, but always *square*. There are rules that allow us, in principle, to calculate the determinant as a single *number* (or a single expression, should the elements involve symbols).

Determinants, being effectively a single quantity, do not have the power and range of applications of matrices, although they are closely related, in the sense that a square matrix has an associated determinant, evaluated by interpreting its array as that of a determinant. Indeed, this is one of the applications of determinants, key examples of which are:

- A matrix is **singular** if and only if its determinant is zero.

- Some formulae, especially in 3-D geometry, can be succinctly written using determinants.

- In a change of variables, determinants measure the resulting change in areas or volumes, which is useful in integration by substitution.

Evaluation of determinants in general is time-consuming, although this is less of a problem when:

- the order is small, e.g., 2×2 or 3×3;

- there is a regular pattern in the rows or columns (not pursued here);

- there are many zero elements.

3.1 Definition of Low-Order Determinants

A **determinant** consists of a square array of elements, written like a matrix, but bounded by vertical lines, e.g.,

$$\begin{vmatrix} a_{11} & a_{12} \\ a_{21} & a_{22} \end{vmatrix}.$$

If the corresponding matrix is A, then this is abbreviated as $\det A$ or $|A|$, although we shall avoid the $|A|$ notation because of the danger of confusion with the absolute value.

The value of a determinant can be defined in several (consistent) ways, but the easiest to translate into practice is based on **recursion**. The value of an $n \times n$ determinant can be given in terms of n determinants, each with order $(n-1) \times (n-1)$. Applying this repeatedly will eventually produce an expression in 1×1 determinants.

We thus have to define a 1×1 determinant $|x|$. The appropriate value is x, which creates a notational problem: if $x < 0$ this conflicts with the absolute value. For this reason we rarely use 1×1 determinants, preferring to stop the recurrence at the 2×2 level. We already know the required value, defined below Frame 2.10.

Frame 3.1   *Value of 2×2 determinant*

$$\det A = \begin{vmatrix} a & b \\ c & d \end{vmatrix} = ad - bc \qquad (3.1)$$

We shall consider the general recurrence in §3.3, but our main applications are for the 3×3 case, so it is worth setting out this special example of the general **cofactor** expansion.

Frame 3.2   *Value of 3×3 determinant*

$$\det A = \begin{vmatrix} a_1 & a_2 & a_3 \\ b_1 & b_2 & b_3 \\ c_1 & c_2 & c_3 \end{vmatrix} = a_1 \begin{vmatrix} b_2 & b_3 \\ c_2 & c_3 \end{vmatrix} - a_2 \begin{vmatrix} b_1 & b_3 \\ c_1 & c_3 \end{vmatrix} + a_3 \begin{vmatrix} b_1 & b_2 \\ c_1 & c_2 \end{vmatrix} \qquad (3.2)$$

There are names for parts of this expansion, which we shall give later. Meanwhile the key features are the 2×2 determinants associated with the elements in the top row – each is found by erasing the row and column containing the associated element – and the alternating signs: $+ - +$.

Example 3.1   In the following calculation, note how useful it is when an element in the top row is zero: we need not work out the associated 2×2 determinant.

$$\begin{vmatrix} 2 & 0 & -1 \\ 1 & 2 & 3 \\ 1 & -1 & -1 \end{vmatrix} = 2 \begin{vmatrix} 2 & 3 \\ -1 & -1 \end{vmatrix} - 0 + (-1) \begin{vmatrix} 1 & 2 \\ 1 & -1 \end{vmatrix}$$

$$= 2\left[2 \times (-1) - 3 \times (-1)\right] - \left[1 \times (-1) - 2 \times 1\right]$$

$$= 2 + 3 = 5.$$

∎

The expression in Frame 3.2 can be expanded using Frame 3.1, to obtain a direct formula, without other determinants.

Frame 3.3   *Alternative expression for 3×3 determinant*

$$a_1 b_2 c_3 + a_2 b_3 c_1 + a_3 b_1 c_2 - a_3 b_2 c_1 - a_2 b_1 c_3 - a_1 b_3 c_2 \qquad (3.3)$$

This should not be memorised as a formula, but as a pattern of so-called "broken diagonals": $+$ for NW–SE and $-$ for NE–SW. In the diagram below, the plain, barred and hatted elements are multiplied separately:

$$\begin{vmatrix} a_1 & \bar{a}_2 & \hat{a}_3 \\ \hat{b}_1 & b_2 & \bar{b}_3 \\ \bar{c}_1 & \hat{c}_2 & c_3 \end{vmatrix} - \begin{vmatrix} \hat{a}_1 & \bar{a}_2 & a_3 \\ \bar{b}_1 & b_2 & \hat{b}_3 \\ c_1 & \hat{c}_2 & \bar{c}_3 \end{vmatrix}.$$

Example 3.2 For the determinant in Example 3.1,

$$\begin{vmatrix} 2 & 0 & -1 \\ 1 & 2 & 3 \\ 1 & -1 & -1 \end{vmatrix} = 2 \cdot 2 \cdot (-1) + 0 \cdot 3 \cdot 1 + (-1) \cdot 1 \cdot (-1)$$

$$- (-1) \cdot 2 \cdot 1 - 0 \cdot 1 \cdot (-1) - 2 \cdot 3 \cdot (-1)$$

$$= -4 + 0 + 1 + 2 - 0 + 6 = 5.$$

■

Ex 3.1 Evaluate $\begin{vmatrix} -2 & -7 \\ 3 & -5 \end{vmatrix}$.

Ex 3.2

(a) Evaluate $\begin{vmatrix} a & 0 \\ b & c \end{vmatrix}$, $\begin{vmatrix} a & b & c \\ 0 & d & e \\ 0 & 0 & f \end{vmatrix}$.

(b) Postulate a rule for determinants of lower-triangular and upper-triangular matrices – see Exercise 2.14 – and try to justify it.

3.2 Properties of Determinants

Determinants have a huge collection of properties, from which we shall extract and illustrate (without proof) a few that have practical application.

Frame 3.4   *Properties of determinants*

$$\det A^T = \det A \tag{3.4}$$

if one row of A is a multiple of another row, $\det A = 0$ (3.5)

multiplying a single row by λ multiplies $\det A$ by λ (3.6)

swapping two rows changes the sign of a determinant (3.7)

subtracting a multiple of one row from another does not

change the determinant's value (3.8)

the determinant of a diagonal matrix is the product

of the diagonal elements (3.9)

$$\det(AB) = (\det A)(\det B) \tag{3.10}$$

$$\det A^{-1} = 1/\det A \tag{3.11}$$

$\det A = 0$ if and only if A is singular (3.12)

One important deduction from (3.4) is that all later statements about *rows* are also true for *columns*.

Example 3.3 We can state without calculation that $\begin{vmatrix} -6 & 1 & 3 \\ 2 & 0 & -1 \\ 4 & -1 & -2 \end{vmatrix} = 0.$

This is because the first column is (-2) times the third. Transposing the determinant would turn these into rows; then (3.5) shows the result to be zero. (This can be verified by direct evaluation.) ∎

The sort of observation in this example is often quite useful for spotting a zero determinant and hence a singular matrix, by (3.12).

There are two collections of results connected with Frame 3.4. One relates to evaluating determinants and will be explored in the next section. The other relates to non-singularity.

From (3.9) we know that $\det I = 1 \times 1 \times \cdots \times 1 = 1$. Then (3.10) gives

$$1 = \det I = \det(AA^{-1}) = (\det A)(\det A^{-1}),$$

from which (3.11) follows, *unless* $\det A = 0$. In such a case there is no value for $\det A^{-1}$ and we conclude A^{-1} does not exist, as stated in (3.12).

(3.10) also shows that if AB is non-singular, so that $\det(AB) \neq 0$, we have $(\det A)(\det B) \neq 0$ as well. Hence both $\det A$ and $\det B$ are non-zero, showing A and B to be non-singular: we cannot have a singular matrix within a chain of products with a non-singular result.

Ex 3.3

(a) Evaluate $\begin{vmatrix} 1 & -2 & 0 \\ -2 & 4 & 3 \\ -1 & 2 & 2 \end{vmatrix}$.

Hint: look carefully at the columns before trying to find a value.

(b) Simplify $\det(\lambda A)$, where A is $n \times n$.

3.3   Evaluation of Determinants and Inverses

If a matrix is non-singular, then a sequence of Gaussian Elimination steps, *as we have implemented them* in §2.9, can reduce it to a diagonal matrix, with the **pivots** on the diagonal. Then, (3.8) shows the determinant is not changed by the elimination steps, (3.7) shows how to deal with row swaps and (3.9) tells us how to calculate the determinant of the final version, giving:

$$\det A = (-1)^r \times \text{product of pivots}, \tag{3.13}$$

where r is the number of row swaps used. This remains true in the singular case since one of the pivots will then be zero and the determinant is zero.

Think about it like this

> This explains why it was important to be strict in the specification of the elimination steps: multiplying or dividing a row will change the value of the determinant, due to (3.6), as will row calculations such as "$x \, \text{Target} - \text{Pivot}$" instead of the correct "$\text{Target} - x \, \text{Pivot}$".

Example 3.4 Evaluate the determinant in Example 3.1.

A	**2**	0	-1	
B	1	2	3	
C	1	-1	-1	
B'	0	**2**	$7/2$	$B - \frac{1}{2}A$
C'	0	-1	$-1/2$	$C - \frac{1}{2}A$
C''	0	0	$5/4$	$C' + \frac{1}{2}B'$

Hence $\det A = 2 \times 2 \times 5/4 = 5$, as before. ∎

Example 3.5 Revisiting Example 2.44, we deduce

$$\begin{vmatrix} 1 & -1 & 0 \\ 2 & -2 & -2 \\ -2 & 1 & 2 \end{vmatrix} = (-1)^1 \times 1 \times (-1) \times (-2) = -2,$$

since **one** row swap was carried out. This value can be verified by direct calculation. ∎

This is the most efficient way to evaluate a large determinant with no special structure, such as having a significant pattern of zero elements. That fact often undermines the usefulness of (3.12) as a practical tool, since once we know the determinant is zero, the Gaussian Elimination will already have told us the matrix is singular.

There is another approach, which is generally expensive on calculations but can be effective in special cases. It is the general version of the recursive method in Frame 3.2.

Select an element a_{ij} and score out the row and column in which it resides, producing an $(n-1) \times (n-1)$ determinant. This is the (i, j)-**minor**, M_{ij}.

Multiplying M_{ij} by $(-1)^{i+j}$ gives the corresponding **cofactor** C_{ij}.

Now choose *any* row or column in the original determinant and calculate as follows.

Frame 3.5   *Row or column cofactor expansion for a determinant*

Add up: element × cofactor, along **any** row or column   (3.14)

Before illustrating this, note that the pattern of $(-1)^{i+j}$ is fixed: it is a *chessboard* pattern:

$$\begin{vmatrix} + & - & + & - & \cdots \\ - & + & - & + & \cdots \\ + & - & + & - & \cdots \\ \vdots & \vdots & \vdots & \vdots & \ddots \end{vmatrix}.$$

The expression in Frame 3.2 can now be confirmed, using the top row of this pattern.

Example 3.6   Evaluate $\begin{vmatrix} 1 & 2 & 0 \\ -1 & 1 & -3 \\ 2 & -2 & 0 \end{vmatrix}$.

Noting that the last column contains only one non-zero element, a cofactor expansion using it will contain just one term, that associated with $a_{23} = -3$. The minor is

$$M_{23} = \begin{vmatrix} 1 & 2 \\ 2 & -2 \end{vmatrix} = -2 - 4 = -6.$$

The cofactor is $(-1)^{2+3} \times (-6) = +6$ and the determinant is

$$0 + (-3) \times 6 + 0 = -18.$$

■

Example 3.7   Evaluate $\begin{vmatrix} 3 & 0 & 0 & -1 \\ 2 & 1 & 3 & 1 \\ 2 & 0 & 0 & -1 \\ 7 & -2 & 0 & 0 \end{vmatrix}$.

First, use column 3, which contains only one non-zero element, in position $(2,3)$. The cofactor requires $(-1)^{2+3} = -1$, so the expansion (ignoring zero values) is

$$(-1) \times a_{23} \times M_{23} = (-1) \times 3 \times \begin{vmatrix} 3 & 0 & -1 \\ 2 & 0 & -1 \\ 7 & -2 & 0 \end{vmatrix}.$$

This new determinant has only one non-zero element in column 2, in position $(3,2)$, again attracting a factor of (-1). The cofactor expansion now becomes

$$(-1) \times 3 \times (-1) \times (-2) \begin{vmatrix} 3 & -1 \\ 2 & -1 \end{vmatrix} = -6(-3 + 2) = 6.$$

■

Cofactor expansions can also be used to invert matrices. The following frame shows the result, although it should not be considered for other than 3×3 matrices, due to the workload.

Frame 3.6   *Inverse of the matrix A*

$$A^{-1} = \frac{1}{\det A} \begin{bmatrix} C_{11} & C_{21} & \cdots & C_{n1} \\ C_{12} & C_{22} & \cdots & C_{n2} \\ \vdots & \vdots & \ddots & \vdots \\ C_{1n} & C_{2n} & \cdots & C_{nn} \end{bmatrix}$$

Thus the cofactors are used to fill the matrix, but **transposed**: the cofactor for a_{ij} is fed into the (j, i) position to produce the **adjugate** matrix. (Then there is a final division by the determinant, assumed non-zero.)

Consider the 2×2 matrix $\begin{bmatrix} a & b \\ c & d \end{bmatrix}$. Corresponding minors and cofactors are:

minors $\qquad a_{11} : d, \qquad a_{12} : c, \qquad a_{21} : b, \qquad a_{22} : a;$

cofactors $\quad a_{11} : +d, \quad a_{12} : -c, \quad a_{21} : -b, \quad a_{22} : +a.$

Feed these (transposed) into a matrix and divide by the determinant:

$$\frac{1}{ad - bc} \begin{bmatrix} d & -b \\ -c & a \end{bmatrix},$$

exactly as in Frame 2.10.

Example 3.8 Invert $A = \begin{bmatrix} 1 & -1 & 0 \\ 2 & -2 & -2 \\ -2 & 1 & 2 \end{bmatrix}$, the matrix in Example 2.44.

Calculate each minor, e.g., that for a_{11} is $\begin{vmatrix} -2 & -2 \\ 1 & 2 \end{vmatrix} = -2$. Construct an array of these, then merge in the $+/-$ pattern:

$$\begin{array}{ccc} -2 & 0 & -2 \\ -2 & 2 & -1 \\ 2 & -2 & 0 \end{array} \qquad \rightarrow \qquad \begin{array}{ccc} -2 & 0 & -2 \\ 2 & 2 & 1 \\ 2 & 2 & 0 \end{array}$$

Finally, transpose this last array and divide by the determinant (-2):

$$A^{-1} = \begin{bmatrix} 1 & -1 & -1 \\ 0 & -1 & -1 \\ 1 & -1/2 & 0 \end{bmatrix}.$$

■

Compare the number of expensive calculations (multiplications, divisions) required by the two inversion methods, for a 20×20 matrix:

Gaussian Elimination : $\quad n^3 = 8000,$

cofactor method : $\qquad n^2(n-1)! + n^2 = 4.9 \times 10^{19},$

assuming all determinants are evaluated by cofactor methods. This shows why Gaussian Elimination reigns supreme for general purpose matrix and determinant work.

Finally, there is a neat **formula** for the 3×3 determinant in (3.3), particularly useful for theoretical calculations in Physics:

$$\det A = \epsilon_{ijk} a_i b_j c_k, \tag{3.15}$$

where ϵ_{ijk} is the **Levi-Civita symbol**, a similar type of symbol to the Kronecker delta in (2.7):

$$\epsilon_{ijk} = \begin{cases} 0 & \text{if any of } \{i, j, k\} \text{ are equal,} \\ +1 & \text{if } (i, j, k) = (1, 2, 3) \text{ or } (2, 3, 1) \text{ or } (3, 1, 2), \\ -1 & \text{if } (i, j, k) = (3, 2, 1) \text{ or } (2, 1, 3) \text{ or } (1, 3, 2). \end{cases} \tag{3.16}$$

Here, we have $+1$ for any subsequence of $123123123123\ldots$ and -1 for any subsequence of its reverse $321321321321\ldots$.

Returning to (3.15), we read it as *three* instances of the *summation convention* explained in §2.5, since there are three pairs of subscripts. Although this looks intimidating, all terms are zero except for the *six* permutations of i, j, k that avoid duplicated values. We have

$$\epsilon_{123}a_1b_2c_3 + \epsilon_{231}a_2b_3c_1 + \epsilon_{312}a_3b_1c_2 + \epsilon_{321}a_3b_2c_1 + \epsilon_{213}a_2b_1c_3 + \epsilon_{132}a_1b_3c_2,$$

which agrees with (3.3) on using (3.16).

Ex 3.4 Use the results of the Gaussian Eliminations in Exercise 2.30 to find the determinants of the three matrices therein.

Ex 3.5 Use cofactor expansions to evaluate $\begin{vmatrix} 2 & 0 & 1 \\ 1 & 3 & -1 \\ 3 & -2 & 3 \end{vmatrix}$, $\begin{vmatrix} 0 & 5 & 0 & 2 \\ 3 & -4 & -2 & 3 \\ 3 & -1 & 0 & 1 \\ 0 & -4 & 0 & -2 \end{vmatrix}$.

Ex 3.6 Evaluate $\begin{vmatrix} \cos\theta & -r\sin\theta & 0 \\ \sin\theta & r\cos\theta & 0 \\ 0 & 0 & 1 \end{vmatrix}$, $\begin{vmatrix} \sin\theta\cos\phi & r\cos\theta\cos\phi & -r\sin\theta\sin\phi \\ \sin\theta\sin\phi & r\cos\theta\sin\phi & r\sin\theta\cos\phi \\ \cos\theta & -r\sin\theta & 0 \end{vmatrix}$.

Ex 3.7 Use the cofactor method to invert $\begin{bmatrix} 1 & 1 \\ -4 & -2 \end{bmatrix}$.

Ex 3.8 Use the cofactor method to invert:

$$\begin{bmatrix} 2 & 2 & -1 \\ -2 & -1 & 0 \\ 1 & 1 & -1 \end{bmatrix}, \quad \begin{bmatrix} 1 & 0 & 1 \\ 0 & 0 & 1 \\ 1 & 1 & 0 \end{bmatrix},$$

comparing your answers with Exercise 2.30.

3.4 Revision Exercises

Ex 3.9 Find the value of α such that $\begin{vmatrix} -2 & 1 & 1 \\ 1 & \alpha & 0 \\ -1 & 2 & -1 \end{vmatrix} = 0$.

Ex 3.10 Use a **systematic** and **fully explained** Gaussian elimination to solve

$$x + y + z = 3,$$
$$2x - 2y + z = 8,$$
$$-2x + 2y \quad\;\; = -6.$$

Find the determinant of the associated matrix.

4 THE VECTOR PRODUCT

This chapter extends the basic theory of vectors by introducing a new *product*, with properties that make it useful for solving problems in three-dimensional geometry. Indeed, it is our most powerful tool for making the leap from two to three dimensions.

4.1 Introduction

The following results from elementary vectors will be heavily used throughout this chapter.

From **position** vectors $\overrightarrow{OA}$ and $\overrightarrow{OB}$, we can calculate the **displacement** vector

$$\overrightarrow{AB} = \overrightarrow{OB} - \overrightarrow{OA}. \tag{4.1}$$

The **magnitude** of the vector $\mathbf{a} = (a_1, a_2, a_3) = a_1\mathbf{i} + a_2\mathbf{j} + a_3\mathbf{k}$ is

$$|\mathbf{a}| = \sqrt{a_1^2 + a_2^2 + a_3^2} \tag{4.2}$$

and a **unit vector** in the direction of $\mathbf{a}$ is

$$\hat{\mathbf{a}} = \frac{\mathbf{a}}{|\mathbf{a}|}. \tag{4.3}$$

The **inner** or **scalar** or **dot** product of vectors $\mathbf{a} = (a_1, a_2, a_3)$ and $\mathbf{b} = (b_1, b_2, b_3)$ is

$$\mathbf{a} \cdot \mathbf{b} = a_1 b_1 + a_2 b_2 + a_3 b_3 = |\mathbf{a}| \, |\mathbf{b}| \cos\theta, \tag{4.4}$$

where θ is the angle between the vectors. We also have

$$\mathbf{a} \cdot \mathbf{a} = a_1^2 + a_2^2 + a_3^2 = |\mathbf{a}|^2. \tag{4.5}$$

If $\mathbf{a} \cdot \mathbf{b} = 0$ then the vectors are **orthogonal**, i.e., they are mutually perpendicular, $\mathbf{a} \perp \mathbf{b}$.

Typical calculations using these are illustrated in the following examples.

Example 4.1 Let $\overrightarrow{OA} = (1, 1, -1)$, $\overrightarrow{OB} = (2, 0, 1)$, $\overrightarrow{OC} = (0, 2, 1)$ and $\angle BAC = \theta$. Then

$$\overrightarrow{AB} = (2, 0, 1) - (1, 1, -1) = (1, -1, 2),$$

$$\overrightarrow{AC} = (0, 2, 1) - (1, 1, -1) = (-1, 1, 2),$$

$$\cos\theta = \frac{\overrightarrow{AB} \cdot \overrightarrow{AC}}{|\overrightarrow{AB}| \, |\overrightarrow{AC}|} = \frac{-1 - 1 + 4}{\sqrt{6}\sqrt{6}} = \frac{1}{3} \quad \Rightarrow \quad \theta = 70.53°.$$

∎

Example 4.2 Let $\mathbf{a} = (3, -12, 4)$ and $\mathbf{b} = (4, 1, 0)$. Then

$$\mathbf{a} \cdot \mathbf{b} = 12 - 12 + 0 = 0 \quad \Rightarrow \quad \mathbf{a} \perp \mathbf{b}.$$

Also,

$$|\mathbf{a}| = \sqrt{9 + 144 + 16} = \sqrt{169} = 13,$$

so a unit vector in the direction of $\mathbf{a}$ is $(3/13, -12/13, 4/13)$.

∎

4.2   The Vector or Cross Product

In addition to the dot product (4.4), there is another way to multiply vectors, with very different properties and applications. Unlike the dot product, it is tied to three dimensions and before we can define it there is an ambiguity about the coordinate system that must be resolved.

Given the usual xy-system shown on the right, should the z-axis point up or down? The normal choice is **UP**, giving a **right-handed** system.

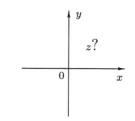

There are several ways to distinguish between a right-handed system and the opposite (a left-handed system). For the former, imagine rotating x to y through $90°$. A screwdriver held in the hand would then drive a (right-handed) screw in the positive z-direction.

Alternatively, the thumb, forefinger and middle-finger can naturally form an approximately orthogonal set of axes. If the right hand is used and the thumb is labelled x and the forefinger y, the middle finger will show z.

Returning to the original aim, we now define the **vector** or **cross** product of two vectors **a** and **b**, written **a**×**b**. As in the case of the dot product, there are two formulae, one for computation and one for applications.

Frame 4.1   *Definition of the vector or cross product*

$$\mathbf{a}\times\mathbf{b} = (a_2 b_3 - a_3 b_2)\mathbf{i} + (a_3 b_1 - a_1 b_3)\mathbf{j} + (a_1 b_2 - a_2 b_1)\mathbf{k} \qquad (4.6)$$

$$\mathbf{a}\times\mathbf{b} = [\,|\mathbf{a}|\,|\mathbf{b}|\sin\theta\,]\,\mathbf{n} \qquad\qquad\qquad (4.7)$$

where θ ($\leqslant 180°$) is the angle between **a** and **b**,

n is a unit vector $\perp$ **a** and **b**, in a right-handed sense,

when rotating **a** to **b**

Example 4.3   Find the vector product of $(1, 2, 3)$ and $(4, 5, 6)$.

$$(1,2,3)\times(4,5,6) = (2\times 6 - 3\times 5)\mathbf{i} + (3\times 4 - 1\times 6)\mathbf{j} + (1\times 5 - 2\times 4)\mathbf{k}$$
$$= (-3, 6, -3)$$

■

The single most important application of the vector product uses the fact that **n**, *and hence* **a**×**b**, *is orthogonal to both* **a** *and* **b**.

This provides a numerical check on calculations: $\mathbf{a}\bullet(\mathbf{a}\times\mathbf{b}) = 0$, and similarly $\mathbf{b}\bullet(\mathbf{a}\times\mathbf{b}) = 0$.

Example 4.4 For the vectors in the previous example:

$$(1, 2, 3) \bullet (-3, 6, -3) = -3 + 12 - 9 = 0,$$
$$(4, 5, 6) \bullet (-3, 6, -3) = -12 + 30 - 18 = 0.$$

∎

Example 4.5 Find a vector orthogonal to both $(1, -1, 1)$ and $(1, 1, 0)$.
  The vector product, in the given order, is:

$$(-1 \times 0 - 1 \times 1)\mathbf{i} + (1 \times 1 - 1 \times 0)\mathbf{j} + (1 \times 1 - (-1) \times 1)\mathbf{k} = (-1, 1, 2).$$

Note that in this case the original two vectors are orthogonal, so these three vectors are all mutually orthogonal and so offer an alternative (orthogonal) coordinate frame, when associated **unit** vectors are calculated. When these are fed into the columns of a matrix, we obtain an **orthogonal matrix**:

$$\begin{pmatrix} \frac{1}{\sqrt{3}} & \frac{1}{\sqrt{2}} & -\frac{1}{\sqrt{6}} \\ -\frac{1}{\sqrt{3}} & \frac{1}{\sqrt{2}} & \frac{1}{\sqrt{6}} \\ \frac{1}{\sqrt{3}} & 0 & \frac{2}{\sqrt{6}} \end{pmatrix}.$$

∎

The $(pq - rs)$ type of calculation in (4.6) is reminiscent of a 2×2 determinant. Looking closely at the detail reveals that the three occurrences are, precisely, a set of cofactors from a determinant with $\mathbf{a}$ and $\mathbf{b}$ in the bottom two rows. Multiplying them by the unit vectors $\mathbf{i}$, $\mathbf{j}$ and $\mathbf{k}$, gives the following alternative formula.

Frame 4.2 *Alternative computational formula for the vector product*

$$\mathbf{a} \times \mathbf{b} = \begin{vmatrix} \mathbf{i} & \mathbf{j} & \mathbf{k} \\ a_1 & a_2 & a_3 \\ b_1 & b_2 & b_3 \end{vmatrix} \tag{4.8}$$

This is a very popular formula, if only because its pattern makes it much easier to memorise than (4.6). We shall use it as the default formula from now on.

Example 4.6 Find the vector product for $(1, 0, 2)$ and $(0, 3, 4)$.

$$\begin{vmatrix} \mathbf{i} & \mathbf{j} & \mathbf{k} \\ 1 & 0 & 2 \\ 0 & 3 & 4 \end{vmatrix} = (0 - 6)\mathbf{i} - (4 - 0)\mathbf{j} + (3 - 0)\mathbf{k} = (-6, -4, 3)$$

∎

This version establishes two important properties, although they can also be deduced using (4.6).

$$\mathbf{b} \times \mathbf{a} = -\mathbf{a} \times \mathbf{b}, \qquad (4.9)$$

since we have swapped two rows in the determinant, thereby preserving its size but changing its sign. (Alternatively, we note that the 'screw' motion reverses, which reverses the direction of **n**.)

$$\mathbf{a} \times \mathbf{a} = \mathbf{0}, \qquad (4.10)$$

since the determinant now has two equal rows and hence is zero. (Alternatively, in (4.7) $\theta = 0$, so $\sin \theta = 0$.)

There is an immediate application for (4.10): it provides a test for two non-zero vectors being **parallel**:

$$\mathbf{u} = k\mathbf{v} \quad \Rightarrow \quad \mathbf{u} \times \mathbf{v} = k\mathbf{v} \times \mathbf{v} = \mathbf{0}.$$

Example 4.7   Find α and β so that $(1, \alpha, \beta)$ is parallel to $(-2, 4, 0)$.

$$\begin{vmatrix} \mathbf{i} & \mathbf{j} & \mathbf{k} \\ 1 & \alpha & \beta \\ -2 & 4 & 0 \end{vmatrix} = (-4\beta)\mathbf{i} - (2\beta)\mathbf{j} + (4 + 2\alpha)\mathbf{k} = \mathbf{0}$$

if $\beta = 0$ and $4 + 2\alpha = 0$, i.e., $\alpha = -2$.

Hence the vector is $(1, -2, 0)$, which is also $-\frac{1}{2}(-2, 4, 0)$, verifying the parallelism.   ∎

The formula (4.7) gives:

$$\mathbf{i} \times \mathbf{j} = \left[1 \times 1 \times \sin 90° \right] \mathbf{n} = \mathbf{n},$$

where **n** is a unit vector perpendicular to both **i** and **j** is a right-handed sense, i.e., it is the vector **k**. There are two similar results, all three being:

$$\mathbf{i} \times \mathbf{j} = \mathbf{k}, \qquad \mathbf{j} \times \mathbf{k} = \mathbf{i}, \qquad \mathbf{k} \times \mathbf{i} = \mathbf{j}. \qquad (4.11)$$

The apparently perverse order in the last of these reflects the **cyclic** order running through all the results: $\mathbf{i} \to \mathbf{j} \to \mathbf{k} \to \mathbf{i} \to \mathbf{j} \to \cdots$.

Together with their reversals, from (4.9), and $\mathbf{i} \times \mathbf{i} = \mathbf{0}$, etc., we can confirm that the formulae in Frame 4.1 are indeed equivalent. We can also use these results to evaluate some simple cases directly.

Example 4.8   Remove the bracketing:

$$\begin{aligned} (\mathbf{i} - \mathbf{j}) \times (\mathbf{j} + \mathbf{k}) &= \mathbf{i} \times \mathbf{j} + \mathbf{i} \times \mathbf{k} - \mathbf{j} \times \mathbf{j} - \mathbf{j} \times \mathbf{k} \\ &= \mathbf{k} \quad - \mathbf{j} \quad - \mathbf{0} \quad - \mathbf{i} \\ &= -\mathbf{i} - \mathbf{j} + \mathbf{k}, \end{aligned}$$

which is consistent with

$$\begin{vmatrix} \mathbf{i} & \mathbf{j} & \mathbf{k} \\ 1 & -1 & 0 \\ 0 & 1 & 1 \end{vmatrix} = (-1-0)\mathbf{i} - (1-0)\mathbf{j} + (1-0)\mathbf{k} = (-1,-1,1).$$

∎

This calculation assumed that the usual algebraic rules hold, particularly those concerning the removal of brackets. This is indeed the case, provided (4.9) is borne in mind.

Example 4.9 Simplify $(\mathbf{a}-\mathbf{b})\times(\mathbf{a}+\mathbf{b})$.

Removing the brackets, just as in normal algebra,

$$\mathbf{a}\times\mathbf{a} + \mathbf{a}\times\mathbf{b} - \mathbf{b}\times\mathbf{a} - \mathbf{b}\times\mathbf{b} = 0 + \mathbf{a}\times\mathbf{b} + \mathbf{a}\times\mathbf{b} - 0 = 2\mathbf{a}\times\mathbf{b}.$$

∎

Ex 4.1 For $\mathbf{a} = \mathbf{i}+\mathbf{j}+\mathbf{k}$ and $\mathbf{b} = 2\mathbf{i}-3\mathbf{k}$, calculate

$$\mathbf{a}\times\mathbf{i}, \quad (\mathbf{a}\times\mathbf{i})\times\mathbf{j}, \quad [(\mathbf{a}\times\mathbf{i})\times\mathbf{j}]\times\mathbf{k}, \quad \mathbf{a}\times\mathbf{b}, \quad (\mathbf{a}\times\mathbf{b})\bullet\mathbf{i}, \quad (\mathbf{b}-2\mathbf{a})\times\mathbf{k}.$$

Ex 4.2 Let $\mathbf{a} = \mathbf{i}+\mathbf{j}$, $\mathbf{b} = -\mathbf{i}+2\mathbf{j}$ and $\mathbf{c} = 2\mathbf{i}+3\mathbf{j}+\mathbf{k}$. Calculate the following:
(a) $\mathbf{b}\times\mathbf{c}$, (b) $\mathbf{a}\times\mathbf{b}$, $\mathbf{b}\times\mathbf{a}$, (c) $(\mathbf{a}+\mathbf{b})\times\mathbf{b}$, (d) $\mathbf{a}\times\mathbf{c}$, $|\mathbf{a}\times\mathbf{c}|$,
(e) $\mathbf{a}\bullet(\mathbf{b}\times\mathbf{c})$, (f) $\mathbf{c}\bullet(\mathbf{b}\times\mathbf{a})$, (g) $\mathbf{a}\times(\mathbf{b}\times\mathbf{c})$, (h) $(\mathbf{a}\bullet\mathbf{c})\mathbf{b} - (\mathbf{a}\bullet\mathbf{b})\mathbf{c}$.

Ex 4.3 Find a vector perpendicular to both $(2,2,1)$ and $(1,-2,2)$. Hence obtain an **orthonormal** system of axes.

Ex 4.4 Show that $|\mathbf{a}\bullet\mathbf{b}|^2 + |\mathbf{a}\times\mathbf{b}|^2 = |\mathbf{a}|^2|\mathbf{b}|^2$.

4.3 Applications of the Vector Product

The vector or cross product has some very direct applications in physical sciences, lying at the heart of some definitions and formulae. It also has indirect applications, through its geometrical properties. We start with the more direct examples.

Consider a force $\mathbf{F}$, applied at a point X with position vector $\mathbf{r}$. Then the force has **moment** or **torque**, about O:

$$\mathbf{M} = \mathbf{r}\times\mathbf{F}. \qquad (4.12)$$

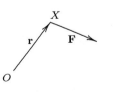

$\mathbf{M}$, being a vector, defines a direction, which is the **axis** about which $\mathbf{F}$ is attempting to rotate the body to which X belongs.

When several forces are involved, the total moment is

$$\mathbf{M} = \sum_i \mathbf{r}_i\times\mathbf{F}_i.$$

For equilibrium, we require $\mathbf{M} = \mathbf{0}$.

Example 4.10   Consider a rod balanced on a fulcrum, with two forces applied.

$$\mathbf{r}_1 = (\alpha, 0, 0), \quad \mathbf{F}_1 = (0, -4, 0),$$
$$\mathbf{r}_2 = (-2, 0, 0), \quad \mathbf{F}_2 = (0, -8, 0).$$

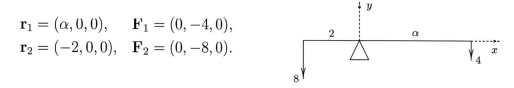

Then the total moment is

$$\mathbf{r}_1 \times \mathbf{F}_1 + \mathbf{r}_2 \times \mathbf{F}_2 = (0, 0, -4\alpha + 16) = \mathbf{0}$$

if $\alpha = 4$, the value at which the rod is balanced. Note that, for a general α, the total moment is a vector perpendicular to the xy-plane.

There is, in fact, a third force acting, the **reaction** at the fulcrum. To save the need to compute its value, the axes are chosen so that its position vector is $\mathbf{0}$ and so it is guaranteed to have zero moment.   ■

Now consider a body spinning about a unit axis $\mathbf{n}$ passing through the origin O, with **angular speed** ω [*omega*].

The **angular velocity** is the vector

$$\boldsymbol{\omega} = \omega\mathbf{n}.$$

The (linear) velocity at a point with position vector $\mathbf{r}$ is

$$\mathbf{v} = \boldsymbol{\omega} \times \mathbf{r}. \qquad (4.13)$$

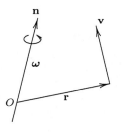

Think about it like this

Note that for a point on the axis itself, $\mathbf{r} = \alpha\mathbf{n}$ so that

$$\mathbf{v} = \omega\alpha\,\mathbf{n} \times \mathbf{n} = \mathbf{0},$$

i.e., points on the axis do not move. We shall return to this context in §4.5.

If we wish to take moments about a point other than O, or if the axis of rotation does not pass through O, the adjustment required is the same, and is typical of the adaptability of vectors.

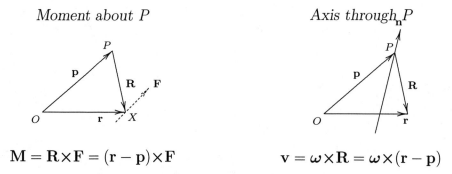

Moment about P	*Axis through P*
$\mathbf{M} = \mathbf{R} \times \mathbf{F} = (\mathbf{r} - \mathbf{p}) \times \mathbf{F}$	$\mathbf{v} = \boldsymbol{\omega} \times \mathbf{R} = \boldsymbol{\omega} \times (\mathbf{r} - \mathbf{p})$

The final application is a geometrical one. The $|\mathbf{a}|\,|\mathbf{b}|\sin\theta$ factor in $\mathbf{a} \times \mathbf{b}$ is reminiscent of the **area** of a triangle: $\frac{1}{2}ab\sin\theta$, where a and b are the lengths of adjacent sides and θ is the angle between. This gives the following formula.

Frame 4.3   *Area of a triangle defined by vectors* **a** *and* **b**

$$A = \frac{1}{2} |\mathbf{a} \times \mathbf{b}| \qquad (4.14)$$

Note that the $|\ldots|$ is *not* an absolute value, but a *magnitude*. It is required to remove the unit vector from the vector product.

Doubling the result in Frame 4.3, gives a direct interpretation of the vector product's magnitude. The area of the parallelogram spanned by **a** and **b** is $|\mathbf{a} \times \mathbf{b}|$.

Hence, if **a** is parallel to **b** the figure collapses, there is no area and $\mathbf{a} \times \mathbf{b} = \mathbf{0}$ as we know from algebraic calculation.

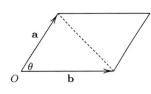

Example 4.11   Find the area of the triangle ABC in Example 4.1.

First of all, we require (displacement) vectors for two sides:

$$\overrightarrow{AB} = \overrightarrow{OB} - \overrightarrow{OA} = (1, -1, 2), \qquad \overrightarrow{AC} = \overrightarrow{OC} - \overrightarrow{OA} = (-1, 1, 2).$$

Then $\overrightarrow{AB} \times \overrightarrow{AC} = \begin{vmatrix} \mathbf{i} & \mathbf{j} & \mathbf{k} \\ 1 & -1 & 2 \\ -1 & 1 & 2 \end{vmatrix} = (-4, -4, 0).$

The area is calculated as $\frac{1}{2} |(-4, -4, 0)| = 2 |(-1, -1, 0)| = 2\sqrt{2}$.   ∎

Note that the vector product should never be used to calculate angles. The same data can be used in the dot product to find $\cos\theta$, which is a much easier calculation. But also, the vector product would deliver only $|\sin\theta|$, which cannot distinguish between acute and obtuse θ; thus, $\sin 120° = \sin 60°$.

Ex 4.5

(a) Find the moment of the force $(2, 1, -1)$, applied at $(1, 0, -1)$, about the origin. Find the moments about $(2, 0, 2)$ and $(3, 1, -2)$.

(b) A body rotates with angular velocity $9 \, \mathrm{rad\,s^{-1}}$ about an axis passing through the origin in the direction $(\frac{1}{3}, -\frac{2}{3}, \frac{2}{3})$. Find the velocity at the point $(1, 1, -2)$.

Ex 4.6

(a) Use the vector product to find the area of the triangle with vertices $(0, 0, 0)$, $(1, -1, 0)$ and $(1, -1, 1)$. Calculate the lengths of the sides of the triangle and hence verify your result.

(b) Consider the points $A\,(1, 1, -1)$, $B\,(-1, 2, -1)$ and $C\,(2, 0, 1)$. Find a vector perpendicular to both $\overrightarrow{AB}$ and $\overrightarrow{AC}$.

Find the area of the triangle ABC.

4.4   Scalar Triple Product

Consider the problem of finding the **volume** of a **parallelepiped**, which is a sort of "squashed" box, with edges parallel to **a**, **b** and **c**.

The area of the base of the figure is

$$|\mathbf{b}\times\mathbf{c}|.$$

Its height is

$$|\mathbf{a}\bullet\mathbf{n}|,$$

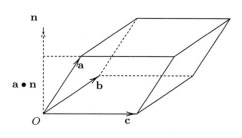

where **n** is a **unit** vector perpendicular to the base, i.e., to **b** and **c**.

Since **n** is parallel to **b**×**c** it can be multiplied by the area of the base to reconstitute that vector product. Multiplying area by height gives what we seek:

$$V = |\mathbf{a}\bullet\mathbf{n}|\,|\mathbf{b}\times\mathbf{c}| = |\mathbf{a}\bullet(\mathbf{b}\times\mathbf{c})|. \tag{4.15}$$

Note that the $|\dots|$ in the final result is an absolute value, rather than a magnitude, since volumes are non-negative. The quantity inside is an important one, known as the **scalar triple product** and is a **scalar** in nature.

Before exemplifying this, we derive is a very useful computational formula for the scalar triple product:

$$
\mathbf{a}\bullet(\mathbf{b}\times\mathbf{c}) = \mathbf{a}\bullet\begin{vmatrix} \mathbf{i} & \mathbf{j} & \mathbf{k} \\ b_1 & b_2 & b_3 \\ c_1 & c_2 & c_3 \end{vmatrix}
$$

$$
= a_1\begin{vmatrix} b_2 & b_3 \\ c_2 & c_3 \end{vmatrix} - a_2\begin{vmatrix} b_1 & b_3 \\ c_1 & c_3 \end{vmatrix} + a_3\begin{vmatrix} b_1 & b_2 \\ c_1 & c_2 \end{vmatrix},
$$

which is a cofactor expansion for the 3×3 determinant in the next frame.

Frame 4.4   *Expression for the scalar triple product*

$$\mathbf{a}\bullet(\mathbf{b}\times\mathbf{c}) = \begin{vmatrix} a_1 & a_2 & a_3 \\ b_1 & b_2 & b_3 \\ c_1 & c_2 & c_3 \end{vmatrix} \tag{4.16}$$

Example 4.12   Find the volume of the cube spanned by **i**, **j** and **k**.

$$\mathbf{i}\bullet(\mathbf{j}\times\mathbf{k}) = \begin{vmatrix} 1 & 0 & 0 \\ 0 & 1 & 0 \\ 0 & 0 & 1 \end{vmatrix} = \det I = 1,$$

as we would expect.   ∎

Example 4.13   Find the volume spanned by $(2, 1, -1)$, $(-1, 2, 1)$ and $(1, -1, 2)$.

$$\begin{vmatrix} 2 & 1 & -1 \\ -1 & 2 & 1 \\ 1 & -1 & 2 \end{vmatrix} = 2(4 + 1) - (-2 - 1) - (1 - 2) = 14,$$

and hence the volume is $|14| = 14$. ∎

Example 4.14   The diagram below shows a rhombic crystal, with vertices $O : (0, 0, 0)$, $A : (59, 0, 0)$, $B : (28, 52, 0)$, $C : (31, 18, 47)$. Find its volume (in the given units).

$$V = \begin{vmatrix} 59 & 0 & 0 \\ 28 & 52 & 0 \\ 31 & 18 & 47 \end{vmatrix}$$

$$= 59 \times 52 \times 47$$

$$= 144\,196,$$

where there is no need to find the absolute value. ∎

The value of the scalar triple product as a determinant reveals some remarkable properties. First of all, we can interchange the $\times$ and $\bullet$:

$$(\mathbf{a} \times \mathbf{b}) \bullet \mathbf{c} = \mathbf{c} \bullet (\mathbf{a} \times \mathbf{b}) = \begin{vmatrix} c_1 & c_2 & c_3 \\ a_1 & a_2 & a_3 \\ b_1 & b_2 & b_3 \end{vmatrix},$$

which has the same value as the original determinant, seen by carrying out the two row swaps $R_2 \leftrightarrow R_3$, $R_1 \leftrightarrow R_2$ in Frame 4.4. The determinant then changes by a factor $(-1)^2 = 1$. Hence

$$\mathbf{a} \bullet (\mathbf{b} \times \mathbf{c}) = (\mathbf{a} \times \mathbf{b}) \bullet \mathbf{c} = [\,\mathbf{a}, \mathbf{b}, \mathbf{c}\,], \qquad (4.17)$$

where we have taken the opportunity to introduce a new, simplified, notation.

The link with a determinant leads us to realise that, given those three vectors, all possible scalar triple products have one of just two values, which in turn are $\pm V$ (where V is the volume of the parallelepiped).

$$[\,\mathbf{a}, \mathbf{b}, \mathbf{c}\,] = [\,\mathbf{b}, \mathbf{c}, \mathbf{a}\,] = [\,\mathbf{c}, \mathbf{a}, \mathbf{b}\,]$$
$$= -[\,\mathbf{a}, \mathbf{c}, \mathbf{b}\,] = -[\,\mathbf{c}, \mathbf{b}, \mathbf{a}\,] = -[\,\mathbf{b}, \mathbf{a}, \mathbf{c}\,].$$

The sign is determined by whether we cycle through $\mathbf{abc}$ in a positive or negative order, where the lists are read 'circularly', i.e., in $\mathbf{abc}$, $\mathbf{c}$ is followed by $\mathbf{a}$.

positive sign:

cycle $\mathbf{a} \to \mathbf{b} \to \mathbf{c} \to \mathbf{a} \to \mathbf{b} \to \cdots$

negative sign:

cycle $\mathbf{a} \to \mathbf{c} \to \mathbf{b} \to \mathbf{a} \to \mathbf{c} \to \cdots$

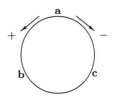

A further application for the scalar triple product is to test for three position vectors being **coplanar**, i.e., lying in the same plane. The volume spanned must be zero, which provides the test.

Frame 4.5   *Test for* **a**, **b** *and* **c** *being coplanar*

$$[\mathbf{a}, \mathbf{b}, \mathbf{c}] = 0$$

This extends to displacement vectors, if interpreted a little differently: it is zero if they *could be* placed in the same plane. Displacement vectors have neither end fixed and so can be moved while remaining parallel to themselves. Hence they could lie in the same plane, but then be moved to destroy that.

Example 4.15 Find α so that the position vectors $(1, 2, 0)$, $(-2, 1, 1)$ and $(-1, \alpha, 2)$ are coplanar.

$$\begin{vmatrix} 1 & 2 & 0 \\ -2 & 1 & 1 \\ -1 & \alpha & 2 \end{vmatrix} = (2 - \alpha) - 2(-4 + 1) + 0$$

$$= 2 - \alpha + 6 = 8 - \alpha,$$

which is zero if $\alpha = 8$.   ■

Ex 4.7 Find the volume of the parallelepiped containing edges OP, OQ and OR, where P is $(1, 1, 2)$, Q is $(2, 3, 5)$ and R is $(1, 5, 5)$.

Ex 4.8

(a) Find the volume of the parallelepiped with edges parallel to AB, AC and AD, where A is $(1, 1, -1)$, B is $(1, 2, 1)$, C is $(0, 1, 2)$ and D is $(2, 2, 0)$.

(b) Find the value of α so that $(3, -1, 1)$, $(-1, 2, \alpha)$ and $(-2, -1, 0)$ are coplanar.

4.5   Vector Triple Product

If we replace the $\bullet$ by a $\times$ in the scalar triple product, we obtain $\mathbf{a} \times (\mathbf{b} \times \mathbf{c})$, which is a legitimate quantity, known as the **vector triple product**.

This time the result is a vector: the product inside the brackets produces a vector, which can then be 'crossed' with the third vector to produce a final vector, which is the value.

This quantity has less direct application, so we shall not pursue it to the same lengths as its companion 'scalar' quantity. It does, however, tend to appear in the midst of calculations and it is useful to know that it can be 'simplified'.

The next frame gives the details. It shows, in passing, that this time the position of the brackets is critical: placing them round $\mathbf{a} \times \mathbf{b}$ rather than $\mathbf{b} \times \mathbf{c}$ retains one part of the answer, but changes the other significantly.

Frame 4.6   *The vector triple product*

$$\mathbf{a} \times (\mathbf{b} \times \mathbf{c}) = (\mathbf{a} \cdot \mathbf{c})\mathbf{b} - (\mathbf{a} \cdot \mathbf{b})\mathbf{c} \tag{4.18}$$
$$(\mathbf{a} \times \mathbf{b}) \times \mathbf{c} = (\mathbf{a} \cdot \mathbf{c})\mathbf{b} - (\mathbf{b} \cdot \mathbf{c})\mathbf{a} \tag{4.19}$$

Think about it like this

This can be memorised by noting the structure of the result:

the answer is a combination of the vectors in the original brackets,

each term contains one copy of each vector,

the first term (+) is ['outside' vectors dotted][middle vector].

Example 4.16   Check this for $\mathbf{a} = (0, 1, 1)$, $\mathbf{b} = (1, 0, 1)$, $\mathbf{c} = (1, 1, 0)$.
Using Frame 4.6,

$$\mathbf{a} \times (\mathbf{b} \times \mathbf{c}) = (0 + 1 + 0)(1, 0, 1) - (0 + 0 + 1)(1, 1, 0) = (0, -1, 1),$$

while a direct calculation gives:

$$\mathbf{b} \times \mathbf{c} = -\mathbf{i} + \mathbf{j} + \mathbf{k}, \qquad \mathbf{a} \times (-\mathbf{i} + \mathbf{j} + \mathbf{k}) = -\mathbf{j} + \mathbf{k}.$$

∎

The next example is typical of its occurrence in real calculations.

Example 4.17   A particle of mass m, at position $\mathbf{r}$ and with velocity $\mathbf{v}$, has its **angular momentum** about O defined as $\mathbf{h} = \mathbf{r} \times (m\mathbf{v})$.

Suppose the particle rotates in a circle about an axis $\mathbf{n}$ so that, from §4.3, it has angular velocity $\boldsymbol{\omega} = \omega \mathbf{n}$. Then

$$\mathbf{v} = \boldsymbol{\omega} \times \mathbf{r}.$$

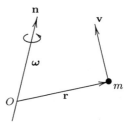

We can now use Frame 4.6 to calculate

$$\mathbf{h} = m\mathbf{r} \times (\boldsymbol{\omega} \times \mathbf{r}) = m \left[(\mathbf{r} \cdot \mathbf{r})\boldsymbol{\omega} - (\mathbf{r} \cdot \boldsymbol{\omega})\mathbf{r} \right].$$

This is somewhat easier to understand and apply, especially if there is some other feature to the problem.

For example, if we know that $\mathbf{r} \perp \mathbf{n}$ then $\mathbf{r} \perp \boldsymbol{\omega}$ and $\mathbf{r} \cdot \boldsymbol{\omega} = 0$. Writing $r = |\mathbf{r}|$, we find the simpler expression $\mathbf{h} = mr^2\omega\mathbf{n}$, i.e., $\mathbf{h} = I\boldsymbol{\omega}$, where $I = mr^2$ is the **moment of inertia** of the particle.   ∎

Ex 4.9 Non-zero vectors $\mathbf{u}$, $\mathbf{v}$ and $\mathbf{w}$ are mutually orthogonal. What is the value of $(\mathbf{u} \times \mathbf{v}) \times \mathbf{w}$?

Ex 4.10 Suppose that $\mathbf{r}$ is any vector and $\mathbf{n}$ is a **unit** vector. Show that

$$\mathbf{r} = (\mathbf{r} \cdot \mathbf{n})\mathbf{n} + \mathbf{n} \times (\mathbf{r} \times \mathbf{n}).$$

Explain what has been achieved on the right-hand side of this equation.
Demonstrate this for the vectors $\mathbf{r} = (1, 2, 3)$ and $\mathbf{n} = (\tfrac{1}{3}, \tfrac{2}{3}, \tfrac{2}{3})$.

4.6   Revision Exercises

Ex 4.11 Given the vectors $\mathbf{a} = (1, 1, -\frac{1}{2})$, $\mathbf{b} = (2, 0, 1)$ and $\mathbf{c} = (2, 1, 1)$, find:

  (a) $\mathbf{a} \times \mathbf{b}$;

  (b) a **unit** vector perpendicular to both $\mathbf{a}$ and $\mathbf{b}$;

  (c) $\mathbf{a} \bullet (\mathbf{b} \times \mathbf{c})$.

Ex 4.12 Given the vectors $\mathbf{a} = (1, -2, 1)$, $\mathbf{b} = (1, 1, -1)$, $\mathbf{c} = (0, 2, 1)$, find the following:

  (a) $\mathbf{a} \times \mathbf{b}$;

  (b) a **unit vector** orthogonal to both $\mathbf{a}$ and $\mathbf{b}$;

  (c) the area of the triangle with vertices O and the other end-points of $\mathbf{a}$ and $\mathbf{b}$;

  (d) the volume of the parallelepiped spanned by $\mathbf{a}$, $\mathbf{b}$ and $\mathbf{c}$.

5 THREE-DIMENSIONAL GEOMETRY

There are three key components in 3-D geometry: points, (straight) lines and planes. Using these, with vector techniques, we can treat problems associated with simple flat surfaces and bodies bounded by such. Most curved bodies and lines require *calculus*, although that often assumes they behave in a simpler manner in small *local* regions.

A **point** has position vector $\mathbf{r} = (x, y, z)$, related to cartesian coordinates (x, y, z).

A **line** is more difficult to handle in 3-D than in 2-D, where it is the natural entity. We shall defer studying lines until later in this chapter.

A **plane**, however, is the natural entity in 3-D and that is where we start.

We shall explore how to define lines and planes in vector terms, also investigating various *intersection* and *angle* problems, such as finding the point at which a line intersects a plane or the angle between a line and a plane.

5.1 The Equation of a Plane

A plane is a flat surface containing lines, with all those lines extending to infinity in both directions. We seek an equation linking the coordinates (x, y, z) of its constituent points.

Every line in the plane is perpendicular to a single direction (pointing out of the plane): the **normal n**.

In this context **n** need not be unit and may point 'up' or 'down'.

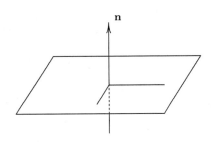

The normal is the single most important feature of a plane and is the key to most computations involving it.

Suppose that $\mathbf{r} = (x, y, z)$ is the position vector of a point P in the plane and $\mathbf{u} = (\alpha, \beta, \gamma)$ is one for a **fixed point** Q in the plane: something must 'anchor' the plane to stop it moving perpendicular to itself.

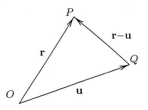

Then $\mathbf{r} - \mathbf{u}$ is a vector parallel to the plane and hence is perpendicular to the normal:

$$(\mathbf{r} - \mathbf{u}) \bullet \mathbf{n} = 0 \quad \Rightarrow \quad \mathbf{r} \bullet \mathbf{n} = d,$$

where $d = \mathbf{u} \bullet \mathbf{n}$ is a constant, whose value we ought to be able to find. This leads to the **vector equation** of the plane.

Suppose that $\mathbf{n} = (a, b, c)$. Expanding the dot product provides the **cartesian equation** of the plane.

Frame 5.1   *The vector and cartesian equations of a plane with normal* $\mathbf{n}=(a,b,c)$

$$\mathbf{r} \cdot \mathbf{n} = d \qquad (d = \mathbf{u} \cdot \mathbf{n}) \qquad\qquad (5.1)$$
$$ax + by + cz = d \qquad\qquad\qquad (5.2)$$

Note that the cartesian form is the natural extension to 3-D of $ax + by = c$, which is a line in 2-D.

Example 5.1   Find the equation of the xy-plane.

This has $\mathbf{k}$ as its normal and contains $(0, 0, 0)$. Hence

$$(x, y, z) \cdot (0, 0, 1) = (0, 0, 0) \cdot (0, 0, 1) \quad \Rightarrow \quad z = 0,$$

which is the standard expression for the xy-plane, in 3-D.   ■

Example 5.2   Find the equation of the plane with normal $(1, 1, -1)$, containing $(3, 2, 1)$.

Since $(3, 2, 1) \cdot (1, 1, -1) = 4$, the vector equation is

$$\mathbf{r} \cdot (1, 1, -1) = 4,$$

while the cartesian equation is

$$x + y - z = 4.$$

■

It is possible to specify a plane in ways other than by stating the normal and a point it contains. We can still produce the equation, usually by making use of vector algebra to convert to the above situation. The vector product is a key tool here.

This is best illustrated by examples.

Example 5.3   Find the plane parallel to the (displacement) vectors $(3, 1, 0)$ and $(3, -1, -1)$, while containing the point $(1, -1, 1)$.

Note that forcing a plane to be parallel to two different lines fixes its orientation, while the given point anchors it in space.

We require the normal, which must be perpendicular to both the given vectors, since they could lie in the plane. The standard method for finding a vector perpendicular to two others is to calculate the vector product:

$$\mathbf{n} = \begin{vmatrix} \mathbf{i} & \mathbf{j} & \mathbf{k} \\ 3 & 1 & 0 \\ 3 & -1 & -1 \end{vmatrix} = -\mathbf{i} + 3\mathbf{j} - 6\mathbf{k}.$$

Then, using the 'anchor' point, the vector equation is

$$\mathbf{r} \bullet (-1, 3, -6) = (1, -1, 1) \bullet (-1, 3, -6) = -10,$$

and the cartesian equation is

$$-x + 3y - 6z = -10 \quad \text{or} \quad x - 3y + 6z = 10,$$

on tidying up the signs. ∎

In 2-D, two points fix a line, whose equation can be found from their coordinates. In 3-D, three points fix a plane. The cartesian equation can be found by forcing the points to satisfy $ax + by + cz = d$. This produces *three* (linear) equations in *four* unknowns a, b, c and d, whose solution is not always straightforward. There is a simple vector method.

Example 5.4 Find the plane containing points $(1, 0, 1)$, $(3, 1, 2)$, $(2, 1, 3)$.

The normal to the plane must be perpendicular to the displacement vectors

$$(3, 1, 2) - (1, 0, 1) = (2, 1, 1), \qquad (2, 1, 3) - (1, 0, 1) = (1, 1, 2),$$

which converts the situation to that in the previous example. Hence

$$\mathbf{n} = \begin{vmatrix} \mathbf{i} & \mathbf{j} & \mathbf{k} \\ 2 & 1 & 1 \\ 1 & 1 & 2 \end{vmatrix} = \mathbf{i} - 3\mathbf{j} + \mathbf{k}.$$

We can now use *any* of the three available 'anchor' points. Choosing the first (and simplest arithmetically), the vector equation is

$$\mathbf{r} \bullet (1, -3, 1) = (1, 0, 1) \bullet (1, -3, 1) = 2,$$

and the cartesian equation is $x - 3y + z = 2$. ∎

Although angle calculations are considered in detail in §5.6, we shall now look at the angle between two planes, to underline the primacy of the **normal** in calculations involving planes.

Two non-parallel planes intersect at an angle, for which there are two measures: θ or $180° - \theta$, depending on how one looks at the situation. *We normally insist on choosing the* **acute** *version.*

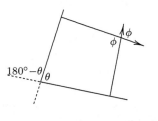

The diagram shows a cross-section of the intersection, with the normals shown, as vectors. We find the angle ϕ between the normals, using the dot product. Then, since the quadrilateral shown contains two right angles, $\theta + \phi = 180°$. The desired solution is therefore ϕ or $180° - \phi$, whichever is acute.

Example 5.5 Find the angle between $-x + y - 2z = 2$ and $2x + y + z = 1$.

Read off the normals (the coefficients of x, y, z): $\mathbf{n}_1 = (-1, 1, -2)$ and $\mathbf{n}_2 = (2, 1, 1)$. Then

$$\cos\phi = \frac{\mathbf{n}_1 \bullet \mathbf{n}_2}{|\mathbf{n}_1|\,|\mathbf{n}_2|} = \frac{-2 + 1 - 2}{\sqrt{6} \cdot \sqrt{6}} = -\frac{1}{2},$$

giving $\phi = 120°$, so we choose the intersection angle as $180° - 120° = 60°$.

Note that the constants in the equations played no role in the calculation. Changing these will move the planes perpendicular to themselves and hence will not change any of the angles involved.   ■

Example 5.6 Find the angle between $x + 2y = 0$ and $2x - y + 2z = 3$.

Read off the normals: $\mathbf{n}_1 = (1, 2, 0)$, $\mathbf{n}_2 = (2, -1, 2)$. We note that $\mathbf{n}_1 \bullet \mathbf{n}_2 = 0$, so the planes intersect at right angles.   ■

Ex 5.1 Find the equations of the planes containing $(1, -1, 1)$ and (a) perpendicular to $(1, 0, -2)$, (b) parallel to $(1, 1, 0)$, $(0, -1, 1)$.

Find the acute angle between these planes.

Ex 5.2 Find the equations of the planes defined by:

(a) containing $(1, -1, 4)$ and perpendicular to $(-2, 1, 5)$;

(b) containing $(1, 1, -1)$ and parallel to $(2, 1, 1)$ and $(1, 2, 1)$;

(c) containing $(1, 2, 3)$, $(-1, 0, 1)$ and $(2, -1, 1)$.

5.2   The Equation of a Line

The cartesian form of a line, which is simple in 2-D, becomes much more complicated in 3-D and it is almost always better to use a *vector equation*. The key to this lies in the **section formula**, giving the vector for a point dividing a line in a given ratio.

Consider the diagram below:

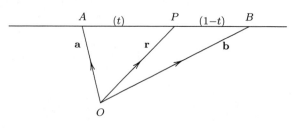

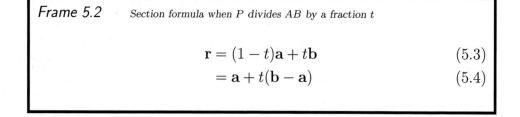

Frame 5.2   Section formula when P divides AB by a fraction t

$$\mathbf{r} = (1 - t)\mathbf{a} + t\mathbf{b} \tag{5.3}$$
$$= \mathbf{a} + t(\mathbf{b} - \mathbf{a}) \tag{5.4}$$

Although the simple derivation of this formula assumes that $0 \leqslant t \leqslant 1$, covering all points between A and B, we can reach points outside AB with other t.

Given a line parallel to a vector $\mathbf{d}$ and containing a fixed ('anchor') point A, with $\overrightarrow{OA} = \mathbf{a}$, we can reach any point P on the line, by proceeding from O to P via A: $\overrightarrow{OP} = \overrightarrow{OA} + \overrightarrow{AP}$ and $\overrightarrow{AP}$ is a multiple of $\mathbf{d}$.

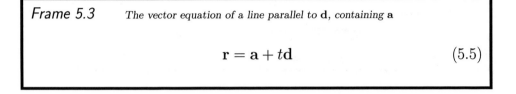

Frame 5.3   *The vector equation of a line parallel to $\mathbf{d}$, containing $\mathbf{a}$*

$$\mathbf{r} = \mathbf{a} + t\mathbf{d} \qquad (5.5)$$

$\mathbf{d}$ (written in place of the original $\mathbf{b} - \mathbf{a}$) is the **direction vector** of the line; its direction is fixed, although any multiple can be used, even a multiple pointing in the reverse direction: $\mathbf{r} = \mathbf{a} + t'\mathbf{d}'$.

$\mathbf{a}$ can be *any* point on the line, so we can also use $\mathbf{r} = \mathbf{b} + s\mathbf{d}$. In these alternative equations, t, t' and s will have different values.

Think about it like this

Think of the line as a motorway, in the direction given by $\mathbf{d}$, with $\mathbf{a}$ and $\mathbf{b}$ as different slip roads. We can use either road to access P on the motorway, but the distances (s, t) will be different.

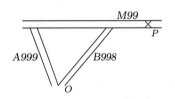

Example 5.7   Find the line in direction $(1, -1, 1)$, containing $(2, 1, 0)$.
Frame 5.3 gives:
$$\mathbf{r} = (2, 1, 0) + t(1, -1, 1).$$

In several calculations, this would be written as $\mathbf{r} = (2 + t, 1 - t, t)$.   ∎

A more usual way to specify a line is by stating two points on it. It is straightforward to convert to the situation in Frame 5.3.

Example 5.8   Find the line containing $(2, 1, 0)$ and $(3, 2, -2)$.
First of all, find the direction: $\mathbf{d} = (3, 2, -2) - (2, 1, 0) = (1, 1, -2)$.
Now proceed as before:

$$\mathbf{r} = (2, 1, 0) + t(1, 1, -2).$$

Alternatively, we could use the other point as 'anchor':

$$\mathbf{r} = (3, 2, -2) + s(1, 1, -2).$$

We can use a multiple of the **d** above, e.g., -2**d**:

$$\mathbf{r} = (2, 1, 0) + u(-2, -2, 4).$$

■

Lines also have **cartesian equations**, obtained by setting $\mathbf{r} = (x, y, z)$ in (5.5) and 'solving' for t.

Frame 5.4   *Cartesian equations of a line*

$$\mathbf{r} = (x, y, z) = (a, b, c) + t(u, v, w)$$
$$\frac{x - a}{u} = \frac{y - b}{v} = \frac{z - c}{w} \quad (= t) \qquad\qquad (5.6)$$

There are several points to note about this version, some of which indicate why we shall rarely use it, much preferring the vector version in Frame 5.3.

1. Note the use of the plural ("equations") in Frame 5.4. This makes the cartesian version much more complicated than in 2-D, reflecting the fact that the plane is the natural 3-D object.

2. The fact that there are two equals signs means there are two equations. Indeed, (5.6) can be read as defining some planes whose intersection is the line.

3. This last feature means that the cartesian equations are not unique; there are lots of planes that can define a line by their intersections. (See the next example.)

4. There is no problem if any of u, v and w is zero: the top line in the fraction is forced to be zero to avoid the problem of dividing by zero, and that delivers the intended information. Thus, if $u = 0$ we must have $x = a$ *always*, so the line is parallel to the yz-plane. Some authors then write

$$x = a; \quad \frac{y - b}{v} = \frac{z - c}{w}.$$

Example 5.9   Rewrite the lines in Examples 5.7 and 5.8 in cartesian form. The first of these is

$$\frac{x - 2}{1} = \frac{y - 1}{-1} = \frac{z(-0)}{1},$$

where the "-0" can be suppressed. (It is not, however, usual practice to change $\frac{y-1}{-1}$ into $\frac{1-y}{1}$.)

The second line can be derived from any of the three versions given. The first two provide:

$$\frac{x-2}{1} = \frac{y-1}{1} = \frac{z}{-2} \quad (=t),$$

$$\frac{x-3}{1} = \frac{y-2}{1} = \frac{z+2}{-2} \quad (=s).$$

■

The cartesian form does have one advantage: it is easy to find (x,y,z), when given the value of any one of the three.

Example 5.10   Test this using the first line in Example 5.9.

Find the point for which $z=0$:

$$x-2 = -(y-1) = 0 \quad \Rightarrow \quad x=2,\ y=1; \qquad (2,1,0).$$

Find the point for which $y=3$:

$$\frac{x-2}{1} = \frac{3-1}{-1} = -2 \quad \Rightarrow \quad x=0; \qquad z = \frac{3-1}{-1} = -2; \qquad (0,3,-2).$$

■

There are numerous intersection and angle problems that can be posed for lines and planes. We now look at four representative ones.

Ex 5.3 Which of the following points lie on the line: $\mathbf{r} = (1,2,1) + t(1,-1,-1)$?

$$(3,0,-1), \qquad (1,0,1), \qquad (0,2,2), \qquad (0,3,2)$$

Write down the cartesian equation of the line, then use it to determine that point on the line for which $y=5$.

Ex 5.4 The line $\mathbf{r} = (1,2,3) + t(1,0,-1)$ has cartesian form:

$$\frac{x-1}{1} = \frac{y-2}{0} = \frac{z-3}{-1}.$$

The division by zero seems dubious. Investigate whether or not this is the case by using it to find which of the following points lie on the line: $(3,2,-1)$, $(2,2,2)$, $(-1,3,5)$.

Note that some people prefer to avoid the issue by writing:

$$\frac{x-1}{1} = \frac{z-3}{-1};\ y = 2.$$

Discuss the situation for $\mathbf{r} = (1,2,3) + t(1,0,0)$ and $\mathbf{r} = (1,2,3) + t(0,0,0)$.

5.3   Intersection of Line and Plane

In normal circumstances, a line ought to pass through a plane at a single point. The easiest way to find this point is to use the **vector** equation of the line and the **cartesian** equation of the plane. Thus, given

$$\mathbf{r} = (a, b, c) + t(u, v, w), \qquad \alpha x + \beta y + \gamma z = \delta,$$

substitute $x = a + tu$, $y = b + tv$, $z = c + tw$ into the equation for the plane:

$$\alpha(a + tu) + \beta(b + tv) + \gamma(c + tw) = \delta,$$

which ought to produce a simple equation for t, from which $\mathbf{r} = (x, y, z)$ for the intersection point can be found.

Example 5.11   Find the intersection of $\mathbf{r} = (1, 1, 0) + t(-1, 2, -1)$ and $x + 2y - z = -1$.

We have $\mathbf{r} = (1 - t, 1 + 2t, -t)$, which lies in the plane if

$$(1 - t) + 2(1 + 2t) - (-t) = -1 \quad \Rightarrow \quad 3 + 4t = -1 \quad \Rightarrow \quad t = -1,$$

leading to the point $\mathbf{r} = \big(1 - (-1), 1 - 2, -(-1)\big) = (2, -1, 1)$.   ■

Example 5.12   Find the intersection of the line in the previous example and $x + y + z = 3$.

We now have

$$(1 - t) + (1 + 2t) + (-t) = 3 \quad \Rightarrow \quad 2 = 3,$$

which is impossible. Hence the line and plane do not intersect, which means the line is parallel to the plane.

Indeed, the plane has normal $(1, 1, 1)$ and $(1, 1, 1) \bullet (-1, 2, -1) = 0$, so the normal is perpendicular to the direction of the line.

Had the plane been $x + y + z = 2$, we would have reached $2 = 2$, which is *always* true, showing that the entire line lies in the plane.   ■

Ex 5.5   Investigate the intersection of the line $\mathbf{r} = (1, 0, 1) + t(0, -2, 1)$ with the planes:

$$2x - y + z = -3, \qquad 2x + y + 2z = 3, \qquad 2x - y - 2z = 0.$$

5.4   Intersection of Two Lines

Unlike the previous case, in normal circumstances two lines in 3-D will *not* intersect. There is simply too much room and they can avoid each other.

Suppose that the lines are

$$\mathbf{r} = \mathbf{a} + t\mathbf{u}, \qquad \mathbf{r} = \mathbf{b} + s\mathbf{v}.$$

Forcing the two **r** to agree gives three equations in two unknowns (s, t), which are unlikely to have a solution. To see if they do, solve two of them, ignoring the third. This will normally give a unique solution. Then substitute this into the third: if it fits, then the lines intersect at the point with that t (or s) value; otherwise, they do not intersect.

Example 5.13 Do $\mathbf{r} = (0, 0, 1) + t(1, 1, 0)$ and $\mathbf{r} = (0, 0, 0) + s(0, 1, 0)$ intersect?

The answer should be *NO*, since the first is parallel to the xy-plane and the second is the y-axis. Making the two **r** equal requires $(t, t, 1) = (0, s, 0)$. The first two components give $t = 0$, $t = s$, which are fine, but the third gives $1 = 0$, which shows there is no intersection. ∎

Example 5.14 Do $\mathbf{r} = (1, 0, 1) + t(1, 2, 1)$ and $\mathbf{r} = (9, 0, 0) + s(0, 16, 9)$ intersect?

Making the two **r** equal requires

$$
\begin{aligned}
1 + t &= 9 &\Rightarrow& \qquad t = 8 \\
2t &= 16s &\Rightarrow& \qquad s = 1 \\
1 + t &= 9s &:& \qquad 1 + 8 = 9 \times 1? \quad \text{(YES)}
\end{aligned}
$$

Hence the lines do intersect and the point of intersection is

$$(1, 0, 1) + 8(1, 2, 1) = (9, 16, 9).$$

Using s, this is also given by $(9, 0, 0) + 1(0, 16, 9) = (9, 16, 9)$. ∎

Example 5.15 Do $\mathbf{r} = (1, -1, 1) + t(2, 1, 1)$ and $\mathbf{r} = (1, 2, 6) + s(-1, 1, 2)$ intersect?

Making the two **r** equal requires

$$
\begin{aligned}
1 + 2t &= 1 - s &\Rightarrow& \quad \text{ADD first two: } 3t = 3 \\
-1 + t &= 2 + s &\Rightarrow& \quad t = 1, \ s = -2 \\
1 + t &= 6 + 2s &:& \quad 1 + 1 = 6 - 4? \quad \text{(YES)}
\end{aligned}
$$

Hence the lines do intersect and the point of intersection is

$$(1, -1, 1) + 1(2, 1, 1) = (3, 0, 2).$$

∎

There is a neat condition for intersection, provided by the **scalar triple product**.

If the lines intersect, then the vectors $\mathbf{a} - \mathbf{b}$, $\mathbf{u}$ and $\mathbf{v}$ must be **coplanar**. Hence, from Frame 4.5,

$$[\mathbf{a} - \mathbf{b}, \mathbf{u}, \mathbf{v}] = 0. \qquad (5.7)$$

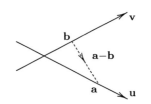

Ex 5.6 Find that value of the constant α for which the two lines $\mathbf{r} = (\alpha, 2, 1) + t(1, -2, 0)$ and $\mathbf{r} = (0, 3, -2) + s(1, -1, 2)$ intersect and that intersection point.

Ex 5.7 Obtain the vector equations of the lines:

(a) passing through $\mathbf{a} = (1, 2, 2)$ and parallel to $\mathbf{u} = (0, 3, 1)$;

(b) passing through $\mathbf{b} = (2, 1, 4)$ and $\mathbf{p} = (1, -1, 1)$.

Calculate $\mathbf{u} \times (\mathbf{b} - \mathbf{p})$ and show that $[\mathbf{b} - \mathbf{a}, \mathbf{u}, \mathbf{b} - \mathbf{p}] = 0$.

Deduce that the two lines are coplanar and use their vector equations to calculate their point of intersection.

5.5   Intersection of Two Planes

Unless they are parallel – when their normals will be multiples of each other – two planes will intersect in a **line**. Our objective is to find the vector equation of that line.

Suppose that π_1 and π_2 are the planes

$$\mathbf{r} \bullet \mathbf{n}_1 = \alpha_1, \qquad \mathbf{r} \bullet \mathbf{n}_2 = \alpha_2,$$

respectively.

Then the direction vector of the common line must be perpendicular to both normals, i.e.,

$$\mathbf{d} = \mathbf{n}_1 \times \mathbf{n}_2,$$

using the key property of the vector product.

To complete the calculation we require an 'anchor' point for the line. This is *any* point on the line, i.e., any point that lies in both planes. Solve the (cartesian) equations of the two planes simultaneously, choosing any one of the infinite number of solutions normally found for two equations in three unknowns.

One method is to set $z = 0$ and solve for x and y, changing to $y = 0$ if this proves unsuccessful, then $x = 0$. (It is only in unusual circumstances that $z = 0$ would encounter difficulties.)

If this gives a point $\mathbf{a}$ the line is $\mathbf{r} = \mathbf{a} + t\mathbf{d}$.

Example 5.16   Find the intersection of the planes:

$$2x - y - z = 2, \qquad \mathbf{n}_1 = (2, -1, -1),$$
$$3x \quad\;\; + z = 5, \qquad \mathbf{n}_2 = (3, 0, 1).$$

The direction of the line is

$$\mathbf{d} = (2, -1, -1) \times (3, 0, 1) = (-1, -5, 3).$$

Set $z = 0$ to obtain $2x - y = 2$, $3x = 5$, so $x = \frac{5}{3}$, $y = \frac{4}{3}$. The line is

$$\mathbf{r} = (\tfrac{5}{3}, \tfrac{4}{3}, 0) + t(-1, -5, 3).$$

In this case, choosing $x = 0$ gives the alternative equation

$$\mathbf{r} = (0, -7, 5) + t(-1, -5, 3),$$

which has a different 'anchor' point. ∎

Example 5.17 Find the intersection of the planes:

$$\begin{aligned} x + y - 2z &= 1, & \mathbf{n}_1 &= (1, 1, -2), \\ -2x - 2y + 4z &= 0, & \mathbf{n}_2 &= (-2, -2, 4). \end{aligned}$$

The direction of the line is

$$\mathbf{d} = (1, 1, -2) \times (-2, -2, 4) = (0, 0, 0).$$

We deduce that $\mathbf{n}_2$ is a multiple of $\mathbf{n}_1$ (in fact $\mathbf{n}_2 = -2\mathbf{n}_1$); the normals, and hence the planes, are parallel. ∎

Ex 5.8 Find the line of intersection of the planes $x - y + 2z = 3$, $x - z = 1$.

5.6 Angles

Most angles can be calculated using the dot product, with **direction vectors** for lines and/or **normals** for planes.

It is sensible to draw a rough diagram, since the result may have to be adjusted. In particular, it is often the case that there is no real distinction between an angle θ and its **supplement** $180° - \theta$. In such cases, it is usual to quote the *acute* angle as the answer.

5.6.1 Angle between planes

This has already been covered in §5.1. This is a case when the acute angle is chosen.

5.6.2 Angle between lines

This angle is defined only if the lines intersect. Then it is merely the angle between the direction vectors. Again, in most cases, the acute angle is chosen.

Example 5.18 Find the angle between the lines in Example 5.15:

$$\mathbf{r} = (1, -1, 1) + t(2, 1, 1), \quad \mathbf{r} = (1, 2, 6) + s(-1, 1, 2).$$

These intersect at $(3, 0, 2)$, but this point is not relevant here. Nor, indeed, are the anchor points $(1, -1, 1)$ and $(1, 2, 6)$. Calculate

$$\cos\theta = \frac{(2, 1, 1) \bullet (-1, 1, 2)}{|(2, 1, 1)| \, |(-1, 1, 2)|} = \frac{1}{\sqrt{6}\sqrt{6}} = \frac{1}{6},$$

giving $\theta = 80.4°$, which is already acute. ∎

5.6.3 Angle between line and plane

This time we find the angle between the direction vector for the line and the normal for the plane, but a final adjustment is necessary in all cases. Consider the diagram below. The direction vector for the line is either **d** or **d**′, depending on the chosen orientation: one is the negative of the other.

Let θ be the angle between **d** (acute, as shown here), or **d**′ (obtuse), and **n**. Then we seek ϕ where:

$$\phi = 90° - \theta \ (\mathbf{d} \text{ case}), \quad \theta - 90° \ (\mathbf{d}' \text{ case}),$$

i.e., use $90° - \theta$ or $\theta - 90°$, whichever is acute.

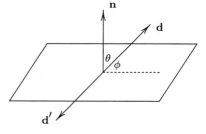

Example 5.19 Find the angle between:

$$\mathbf{r} = (1, -1, 1) + t(2, 1, 1), \qquad \mathbf{d} = (2, 1, 1),$$
$$-x + y - 2z = 3, \qquad\qquad \mathbf{n} = (-1, 1, -2).$$

$$\cos\theta = \frac{\mathbf{d} \cdot \mathbf{n}}{|\mathbf{d}|\,|\mathbf{n}|} = \frac{-2 + 1 - 2}{\sqrt{6}\,\sqrt{6}} = -\frac{1}{2},$$

which gives $\theta = 120°$. Since this is obtuse, we have the **d**′ situation and we conclude:

$$\phi = 120° - 90° = 30°.$$

∎

Ex 5.9 Find the angle between the lines in Exercise 5.6:

$$\mathbf{r} = (\alpha, 2, 1) + t(1, -2, 0), \qquad \mathbf{r} = (0, 3, -2) + s(1, -1, 2),$$

assuming that α has been chosen so that they intersect.

Ex 5.10 Find the point at which the line $\mathbf{r} = (1, 0, -1) + t(-1, 1, 2)$ intersects the plane $\mathbf{r} \cdot (1, 2, 2) = -6$.

Find the angle between the line and the plane.

5.7 Revision Exercises

Ex 5.11 Find the cartesian equation of the plane through $(2, -3, 1)$ and with normal in the direction $(1, 1, -2)$.

A second plane has equation $x - 2y + 3z = 4$. Write down the direction of its normal.

Find, in degrees correct to 2 dp, the **acute** angle between the planes.

Ex 5.12 Given the line L and plane π:

$$L: \quad \mathbf{r} = (2, -1, 1) + t(1, -1, 0), \qquad \pi: \quad x - 2y + z = 2,$$

(a) find the point at which L intersects π;

(b) find the normal to π;

(c) find the acute angle between L and π.

Ex 5.13 Consider the lines:

$$\mathbf{r} = (1, 0, 1) + t(1, -1, 1), \qquad \mathbf{r} = (-2, 1, -3) + s(1, 1, 2).$$

(a) Show that the lines intersect, finding the point of intersection.

(b) Find the acute angle between the lines, in degrees to 2 dp.

(c) Find the (cartesian) equation of the plane in which the two lines both lie.

6 PROBABILITY

Scientists, engineers and social scientists often conduct experiments or surveys where what is being measured has a **random** or **stochastic** element. The **statistical** analysis of the results has various objectives, such as:

- to extract the most reliable numerical measure;

- to judge the significance of the observations.

To achieve both of these requires a measure of how likely each outcome of the experiment is, i.e., a measurement of its **probability**.

In addition to its use in statistics, probability underpins some fundamental topics in science, such as quantum theory and statistical mechanics, the latter including the kinetic theory of gases.

6.1 Sets

Although we shall start by assessing how to assign a probability measure to 'elementary' events, such as obtaining *Heads* when a coin is tossed, we soon encounter 'compound' events, such as obtaining *Heads* on the first toss and no *Heads* on the following two. These events are handled by a notation and set of rules borrowed from *Set Theory*. Indeed, at a deep level, Set Theory is involved in the theoretical definition of probability itself, although we shall adopt a more practical approach.

A **set** of **elements** is just a collection of well-defined objects, with no ordering in the collection, unlike a **list**. We are interested in the interplay between different sets, for which a useful device is a pictorial representation known as a **Venn Diagram**.

Example 6.1   Consider a class of students.

U = **universe**,

F = set of all males,

M = set of all females

$\quad = \overline{F}$, the **complement** of F.

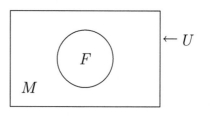

The terms **universe** and **complement** are general ones.

The complement of A represents all elements in U, but **not** in A. It is written $\overline{A}$, $C(A)$, A' or $\mathfrak{C}(A)$, although we shall prefer the first version. Note that $\overline{\overline{A}} = A$.

The universe is the set of all elements under investigation. The complement of the universe is the **empty set**, written $\emptyset$, which contains no elements: $\emptyset = \overline{U}$.

There are two key ways to combine sets:

union (OR): $A \cup B$ = set of elements in A **or** B **or** both,   (6.1)

intersection (AND): $A \cap B$ = set of elements in both A **and** B.   (6.2)

Think about it like this

∪ is sometimes pronounced as 'cup' and ∩ as 'cap', but it may be found more helpful to use 'or' and 'and', since they indicate the meaning. That said, great care must be taken since everyday English can be imprecise: "This class consists of male and female students" should be interpreted as $M \cup F$ (M **or** F) rather than $M \cap F$, assuming no student is both male and female!

The following Venn Diagram shows their representation.

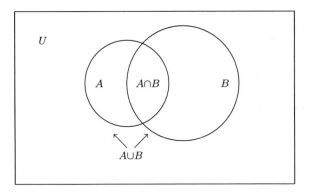

It is often the case, in probability calculations, that it is easier to calculate the *opposite* of what we wish, i.e., to work with the *complement*. The following rules, which can be verified by interpreting each side using the diagram above, are helpful:

$$\overline{A \cup B} = \overline{A} \cap \overline{B}, \qquad \overline{A \cap B} = \overline{A} \cup \overline{B}. \tag{6.3}$$

Example 6.2 Members of a class of 10 Mathematics students also study Chemistry (C), Engineering (E) and Geology (G):

$$
\begin{aligned}
C &= \{a, b, c, d\}, \\
E &= \{b, d, f, g, h\}, \\
G &= \{a, c, e, i\} \\
C \cup E &= \{a, b, c, d, f, g, h\}, \\
C \cap E &= \{b, d\}, \qquad E \cap G = \emptyset.
\end{aligned}
$$

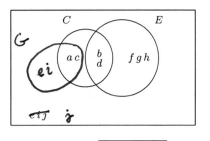

We also have $C \cup E \cup G = \{a, b, c, d, e, f, g, h, i\}$, so that $\overline{C \cup E \cup G} = \{j\}$, which identifies the only student in the class not taking one of these three subjects.

The first of the rules in (6.3) is illustrated by $A = C$, $B = E$:

$$
\begin{aligned}
\overline{C \cup E} &= \{e, i, j\}, \\
\overline{C} \cap \overline{E} &= \{e, f, g, h, i, j\} \cap \{a, c, e, i, j\} = \{e, i, j\}.
\end{aligned}
$$

■

6.2   Assignment of Probability

Suppose we conduct an 'experiment' whose outcome cannot be predicted, in the sense that a repetition may produce a different outcome; it is **random** or **stochastic**. We wish to measure the likelihood of each possible outcome: its **probability**.

The set U of all possible outcomes is the **sample space**. (Its contents are what we might find if we "sample" the experiment.)

An **event** is a subset A of U, to which we seek to allocate a **probability**, written $P(A)$ or $\Pr(A)$ or $\mathbb{P}(A)$.

Informally, $P(A)$ should be proportional to the 'size' of A. To achieve a standard that allows us to compare probabilities in different contexts, the chosen measure is the size of A *relative to* U. This idea leads to the following desirable properties for our measure.

Frame 6.1   Properties of $P(A)$

$$0 \leqslant P(A) \leqslant 1 \tag{6.4}$$

$$P(U) = 1, \qquad P(\emptyset) = 0 \tag{6.5}$$

$$P(\overline{A}) = 1 - P(A) \tag{6.6}$$

$$A \text{ subset of } B \quad \Rightarrow \quad P(A) \leqslant P(B) \tag{6.7}$$

Notation

> There is no necessity for $P(A)$ to be defined as a number in $[\,0,1\,]$, but this is the universal convention. For convenience, however, it is sometimes the case that a value will be quoted as $100P(A)\%$.

There are three principal ways in which to assign probabilities to events.

1. **Experimental**

   Suppose that N trials produce M instances of the event A. Then an estimate of the probability is $P(A) = \frac{M}{N}$.

   Example 6.3   A coin is tossed 100 times, producing 55 'Heads' (H) and 45 'Tails' (T).

   We may decide to use $P(H) = 0.55$, $P(T) = 0.45$ in our subsequent calculations. But this is not reliable: a second experiment could produce quite different results.   ■

2. **Model-based**

   We identify all of the simplest – **elementary** – events and assume they obey simple rules. The most common such rule is that they are all equally likely and hence have equal probability.

Example 6.4 We may assume our coin in the previous example is unbiased; it is often called **fair**. The only elementary events are H and T. They must have equal probability and, between them, they account for all the probability. Hence $P(H) = P(T) = 0.5$. ∎

3. **Personal**

We make a guess based on our own intuitions or past experience, e.g., as a gambler does when deciding appropriate odds at which to bet on a horse. We shall not pursue this; it is not very different from the experimental measure.

Our approach will be to concentrate on **models**, eventually using **experiments** to test their validity.

Example 6.5 If a coin is fair, how likely is it to get 55 or more H in an experiment (as in Example 6.3).

The answer – using a method considered later – is that the probability of 55 or more H is 0.184. This is low, but not unreasonably so. It is not, on its own, sufficient evidence to disprove the fairness of the coin. ∎

There are several **standard models**, used to mimic real situations.

- **Coin**: as above.

- **Die**: a six-sided (unbiased) die has $P(1) = P(2) = P(3) = P(4) = P(5) = P(6) = \frac{1}{6}$.

- **Bag of balls**: usually a mixture, e.g., of colours.

  Example 6.6 A bag contains 4 black (B) and 6 white (W) balls; one is drawn at random. Then $P(B) = 0.4$, $P(W) = 0.6$. ∎

- **Cards**: such as a standard pack of 52, without Jokers.

  Example 6.7 A card is selected at random: $P(\heartsuit) = \frac{1}{4}$, $P(\mathrm{A}) = \frac{1}{13}$, where A represents an 'Ace'. ∎

The preferred term for such 'experiments' is **sampling**, the idea being that there is a set of all possible outcomes, which we *sample* to obtain the result. For the **bag** and the **card** models, there are two fundamentally different types:

sampling **with** *and* **without** *replacement.*

Example 6.8 Returning to Example 6.6, if a ball is **replaced** after each sample, $P(B) = 0.4$ in every case.

Otherwise, repeated sampling leads to variable probabilities. Suppose we label the sample number by $\#n$ for the nth selection:

$$\text{if } \#1 = B \text{ then } P(\#2 = B) = \frac{3}{9},$$
$$\text{if } \#1 = W \text{ then } P(\#2 = B) = \frac{4}{9}.$$

Note the use of $P(X = x)$ to denote the probability of a sampling labelled X resulting in the value x, a notation to be developed in §7.1. ∎

The **coin** and **die** models are always *with replacement*, since coins and dice have no memory of what has previously occurred.

These basic models can be compounded in various ways to build more elaborate ones.

Example 6.9 A fair coin is tossed twice (or two coins are tossed together). What are the outcomes and their probabilities?

The order of tossing is important, as is the distinction between the two coins, if that model is preferred. In either case there are four outcomes: HH, HT, TH, TT, which should be equally likely, so each has probability $1/4$. ∎

A useful tool in analysing multiple sampling from *non-replacement* models is the **binomial coefficient** $\binom{n}{r}$. This counts the number of ways in which r objects can be selected from n, without replacement and with the order unimportant. If these are all equally likely, each has probability $1/\binom{n}{r}$.

Example 6.10 The number of possible outcomes in the UK *National Lottery* is

$$\binom{49}{6} = 13,983,816,$$

since it is not allowed to choose the same number twice and the order of choice is irrelevant. Hence the probability of winning the jackpot is about 7×10^{-8}, or 1 in 14 million.

To find the probability (p) of winning the lowest prize, by getting three correct numbers from the six chosen, we first count how many draws (N), out of all possible draws (above), produce this. We must choose 3 of the 6 winning numbers and 3 of the 43 non-winning numbers:

$$N = \binom{6}{3}\binom{43}{3}, \qquad p = N \Big/ \binom{49}{6} \simeq 0.0177.$$

∎

Example 6.11 Suppose we deal a hand of two cards from a shuffled pack. There are $\binom{52}{2}$ different possible hands.

$$P(\text{AK}) = \binom{4}{1} \times \binom{4}{1} \Big/ \binom{52}{2}.$$

(There are $4 \times 4 = 16$ different AK combinations.)

Similarly, for a hand of three cards,

$$P(3 \text{ Aces}) = \binom{4}{3} \Big/ \binom{52}{3}.$$

(There are $\binom{4}{3} = 4$ different sets of three aces.) ∎

Ex 6.1 Four numbers are chosen at random from the set $\{1, 2, 3, \ldots, 10\}$, allowing repetition. What is the probability that they are all different?

Ex 6.2 A college has a class of 100 students and it is known that:

60 read French, 40 German, 10 Italian; 4 read French and Italian, 6 German and Italian, 4 French and German; 2 read all three languages.

A student is selected from the class at random. What are the probabilities that the student reads (a) precisely two languages, (b) at least one language?

Ex 6.3 Construct the entire sample space, i.e., a list of all possible outcomes, when two fair dice are thrown, recording their readings separately, e.g., as $(1, 1)$.

Hence find the probabilities for the events:

a 1 or a 6 is included; there is no double; the sum of the throws is 9; the sum is more than 9; the readings differ by 4; the maximum reading is 4 or 5.

Ex 6.4

(a) **Betting odds** are a different way to specify probabilities. The odds 'a to b on' or, equivalently, 'b to a against' means the event is rated to have probability $\dfrac{a}{a+b}$. Thus '10 to 1' on has probability $^{10}/_{11}$, while '7 to 1' against has probability $^1/_8$.

Calculate the probabilities for 'evens' (1 to 1), 2 to 1 on, 5 to 2 against, 100 to 8 against.

(b) Calculate the odds for probabilities $^3/_4$ and $^1/_5$.

(c) To calculate the odds for a 'treble', i.e., three horses winning in separate races, the odds are converted to probabilities, multiplied and converted back to odds. Find the odds for the treble: 2 to 1, 7 to 2, 100 to 30 (all 'against').

6.3 The Addition Rule

Constructing compound models by listing elementary outcomes, as done in Example 6.9, is time-consuming and it is better to seek *rules* that allow the probabilities to be calculated from the simpler models.

Suppose the areas in the Venn Diagram are scaled versions of the associated probabilities. Then we can perform calculations using those areas. An immediate result is a rule for combining probabilities.

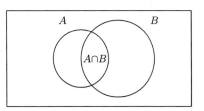

The total area covering A and B can be found by summing the separate areas for A and B, provided we subtract the common area representing $A \cap B$, since it would otherwise be counted twice. This leads to the **addition rule**.

Frame 6.2   *The addition rule for probability*

$$P(A \cup B) = P(A) + P(B) - P(A \cap B) \qquad (6.8)$$

There is a very useful special case, when $A \cap B = \emptyset$. This means that A and B cannot both occur and the term for such a situation is that the events are **mutually exclusive**.

Frame 6.3   *The addition rule for mutually exclusive events*

$$P(A \cup B) = P(A) + P(B) \quad \text{if } A \cap B = \emptyset \qquad (6.9)$$

Example 6.12 Suppose that 90% of a group of people can ride a bicycle, while 80% can drive a car. Then, writing these properties as B and C, we have, for an individual in the group, $P(B) = 0.9$, $P(C) = 0.8$. What is the probability that this person can either ride a bike or drive a car?

The simple-minded approach, using (6.9),

$$P(B \text{ or } C) = P(B \cup C) = P(B) + P(C) = 1.7,$$

clearly fails: no probability can exceed 1. The problem here is that the properties are not mutually exclusive: there are people who can do both. We cannot answer this question without knowing how many. Suppose it is 75%: $P(B \cap C) = 0.75$. Then (6.8) gives

$$P(B \cup C) = 0.9 + 0.8 - 0.75 = 0.95.$$

■

Note the shorthand notation here, choosing a letter that represents a property to stand for "x has the property X".

Example 6.13 In a group of 100 students, 60 speak F(rench), 30 speak G(erman) and 10 speak both.

$$P(F \cup G) = 0.6 + 0.3 - 0.1 = 0.8.$$

It is possible to analyse the given data and deduce that 20 speak N(either) language. This follows much more simply from the rules of probability:

$$P(N) = 1 - P(\overline{N}) = 1 - P(F \cup G) = 1 - 0.8 = 0.2.$$

It is very common in this subject to calculate the probability of the exact opposite of what is asked, then subtract from 1.   ■

For the remainder of this section we concentrate on **mutual exclusivity** and use (6.9).

Example 6.14 A fair die is thrown. $P(5 \text{ or } 6) = \frac{1}{6} + \frac{1}{6} = \frac{1}{3}$, since the events of throwing a 5 and a 6 clearly cannot occur simultaneously. ∎

This special case can be easily extended to many events. (The general case can also be extended, but the resulting formula is very complicated.)

$$P(A_1 \cup A_2 \cup \cdots \cup A_n) = P(A_1) + P(A_2) + \cdots + P(A_n), \qquad (6.10)$$

if $A_i \cap A_j = \emptyset$ for all i and j, $i \neq j$.

Example 6.15 Find the probability of obtaining a 'Flush' in poker: five cards of the same suit.

There are $\binom{52}{5}$ different hands that can be dealt. Of these, there are $\binom{13}{5}$ different sets of 5 Hearts, for example. Hence

$$p = P(5 \times \heartsuit) = \binom{13}{5} \Big/ \binom{52}{5}.$$

The probabilities for ♣, ♢ and ♠ are the same, by symmetry. These events are mutually exclusive, so

$$P(\text{Flush}) = p + p + p + p \simeq 0.02.$$

∎

A consequence of (6.10) is that if the full set of outcomes is divided into mutually exclusive sets then their probabilities sum to 1.

Example 6.16 On a given day, there is a 40% chance of precipitation, with rain three times as likely as snow, the latter including hail and sleet. Then, with obvious notation,

$$P(R) + P(S) = 0.4, \quad P(R) = 3P(S),$$

which can be solved to find

$$P(S) = 0.1, \ P(R) = 0.3, \ P(\text{Dry}) = 0.6.$$

∎

This division into mutually exclusive sets of outcomes underpins the very useful method of **tree diagrams**, where a 'branch' of the tree is used for each outcome. We draw the tree, identify branches delivering our desired property, then calculate the probability using (6.10), relying on mutual exclusivity.

Example 6.17 A bag contains 3 B(lack), 2 W(hite) and 5 B/W striped balls. One ball is chosen at random. What is the probability that it contains Black? The simplest approach is to use the reverse: $1 - P(W) = 1 - \frac{2}{10} = 0.8$, but we pursue a direct approach here.

The required probability is the sum of the probabilities for the two relevant branches:

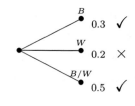

$$0.3 + 0.5 = 0.8,$$

indicated by ✓ on the **leaf**, as such an end-point is often known.

∎

The real power of tree diagrams, as we see later, is when there are several components in the model. To incorporate this element requires us to derive a further rule.

Ex 6.5 A coin is weighted so that 'Heads' is twice as likely as 'Tails'. Find $P(\text{Heads})$ and $P(\text{Tails})$.

Ex 6.6

(a) Suppose $P(A \cup B) = {}^2\!/_3$ and $P(A) = {}^1\!/_4$. Find $P(B)$ when i. A and B are mutually exclusive, ii. $P(A \cap B) = {}^1\!/_{12}$.

(b) **Mutually exclusive** events A and B have probabilities $P(A) = {}^1\!/_6$ and $P(B) = {}^1\!/_2$. Compute $P(\overline{A})$, $P(A \cup B)$, $P(A \cap \overline{B})$, $P(\overline{A \cup B})$.

6.4   Conditional Probability

A key value that the previous section required, but had no way to provide, is $P(A \cap B)$, i.e., the probability that the events A and B both occur. The difficulty with this quantity is that one event may depend on the other. This can range from A guaranteeing B, to A prohibiting B, as well as A making B more or less likely. For example, let A be the event that, in a game of cards, Player 1 holds four Aces and B that Player 2 holds one Ace. Clearly, if A occurs, B cannot occur, so $P(A \cap B) = 0$.

More realistic examples are:

- the chance of finding oil in one sector increases if it is found in an adjacent sector;

- an insurance company alters its judgement of an individual based on sex, smoking habits, family medical history, etc.;

- a person is more likely to get the flu if their partner has the flu.

This possible dependency is encapsulated in the idea of **conditional** probability, which we define and notate as follows.

Frame 6.4   *Definition of conditional probability*

$P(B|A) = $ the probability that B occurs, given that A occurs

---

In general, $P(B|A) \neq P(B)$.

Example 6.18   Two dice are thrown and the values are added, with a result of 8. What is the probability that one die shows a six?

The possible throws are, with the dice in order:

$$\mathbf{6+2}, \quad 5+3, \quad 4+4, \quad 3+5, \quad \mathbf{2+6},$$

where the emboldened ones are those showing a six. These are all equally likely, so

$$P(\text{one shows six}|\text{sum is 8}) = \tfrac{2}{5}.$$

Without knowing the sum of the faces, the probability is, using (6.8),

$$P(\text{one shows six}) = P(\text{1st is six}) + P(\text{2nd is six}) - P(\text{both are six})$$
$$= \tfrac{1}{6} + \tfrac{1}{6} - \tfrac{1}{36} = \tfrac{11}{36},$$

which is different.   ∎

This concept is particularly relevant for *selection without replacement*, since later selections depend on earlier ones.

Example 6.19   A bag contains 2 *W*hite and 3 *B*lack balls. For sampling with replacement, $P(B) = \tfrac{3}{5}$ for every selection. Otherwise, for a second draw:

$$P(B|W \text{ drawn first}) = \tfrac{3}{4}, \qquad P(B|B \text{ drawn first}) = \tfrac{1}{2}.$$

∎

Ex 6.7   Two fair dice are thrown, generating probabilities as in Exercise 6.3. Given that the sum of the numbers is 8, find the probability that both are even.

The experiment is repeated until as sum of either 6 or 7 is recorded. What is the probability that this stops with a total of 7?

6.5   The Product Rule

The most useful rule for calculating $P(A \cap B)$ – the **product rule** – depends on conditional probability.

Frame 6.5   *The product rule for probability*

$$P(A \cap B) = P(A)P(B|A) = P(B)P(A|B) \qquad (6.11)$$

This rule can be used to calculate *any* of these three quantities, given the value of the other two. Its most common uses are to calculate $P(A \cap B)$, and to calculate one of the conditional probabilities from the value of the other.

Before looking at examples of conditional probability, there is one important special simple case, which applies when the events A and B are

independent. By this we mean that B's probability does not depend on A, and *vice versa*. Thus $P(B|A) = P(B)$ and (6.11) becomes

$$P(A \cap B) = P(A)P(B). \qquad (6.12)$$

This is often taken as the definition of **independence**.

Frame 6.6   *Definition of independent events*

$$P(A \cap B) = P(A)P(B) \quad or \quad P(B|A) = P(B) \quad or \quad P(A|B) = P(A)$$

The more usual procedure in practice is to argue, *on physical grounds*, that A and B must be independent, then to use (6.12). Typical of such arguments are that dice cannot influence each other so throws of two dice or repeated throws of one die are independent, and that atoms in a radioactive specimen decay independently of each other.

Events must never be assumed to be independent without good evidence; the alluringly simple (6.12) will otherwise give false results.

Example 6.20   A bag contains 5 *B*lack balls and 5 *W*hite balls and two are drawn. What is the probability that both are Black?

Replacement: The draws are independent, so (6.12) gives $P(BB) = \frac{1}{2} \times \frac{1}{2} = \frac{1}{4}$.

Non-replacement: After drawing one Black, we are left with $5W$, $4B$, so the probability for the next to be Black is $\frac{4}{9}$. Hence

$$P(BB) = P(\text{1st } B)P(\text{2nd } B|\text{1st } B) = \frac{1}{2} \times \frac{4}{9} = \frac{2}{9},$$

which is less than $\frac{1}{4}$.   ■

> *Think about it like this*
>
> The following outlines the justification for (6.11). Suppose we know that A occurs. Then the probability for B must be conditional. When we use the Venn diagram in §6.1, we have to exclude all parts that do not occur inside A, which means two things. The sets for all other events must have their non-A parts removed, which we can do using an intersection: the relevant part of B is $A \cap B$. Also, all the individual (mutually exclusive) probabilities add up to $P(A)$, not 1, so we need to *rescale* them by dividing by that sum, $P(A)$. Hence
>
> $$P(B|A) = \frac{P(A \cap B)}{P(A)},$$
>
> which rearranges to give (6.11).

Example 6.21   In Example 6.18, suppose A represents the sum of 8. Only 5 of the 36 elementary events are in A, their probabilities adding up to $P(A) = \frac{5}{36}$. When we consider getting a six, B say, only 2 of the 11 such events overlap with A, so $P(A \cap B) = \frac{2}{36}$. Dividing by $P(A)$, to rescale this probability, gives $\frac{2}{5}$ as before.   ■

We shall now concentrate on cases where **independence** can be assumed, returning to the more general case when we develop tree diagrams further.

Example 6.22 A coin is tossed twice. Then $P(HH) = \frac{1}{2} \times \frac{1}{2} = \frac{1}{4}$, which we could have calculated by allocating the probability evenly across the four elementary events: $HH,\ HT,\ TH,\ TT$. ∎

Example 6.23 A gambler bets on three horses, with probabilities of winning – as judged by the bookmaker – $\frac{1}{2}$, $\frac{2}{3}$, $\frac{1}{10}$.

We can reasonably assume the races are independent of each other, so the probability of winning a *treble*, through all three horses winning, is

$$P(\text{Treble}) = \frac{1}{2} \times \frac{2}{3} \times \frac{1}{10} = \frac{1}{30},$$

so a stake of £1 should result in £30 being paid back. ∎

The product rule is particularly useful for calculating

$$P(\text{all events occur}) \quad \text{and} \quad P(\text{no event occurs}).$$

The first of these is a straightforward generalisation of (6.12):

$$P(A_1 \cap A_2 \cap \cdots \cap A_n) = P(A_1)P(A_2)\cdots P(A_n) \quad \text{(independent events)}.$$

The second is the same, but using $\overline{A_k}$: no event occurs if all events fail to occur.

It is a short step to a very useful formula:

$$P(\text{at least one event occurs}) = 1 - P(\text{no event occurs}), \tag{6.13}$$

a value that is usually very time-consuming to calculate directly, as the next example shows.

Example 6.24 [*The first significant probability calculation, due to Fermat.*] A professional gambler discovered that betting on throwing at least one six in four throws of a die wins in the long-term, but betting on throwing at least one double-six in 24 throws of two dice loses. Why?

For the first case, $P(\text{non-6}) = \frac{5}{6}$, so $P(\text{all non-6}) = \left(\frac{5}{6}\right)^4$. Hence

$$P(\text{at least one six}) = 1 - \left(\frac{5}{6}\right)^4 \simeq 0.518.$$

We analyse the second case similarly, with $P(66) = \frac{1}{36}$, $P(\text{non-66}) = \frac{35}{36}$:

$$P(\text{at least one double-six}) = 1 - \left(\frac{35}{36}\right)^{24} \simeq 0.491.$$

∎

We finish with application of the product rule to the important practical problem of **Reliability** of a device constructed by connecting individual components. In the simplest model we wish to connect two components A and B to form the device D. Let

$$P(A) = \text{probability of } A \textbf{ failing, etc.}$$

and we assume that such failures are **independent** of each other, i.e., one component failing does not affect the other's performance. We note that

$$\text{probability that } A \text{ does not fail} = P(\overline{A}) = 1 - P(A).$$

There are two ways to connect A and B.

Series

$$\text{———}\ A\ \text{———}\ B\ \text{———}$$

$$P(D) = P(\text{one fails}) = 1 - P(A \text{ works and } B \text{ works})$$
$$= 1 - [1 - P(A)][1 - P(B)]$$
$$P(D) = P(A) + P(B) - P(A)P(B). \tag{6.14}$$

Note that the product rule was used in the middle step, reflecting the "and" (as well as independence).

Parallel

$$P(D) = P(\text{both fail}) = P(A)P(B). \tag{6.15}$$

Note that again independence was relied upon.

Example 6.25 Suppose A is 90% reliable and B is 80% reliable. Then $P(A) = 0.1$, $P(B) = 0.2$ and

$$\begin{aligned}\text{series:} \quad & P(D) = 0.1 + 0.2 - 0.1 \times 0.2 = 0.28,\\ \text{parallel:} \quad & P(D) = 0.1 \times 0.2 = 0.02.\end{aligned}$$

We see that the parallel device is much safer. That ought to be clear from commonsense, but we now have a measure to show how much safer it is. ■

Ex 6.8 Suppose that $P(A) = 0.4$, $P(B) = 0.6$ and $P(B|A) = 0.8$. Find:

$$P(A \cap B), \quad P(A \cup B), \quad P(A|B), \quad P(B|\overline{A}), \quad P(\overline{A}|\overline{B}).$$

Ex 6.9 Two cards are drawn at random from 10 cards numbered 1 to 10. Find the probability that the sum is odd if (a) the two cards are drawn together, (b) the first is replaced before the second is drawn.

Ex 6.10 A circuit consists of three components A, B, C in series. A is itself built from two components A_1 and A_2 in parallel, C is built from C_1, C_2 and C_3 in parallel, while B is a single component. Find the probability of overall failure, given the individual probabilities of failure and assuming *independence*:

$$P(A_1) = 0.2, \ P(A_2) = 0.1; \quad P(B) = 0.05;$$

$$P(C_1) = 0.2, \ P(C_2) = 0.25, \ P(C_3) = 0.2.$$

6.6 Tree Diagrams

We can extend the simple tree diagram, introduced in §6.3, to deal with multiple events, which we can think of as sequences of 'simple' events.

At the end of each branch for the first event, we draw new branches to cover **all** possibilities in the second, *assuming that the indicated outcome of the first event has taken place.* This last statement is key to the calculations: the method relies on **mutually exclusivity** of the branches and **conditional probabilities** assigned to each. It is summed up as follows.

Frame 6.7   *Method of tree diagrams*

1. Assign probabilities to all parts of each branch: these will be **conditional** probabilities.

2. Multiply probabilities along each branch (**product rule**).

3. Add up the relevant values found in 2 (**addition rule**).

Example 6.26   A box contains 9 bulbs, of which 3 are defective (D). Select 2 bulbs, *without replacement*, and test them.

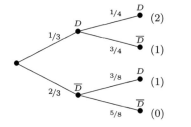

For the top two branches, the second draw has 2 defective bulbs out of 8, while for the bottom two, it is 3 out of 8. The probabilities differ on account of that. The number of defectives is written at the end of each 'leaf' and informs the calculation of the probabilities.

$$P(0D) = \tfrac{2}{3} \cdot \tfrac{5}{8} = \tfrac{5}{12},$$
$$P(1D) = \tfrac{1}{3} \cdot \tfrac{3}{4} + \tfrac{2}{3} \cdot \tfrac{3}{8} = \tfrac{6}{12},$$
$$P(2D) = \tfrac{1}{3} \cdot \tfrac{1}{4} = \tfrac{1}{12}.$$

Note that these add to 1, as we would expect.   ■

In some situations, e.g., sampling until an event occurs, the sampling and the tree can go on for ever. Summing the probabilities then needs infinite series.

Example 6.27   *A* and *B* play a game: a coin is tossed repeatedly until two consecutive tosses are the same. If this occurs on an **even**-numbered throw, *A* wins; if on an **odd**-numbered throw, *B* wins.

The first part of the tree diagram is shown below, with leaves labelled by the winner. It goes on forever, but we now have enough data to set up the probability sums. Note the symmetry between the top and bottom, which allows us to use just one half, and double the result.

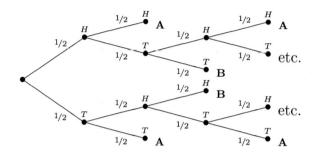

We find geometric series in the results:

$$P(A \text{ wins}) = 2\left[\frac{1}{4} + \frac{1}{16} + \frac{1}{64} + \cdots\right] = 2\frac{1/4}{1 - 1/4} = \frac{2}{3},$$

$$P(B \text{ wins}) = 2\left[\frac{1}{8} + \frac{1}{32} + \frac{1}{128} + \cdots\right] = 2\frac{1/8}{1 - 1/4} = \frac{1}{3}.$$

■

One of the most useful applications of the general product rule comes from the fact that there are two expressions for $P(A \cap B)$ in Frame 6.5:

$$P(A \cap B) = P(A)P(B|A) = P(B)(P(A|B)$$

can be rearranged to give

$$P(B|A) = \frac{P(A|B)P(B)}{P(A)}, \tag{6.16}$$

i.e., we can *reverse* conditional probabilities.

Think about it like this

It is often the case that we can measure one conditional probability but require the other. Equations such as (6.16) provide the necessary formulae. This is known as **Bayesian analysis** and we shall use tree diagrams to illustrate it.

Example 6.28 A box contains three coins: two are fair and the other is double-headed. A coin is chosen at random and tossed. If it shows *Heads*, what is the probability it is double-headed?

Let F = fair and D = double-headed. The crux of the problem is that we know $P(H|D)$, which must be 1, but wish to know $P(D|H)$.

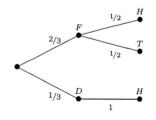

Sum the first and third branches to find $P(H)$, while $P(D)$ can be read off the tree:

$$P(H) = 2/3 \cdot 1/2 + 1/3 \cdot 1 = 2/3,$$
$$P(D) = 1/3.$$

Then (6.16) gives $P(D|H) = \dfrac{1 \times \frac{1}{3}}{\frac{2}{3}} = \frac{1}{2}.$

∎

The next example is a more practical one and its result is quite surprising. It illustrates well the ability to calculate a quantity that cannot be easily measured.

Example 6.29 A medical condition C affects 2% of the population. There is a test T, which shows positive for 90% of those with the condition and falsely positive for 1% of those without it.

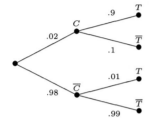

Sum the first and third branches to find the probability of a positive result:

$$P(T) = .02 \times .9 + .98 \times .01 = 0.0278,$$

while the first branch gives

$$P(C \cap T) = .02 \times .9 = 0.018.$$

Then the probability that a positive test shows the person has the condition is

$$P(C|T) = \frac{P(C \cap T)}{P(T)} = \frac{.018}{.0278} = \frac{180}{278} \simeq 0.65.$$

Then $P(\overline{C}|T) \simeq 0.35$ and we find that about one-third of those who test positively do *not* have the condition. ∎

Ex 6.11 A coin is thrown twice. What is the probability that two 'Heads' appear, given that the first throw is a 'Head'? What is the probability that two 'Heads' appear, given that at least one throw is a 'Head'?

Ex 6.12 Heather produces 30% of a bank's economic forecasts and Trevor produces the rest. Heather's forecasts are correct 75% of the time and Trevor's are correct 60% of the time. If a forecast, chosen at random, is correct, what is the probability that it was produced by Heather?

Ex 6.13 A company owns drilling rights in the North Sea. From geological records they know that high quality oil deposits are found 20% of the time, low quality deposits 30% of the time and no oil 50% of the time. Pre-drilling seismic tests give positive results on 70% of high quality sites, 35% of low quality sites and 10% on sites with no oil.

(a) Find the overall probability of a positive result in the seismic test.

(b) If the result is positive, what is the probability of finding oil at the site, based on that information?

6.7 Revision Exercises

Ex 6.14 A die is thrown twice. Let A denote "the number of spots on the first throw" and B denote "the total score of both throws". Calculate $P(A = 2)$, $P(B = 6)$ and $P(B = 7)$. Is either the event $B = 6$ or the event $B = 7$ independent of the event $A = 2$?

Ex 6.15 A bag contains 3 **red** balls, 4 **green** balls and 1 **black** ball. Balls are drawn at random, one after the other **without replacement**, until either two of the balls that have been drawn are of the same colour, or the black ball is drawn. Calculate:

(a) the probability that the process stops without the black ball having been drawn;

(b) the probability that there are precisely two draws made;

(c) the probability that the black ball has been drawn, given that precisely two draws were required.

Ex 6.16 A bag contains 2 **red** balls, 3 **blue** balls and 4 **green** balls. Two balls are drawn at random, one after the other **without replacing the first**. Calculate:

(a) the probability that both balls are the same colour;

(b) the probability that the second ball is green;

(c) the probability that the first ball is red, given that the second is known to be green.

7 DISCRETE DISTRIBUTIONS

The isolated probability calculations carried out in the previous chapter are valuable for some contexts, but in most cases we wish to view the whole picture, i.e., to have a complete set of probabilities encompassing all events, preferably bundled into mutually exclusive sets, as used in tree diagrams.

One particularly useful way to control this is to allocate a *number* to each outcome. Once we have such a number, we can marry it to the probabilities to calculate informative information, such as an *average* value. These numbers are thought of as values of a **random variable**. A specification of *all* possible values of the random variable, and their associated probabilities, is a **probability distribution**: a statement of how the available probability has been "distributed" among the outcomes.

7.1 Random Variables

Statistically-based experiments, or **trials**, often measure a number, thought of as one of the possible values of a variable, X say. This can be an artificial code or a natural part of the model. The following examples illustrate the wide range of possibilities:

1. the number on the face of a die (**natural**);

2. coin toss: $X = 1$ for *Heads*, $X = 0$ for *Tails* (**encoded**);

3. sum of the throws of two dice (not an *elementary* event, so this simplifies the structure by having fewer cases to deal with);

4. number of defectives in a sample (as in Example 6.26);

5. the net win at roulette (can be negative);

6. the lifetime of a light bulb;

7. the time between arrivals at a checkout.

The variables involved here are called **random variables**, since the values for any given trial cannot be predicted. They are almost always notated by capital letters, including Greek letters.

There is a fundamental distinction between the cases 1–5 and 6–7. The values for the former cases are isolated, like the natural numbers $\mathbb{N}$: the random variable is **discrete**.

The values for the latter can take any value in an **interval** in $\mathbb{R}$: the random variable is **continuous**. We shall defer consideration of these until the next chapter.

Whatever the context, the events for different values of the random variable must be **mutually exclusive**, else many of the calculations that follow are invalid. This is similar to the restriction on ordinary variables for functions, where one input value can produce only one output value. Here, one outcome can produce only one value of the variable.

7.2   Probability Distributions

Once we identify all possible values of a random variable X, and the probability that each occurs, we have defined a **(probability) distribution**. Associated with this is a key function – where "function" is used in its normal sense – called the **probability function**. Some people insert the word "**density**" but we shall reserve this for continuous distributions.

Frame 7.1   *The probability function and its properties*

$$f(x) = P(X = x) \qquad (7.1)$$

$$0 \leqslant f(x) \leqslant 1 \qquad (7.2)$$

$$\sum_{\text{all } k} f(x_k) = 1 \qquad (7.3)$$

(7.1) defines $f(x)$ to be the probability of obtaining that value of X and (7.2) is a consequence of $f(x)$ being a probability. (7.3), which relies on mutual exclusivity, shows that we have covered all possibilities.

The probability function can sometimes be specified by a formula (see §§7.4–7) but meanwhile we look at examples using tables and graphs.

Example 7.1   In Example 6.26 we found the probabilities for all possible draws of two bulbs from a box. The random variable was a natural one: the number of defectives.

The probabilities to be plotted are those in following table, using values referred to above:

x	0	1	2
$f(x)$	$5/12$	$6/12$	$1/12$

■

Example 7.2   Three fair coins are tossed and the number of *Heads* defines the random variable X. There are eight possibilities, listed as follows, with the number of *Heads* shown:

$$HHH\,(3),\ HHT\,(2),\ HTH\,(2),\ HTT\,(1),\ THH\,(2),\ THT\,(1),\ TTH\,(1),\ TTT\,(0).$$

Since each of these outcomes is equally-likely, we can calculate probabilities as follows:

x	0	1	2	3
$f(x)$	$1/8$	$3/8$	$3/8$	$1/8$

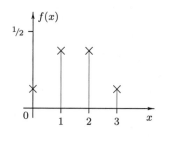

■

Example 7.3 Two four-sided dice are thrown and the numbers on the faces are added. There are 16 elementary events, each with probability $1/16$. The table on the left shows how the totals are distributed, which feeds into the table on the right, defining the probability function.

	1	2	3	4
1	2	3	4	5
2	3	4	5	6
3	4	5	6	7
4	5	6	7	8

x	2	3	4	5	6	7	8
$f(x)$	$1/16$	$2/16$	$3/16$	$4/16$	$3/16$	$2/16$	$1/16$

Note that the probabilities sum to 1. ∎

There is a further useful function associated with all distributions: the **(cumulative) distribution function**. The bracketed word is a helpful reminder of its definition, but the function is so frequently used that it is often omitted.

Its definition and principal property are given in the following frame.

Frame 7.2   *The cumulative distribution function*

$$F(x) = P(X \leqslant x) = \sum_{y \leqslant x} f(y) \qquad (7.4)$$

$$P(a < X \leqslant b) = F(b) - F(a) \qquad (7.5)$$

The mutual exclusivity gives the summation formula and the obvious formula

$$\sum_{y \leqslant a} f(y) + \sum_{a < y \leqslant b} f(y) = \sum_{y \leqslant b} f(y)$$

rearranges to give (7.5).

From its definition we see that $F(x)$ never decreases, while $F(-\infty) = 0$ and $F(\infty) = 1$.

Example 7.4 Draw the graph of $F(x)$ for the distribution in Example 7.2.

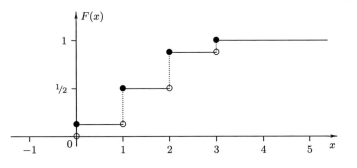

∎

Think about it like this

> The graph in this example shows a serious drawback to $F(x)$: it is defined piecewise and is discontinuous. Its key role is in **continuous** distributions. For those, it is the counterpart to $f(x)$ that proves difficult to use, while the distribution function has much simpler properties and is generally a continuous function.

Ex 7.1 Two fair dice are thrown. Let N be the larger of the two numbers. Find $P(N = k)$ for $k = 1, 2, \ldots, 6$.

Ex 7.2 A die has faces numbered from 1 to 6 and is weighted so that the probability of throwing n in a single throw is proportional to n, i.e., it is λn for some constant λ. Find λ.

7.3 Distribution Parameters

The numerical values of a random variable allow us to define and calculate certain 'summary' values, called **parameters**, which give an overall picture of the distribution. In *Statistics*, we carry out practical trials to measure certain values, which are direct counterparts of these parameters. These measures are, in fact, called **statistics**. As we shall see much later, using just two of these statistics can often allow us to draw conclusions from statistical trials irrespective of the details of the underlying distribution.

7.3.1 Mode

The **mode** for a distribution is the most probable value of X, i.e., the value x for which $f(x)$ is a maximum.

Example 7.5 For the four-sided dice in Example 7.3, the mode is 5, with probability $4/16$.

For the three coins in Example 7.2, there are two modes: 1 and 2, with equal probabilities $3/8$. ∎

The mode is mostly used in 'descriptive', rather than computational, statistical work.

7.3.2 Median

The median is the 'middle' value in the sense that the probability of lying on each side is exactly $1/2$. Thus $F(m) = 1/2$.

Frame 7.3   *The definition of the median*

$$m = F^{-1}(0.5) \qquad (7.6)$$

This definition relies on the **inverse function** for $F(x)$, which may not exist. As we see in the following examples, this means that the median may not be defined or may have an infinite number of values.

Example 7.6   Consider a single coin toss.

Define

$$X = \begin{cases} 0 & \text{for } \textit{Tails}, \\ 1 & \text{for } \textit{Heads}, \end{cases}$$

each value having probability $\frac{1}{2}$.

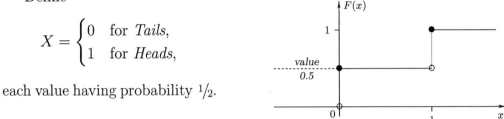

The distribution function's graph shows that $F(x) = 0.5$ for $0 \leqslant x < 1$, so there are an infinite number of 'medians'. A commonsense choice is the mid-point $\frac{1}{2}$, although this is not a possible value of X. ∎

Example 7.7   Consider the choice of one card from a set of three.

We have $X = 1, 2, 3$, each with probability $\frac{1}{3}$. There is no x for which $F(x) = 0.5$, although $x = 2$ is an obvious commonsense choice, as the graph suggests.

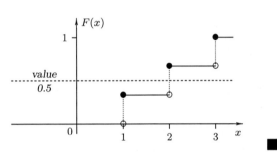

∎

Nevertheless, the definition in Frame 7.3 is useful for *continuous* distributions, where we rarely encounter problems in defining the inverse function.

7.3.3   Expected Value (Mean)

For computational, rather than descriptive, purposes, a better measure of the centre of the distribution is the **expected value** or **mean**, defined and notated as follows.

Frame 7.4   *Expected value or mean of a distribution*

$$E(X) = \mu_X = \sum_k x_k P(X = x_k) = \sum_k x_k f(x_k) \qquad (7.7)$$

The rationale for this definition is as follows. Suppose we take a sample of N values, where each x_k appears with a **frequency** f_k times. Then the **average** of the sample (in the everyday sense of the word) is

$$\frac{f_1 x_1 + f_2 x_2 + \cdots + f_n x_n}{N} = \frac{f_1}{N} x_1 + \frac{f_2}{N} x_2 + \cdots + \frac{f_n}{N} x_n \simeq \mu_X,$$

since $\frac{f_k}{N} \simeq f(x_k)$ when the sample is a representative one. Thus the mean and the average are approximately the same. Indeed, 'mean' is another word for 'average'.

Example 7.8   Consider a six-sided die, where the probabilities are all $\frac{1}{6}$.
The mean score is

$$\mu_X = 1 \times \tfrac{1}{6} + 2 \times \tfrac{2}{6} + \cdots + 6 \times \tfrac{1}{6} = 21 \times \tfrac{1}{6} = 3.5.$$

∎

Example 7.9   Consider the tossing of three coins, as in Example 7.2.
The mean number of *Heads* is

$$\mu_X = 0 \times \tfrac{1}{8} + 1 \times \tfrac{3}{8} + 2 \times \tfrac{3}{8} + 3 \times \tfrac{1}{8} = \tfrac{12}{8} = 1.5.$$

∎

Example 7.10   Consider the number of defective bulbs in Example 6.26.
The mean number of defectives is

$$\mu_X = 0 \times \tfrac{5}{12} + 1 \times \tfrac{6}{12} + 2 \times \tfrac{1}{12} = \tfrac{8}{12} = \tfrac{2}{3}.$$

∎

The mean in all of these examples is a value that cannot be achieved by the random variable X. This is not unusual and is not a problem, since the mean is related to repeated sampling, not to a single sample. A typical application is to the situation when there are N samples and the outcomes are added, e.g., a gambler playing a game with mean winnings μ_X will "expect" to win an approximate amount $N\mu_X$ in N games. This helps explain the name **expected value**.

7.3.4   Variance

There is one further type of measure required for a distribution; once we have it we can make great advances in statistical calculations. We need to measure **dispersion**, i.e., how spread out a distribution is (about its mean). We would expect the result of throwing a die to have a larger spread than the result of tossing three coins, since the latter has the probabilities near the mean larger than the other values.

There are two such quantities; the easier to investigate is the **variance**. There are two equivalent formulae: the first is the theoretically justified one and the second is the computational one.

Frame 7.5   *Variance of a distribution*

$$\mathrm{Var}(X) = \sum_k (x_k - \mu_X)^2 P(X = x_k) = \sum_k (x_k - \mu_X)^2 f(x_k) \quad (7.8)$$

$$\mathrm{Var}(X) = \sum_k x_k^2 f(x_k) - \mu_X^2 = E(X^2) - [E(X)]^2 \quad\quad\quad (7.9)$$

Think about it like this

The idea for the variance is that we wish a representative value of the difference of the values of X from the mean μ, i.e., $X - \mu$. We cannot simply average these because the positive and negative values would cancel each other out. But if we *square* the values first, we banish negative values and get a true measure of the spread: $E\left[(X - \mu)^2\right]$, an 'average' value of $(X - \mu)^2$.

For convenience, we often suppress the subscript in μ_X when there is no ambiguity.

Example 7.11 Consider the tossing of three coins, as in Example 7.2. The mean, from Example 7.9, is $\mu = {}^3\!/_2$. Aiming to use (7.8), we construct the table:

x_k	0	1	2	3
$(x_k - \mu)^2$	$9\!/_4$	$1\!/_4$	$1\!/_4$	$9\!/_4$
$f(x_k)$	$1\!/_8$	$3\!/_8$	$3\!/_8$	$1\!/_8$

Then multiply and add the last two rows:

$$\operatorname{Var}(X) = \tfrac{9}{32} + \tfrac{3}{32} + \tfrac{3}{32} + \tfrac{9}{32} = {}^3\!/_4.$$

The formula (7.9) finds:

$$\operatorname{Var}(X) = 0^2 \times {}^1\!/_8 + 1^2 \times {}^3\!/_8 + 2^2 \times {}^3\!/_8 + 3^2 \times {}^1\!/_8 - \left({}^3\!/_2\right)^2 = {}^3\!/_4.$$

Note that this answer can be interpreted as $3 \times {}^1\!/_2 \times {}^1\!/_2 = n \times P(H) \times P(\overline{H})$, where n is the number of coins. We see in §7.6 that this is no accident. ■

Before looking at further examples, it is informative to see why the two versions are the same. From (7.8),

$$\operatorname{Var}(X) = \sum_k \left[x_k^2 - 2\mu x_k + \mu^2\right] f(x_k)$$
$$= \sum_k x_k^2 f(x_k) - 2\mu \sum_k x_k f(x_k) + \mu^2 \sum_k f(x_k)$$
$$= E(X^2) - 2\mu\mu + \mu^2 \times 1$$
$$= E(X^2) - \mu^2,$$

using (7.7) and the fact that the probabilities add to 1.

Example 7.12 Consider a six-sided die, whose mean was found in Example 7.8 to be 3.5.

$$\operatorname{Var}(X) = 1^2 \times {}^1\!/_6 + 2^2 \times {}^1\!/_6 + \cdots + 6^2 \times {}^1\!/_6 - \left({}^7\!/_2\right)^2 = \tfrac{91}{6} - \tfrac{49}{4} = \tfrac{35}{12}.$$

We see that this is indeed larger than the variance for three coins $({}^3\!/_4)$. ■

Example 7.13 Consider the defective bulbs in Example 6.26, whose mean was found in Example 7.10 to be ${}^2\!/_3$.

$$\operatorname{Var}(X) = 0^2 \times {}^5\!/_{12} + 1^2 \times {}^6\!/_{12} + 2^2 \times {}^1\!/_{12} - \left({}^2\!/_3\right)^2 = {}^{10}\!/_{12} - {}^4\!/_9 = {}^7\!/_{18}.$$

■

7.3.5   Standard Deviation

The variance $\mathrm{Var}(X)$ has one drawback for practical statistical work: its measurement unit (if there is one) is the square of that for X. This is easily remedied, by using the **standard deviation**.

Frame 7.6   *Standard deviation of a distribution*

$$\sigma_X = \sqrt{\mathrm{Var}(X)} \qquad\qquad (7.10)$$

Think about it like this

This does not make the variance redundant, since the algebraic difficulties involved with the square root means the necessary theoretical work associated with the standard deviation has to be done for the variance, before using the square root.

Notation

The subscript X is sometimes omitted, when the context is clear. Some authors use σ_X^2 to notate $\mathrm{Var}(X)$.

Example 7.14   For the three coins in Example 7.2 the standard deviation is $\sigma_X = \sqrt{3/4} = \sqrt{3}/2$. ∎

Example 7.15   Consider the four-sided dice in Example 7.3.

This symmetric distribution has 5 as both its mode and median. The other parameters are

$$E(X) = \frac{1}{16}\left[2 \times 1 + 3 \times 2 + 4 \times 3 + 5 \times 4 + 6 \times 3 + 7 \times 2 + 8 \times 1\right]$$

$$= \frac{1}{16}\left[2 + 6 + 12 + 20 + 18 + 14 + 8\right] = 5,$$

$$\mathrm{Var}(X) = \frac{1}{16}\left[2^2 \times 1 + 3^2 \times 2 + \cdots + 8^2 \times 1\right] - 5^2$$

$$= 27.5 - 25 = 2.5,$$

$$\sigma_X = \sqrt{2.5}.$$

∎

Ex 7.3   A fair 4-sided die has the numbers 1, 2, 3 and 4 inscribed on its faces, those being the values of a random variable X. Find the probability distribution for X, its mean and variance.

Ex 7.4   A bag contains 4 red and 2 blue counters. One counter at a time is removed from the bag but not replaced, until a blue counter appears. What is the expected number of counters drawn from the bag?

Ex 7.5   In a set of 5 objects, one is special. One object is selected at random and inspected to see if it is the special one. If so, the process stops. Otherwise the experiment is repeated, with the selected object **not replaced**. Let X be the number of selections required to obtain the special one, so X is from 1 to 5.

Find the probability distribution for X, graph the probability function and the distribution function. Calculate $P(X \leqslant 2)$, $P(X > 3)$ and $E(X)$. Suggest a value for the median.

Ex 7.6

(a) Calculate the mode and mean for the random variable N in Exercise 7.1.

(b) Calculate the mean, variance and standard deviation of the score obtained when the die in Exercise 7.2 is thrown.

7.4   Uniform Distribution

We now examine four key distributions that appear frequently in practice. It makes good sense to find the properties of the general forms of these, rather than have to undertake the work every time one appears.

Two are *finite*, in the sense of having a random variable taking values from 0 or 1 to n, while the other two are *infinite*, since the variables range from 0 or 1 to ∞.

The first is the **uniform** distribution, in which the values from 1 to n occur with equal probability:

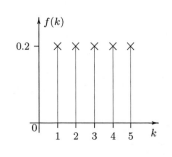

$$P(X = k) = \frac{1}{n} \quad (1 \leqslant k \leqslant n).$$

The graph shows the probability function for $n = 5$.

We can find the mean and variance using standard summation formulae:

$$E(X) = [1 + 2 + \cdots + n]\frac{1}{n} = \frac{n(n+1)}{2}\frac{1}{n} = \frac{n+1}{2},$$

$$\mathrm{Var}(X) = [1^2 + 2^2 + \cdots + n^2]\frac{1}{n} - \left(\frac{n+1}{2}\right)^2$$

$$= \frac{n(n+1)(2n+1)}{6}\frac{1}{n} - \frac{(n+1)^2}{4}$$

$$= \frac{n+1}{12}[4n + 2 - 3n - 3] = \frac{n^2 - 1}{12}.$$

We have already encountered the uniform distribution: a fair coin ($n = 2$), a fair die ($n = 6$), a pack of cards ($n = 52$).

To sum up, for the general case:

Frame 7.7   *Uniform distribution on {1,2,...,n}*

$$f(k) = \frac{1}{n} \quad (1 \leqslant k \leqslant n) \tag{7.11}$$

$$E(X) = \frac{n+1}{2} \tag{7.12}$$

$$\text{Var}(X) = \frac{n^2 - 1}{12} \tag{7.13}$$

Example 7.16   For a coin with $P(\text{Tails}) = 1$, $P(\text{Heads}) = 2$,

$$E(X) = \tfrac{3}{2}, \qquad \text{Var}(X) = \frac{4-2}{12} = \tfrac{1}{4}.$$

This is similar to Example 7.6, where we used values 0 and 1. There the mean is $\tfrac{1}{2}$; here it is $\tfrac{1}{2} + 1$. As we would expect, adding one to the values adds one to the mean. The variance, however, is unchanged. It measures the *spread* about the mean and so is unaffected when all values (and hence the mean) are moved by the same amount.   ■

Example 7.17   Consider $n = 10$. Then $E(X) = 5.5$ and $\text{Var}(X) = \frac{99}{12} = \frac{33}{4}$. More useful is the set of values $\{0, 1, \ldots, 9\}$, i.e., $Y = X - 1$. Then

$$E(Y) = 5.5 - 1 = 4.5, \qquad \text{Var}(Y) = \tfrac{33}{4}.$$

■

This example illustrates an important use of the uniform distribution. It controls streams of **random numbers**, i.e., sequences of numbers that are all of equal probability and occur at random, as if sampled from a uniform distribution. They are used in *simulation* programs. Those for a uniform random variable are fundamental, in the sense that a stream fitting a different distribution is usually derived from a uniform stream.

Example 7.18   To get a set of numbers uniformly distributed on $[\,0, 1\,]$ we could generate ones from 0 to 10,000, then divide by 10^4.   ■

Ex 7.7   Find the probability distribution, mean and variance for the result of throwing a fair die. Verify that these results agree with the uniform distribution on $\{1, 2, 3, 4, 5, 6\}$.

7.5   Geometric Distribution

We first define a simple random process that underpins the key distributions in this section and the next.

A process with a probability p of *success* and probability q of *failure*, with $p + q = 1$, is a **Bernoulli trial**. We shall now use repeated (identical) Bernoulli trials, with an important assumption: *they are independent*. (This allows use of the simple form of the product rule.)

Suppose that X measures the number of trials needed to achieve a first success. Then, the product rule gives

$$X = k \quad \Rightarrow \quad k-1 \text{ failures, then success} \quad \Rightarrow \quad f(k) = P(X = k) = q^{k-1}p.$$

Note that

$$\sum_k f(k) = p + qp + q^2p + q^3p + \cdots$$

$$= p\left[1 + q + q^2 + \cdots\right] = p\frac{1}{1-q} = 1,$$

since $p + q = 1$. The sum involved is the geometric series, revealing the underlying sequence of probabilities to be a geometric progression; hence this is known as a **geometric distribution**. It has applications in *quality control*.

The expected value is

$$E(X) = p + 2qp + 3q^2p + 4q^3p + \cdots$$

$$= p\frac{d}{dq}\left[1 + q + q^2 + q^3 + \cdots\right]$$

$$= p\frac{d}{dq}\left[\frac{1}{1-q}\right]$$

$$= p(1-q)^{-2} = p\frac{1}{p^2} = \frac{1}{p}.$$

Alternatively, one can argue that in N trials we expect Np successes, which are spaced out by $\frac{N}{Np} = \frac{1}{p}$, on average.

The variance can be found similarly. The key data are given in the following Frame.

Frame 7.8   *Geometric distribution with parameter p*

$$f(k) = q^{k-1}p \quad (k \geqslant 1) \tag{7.14}$$

$$E(X) = \frac{1}{p} \tag{7.15}$$

$$\text{Var}(X) = \frac{q}{p^2} \tag{7.16}$$

Example 7.19   Consider the case $p = q = 1/2$.

$$P(X = k) = (1/2)^{k-1} \, 1/2 = 2^{-k},$$

$$E(X) = \frac{1}{1/2} = 2,$$

$$\text{Var}(X) = \frac{1/2}{(1/2)^2} = 2.$$

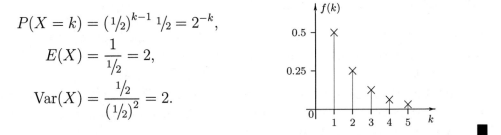

Example 7.20 One in every 100 cans of fizz has a special ring pull. What is the maximum number I may have to buy to ensure I have a 50–50 chance of finding one? We assume the stock of cans in infinite, so we are effectively "sampling with replacement", to ensure the trials are **independent**.

We seek N such that

$$P(X = 1) + P(X = 2) + \cdots + P(X = N) \simeq 0.5.$$

Let $p = 0.01$, $q = 0.99$. Then

$$p + qp + q^2 p + \cdots + q^{N-1}p = p\left[\frac{1 - q^N}{1 - q}\right] = 1 - q^N,$$

which we could have found more easily by

$$P(X \leqslant N) = 1 - P(X > N) = 1 - P(N \text{ failures}) = 1 - q^N.$$

We therefore require

$$1 - 0.99^N \simeq 0.5 \quad \Rightarrow \quad 0.99^N \simeq 0.5 \quad \Rightarrow \quad N \simeq \frac{\ln 0.5}{\ln 0.99} \simeq 69.$$

∎

Ex 7.8 Two fair coins are tossed together. How many times, on average, does this have to be done to obtain: (a) two heads and (b) one head and one tail?

Ex 7.9 An event has a probability p of occurring (and $q = 1 - p$ of not occurring). A series of independent trials is carried out. Find the probabilities that the first occurrence is (a) at an even-numbered trial, (b) at an odd-numbered trial. Verify they add to one.

Ex 7.10 A gambler plays a game with probability $1/2$ of winning, when he receives back the original stake doubled. He adopts the following scheme: he gambles 1 unit on the first game. If he wins, he banks the winnings and starts again. If he loses, he doubles the stake on the next game, and so on until he wins.

Suppose that, in a 'losing' sequence, he requires X games to get a win. Show that $P(X = n) = 1/2^n$. Show that the net win in any sequence is 1 unit.

In spite of this, the strategy is known as **Gambler's Ruin**. Why?

7.6   Binomial Distribution

The most important of all discrete distributions – the **binomial distribution** – is also based on *Bernoulli trials*, but this time a fixed number of trials, n. X counts the number of successes; we seek $P(X = k)$ for all possible k.

This value can be deduced in many ways, e.g., by analysing a tree diagram. In this case we have a **binary** tree: from each point there are **two** branches, success (S) and failure (F).

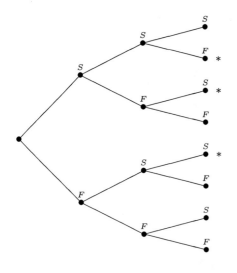

In general there are 2^n branches, since each of the n decisions doubles the number; in the case illustrated to the left, there are $8 = 2^3$.

We seek to identify all branches with $k\,S$ and $(n-k)\,F$. There are precisely $\binom{n}{k}$ ways in which to select k of the n segments in a branch, to label them as S.

For the example on the left, there are $\binom{3}{2}$ asterisked branches, each with $2\,S$ and $1\,F$.

Now, using the product rule and relying on *independence*, each branch has probability $p^k q^{n-k}$. Hence, using the addition rule, as usual for a tree diagram:

$$P(X = k) = \binom{n}{k} p^k q^{n-k}.$$

These are the probabilities for the distribution, often notated as $\mathrm{Bin}(n, p)$.

Note again that independence is essential: the sampling must be "with replacement".

Example 7.21 For the three coins considered in Example 7.2, we have $\mathrm{Bin}\,(3, \tfrac{1}{2})$. Then $q = \tfrac{1}{2}$ also and

$$P(X = 0) = \binom{3}{0} \left(\tfrac{1}{2}\right)^0 \left(\tfrac{1}{2}\right)^3 = \tfrac{1}{8},$$

$$P(X = 1) = \binom{3}{1} \left(\tfrac{1}{2}\right)^1 \left(\tfrac{1}{2}\right)^2 = \tfrac{3}{8},$$

$$P(X = 2) = \binom{3}{2} \left(\tfrac{1}{2}\right)^2 \left(\tfrac{1}{2}\right)^1 = \tfrac{3}{8},$$

$$P(X = 3) = \binom{3}{3} \left(\tfrac{1}{2}\right)^3 \left(\tfrac{1}{2}\right)^0 = \tfrac{1}{8}.$$

These are exactly the values found earlier by listing all cases, but now delivered by a formula. $\blacksquare$

The probabilities in this example added to 1, as they must. We can easily confirm this is true in general:

$$\sum_k P(X = k) = \sum_{k=0}^{n} \binom{n}{k} p^k q^{n-k} = (q + p)^n = 1^n = 1,$$

using the **Binomial Theorem**.

Further algebra of a binomial type gives simple formulae for the mean and variance.

Frame 7.9   *Binomial distribution* Bin(n,p)

$$f(k) = \binom{n}{k} p^k q^{n-k} \quad (0 \leqslant k \leqslant n) \qquad (7.17)$$

$$E(X) = np \qquad (7.18)$$

$$\text{Var}(X) = npq \qquad (7.19)$$

The mean value is a natural one: for large n we 'expect' np successes.

Example 7.22 For tossing three coins, where $n = 3$, $p = \frac{1}{2}$, we found in Examples 7.9 and 7.11:

$$E(X) = \tfrac{3}{2} = 3 \times \tfrac{1}{2}, \qquad \text{Var}(X) = \tfrac{3}{4} = 3 \times \tfrac{1}{2} \times \left(1 - \tfrac{1}{2}\right).$$

■

The probabilities calculated in Example 7.21 are symmetrical, which is true whenever $p = \frac{1}{2}$. The graph on the right is Bin$(5, \frac{1}{2})$.

The distribution can be very asymmetrical for p near 0 or 1, as the next example shows.

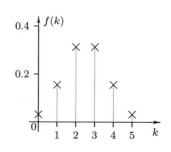

Example 7.23 Suppose we throw three fair dice and count the number of sixes. The distribution here is Bin$(3, \frac{1}{6})$.

Using binomial coefficients 1, 3, 3, 1, we find:

$$P(X = 0) = \left(\tfrac{1}{6}\right)^0 \left(\tfrac{5}{6}\right)^3 = {}^{125}/_{216},$$

$$P(X = 1) = 3\left(\tfrac{1}{6}\right)^1 \left(\tfrac{5}{6}\right)^2 = {}^{75}/_{216},$$

$$P(X = 2) = 3\left(\tfrac{1}{6}\right)^2 \left(\tfrac{5}{6}\right)^1 = {}^{15}/_{216},$$

$$P(X = 3) = \left(\tfrac{1}{6}\right)^3 \left(\tfrac{5}{6}\right)^0 = {}^{1}/_{216}.$$

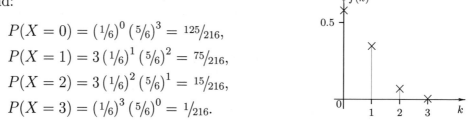

The formulae in Frame 7.9 give $E(X) = 3 \times \frac{1}{6} = \frac{1}{2}$ and $\text{Var}(X) = 3 \times \frac{1}{6} \times \frac{5}{6} = \frac{5}{12}$. We can verify these directly, e.g.,

$$E(X) = \frac{1}{216} \left[0 \times 125 + 1 \times 75 + 2 \times 15 + 3 \times 1 \right] = \frac{108}{216} = \frac{1}{2}.$$

■

The binomial distribution is fundamental for statistical models where a *binary* test is made: working/faulty, yes/no, agree/disagree, win/lose, etc. We end this section with some realistic calculations, which will reveal a serious computational problem with the binomial distribution, one we shall tackle later.

Example 7.24 A piece of equipment whose reliability is critical is designed to work if at least **two** of its **eight** components function. The probability of a failure of any one, in a given period, is 0.1 *and* failure events are **independent**.

Let X be the number failing in the period. Then X is distributed as Bin(8, 0.1). We require to find

$$P(\text{total fail}) = P(X = 8) + P(X = 7)$$
$$= 0.1^8 + \binom{8}{1} 0.1^7 (1 - 0.1) = 0.000\,000\,73.$$

∎

Example 7.25 A die is thrown 40 times and a *six* appears three times. Is the die biased?

Assume it is *not* biased and let X be the number of sixes that appear. X is distributed as Bin $(40, \,^1/_6)$. To judge the performance, we calculate the probability of getting **three or fewer** sixes. If this is small, our assumption – that the die is unbiased – is suspect.

$$P(X \leqslant 3) = P(X = 0) + P(X = 1) + P(X = 2) + P(X = 3)$$
$$= \left(\tfrac{5}{6}\right)^{40} + \binom{40}{1}\left(\tfrac{5}{6}\right)^{39}\left(\tfrac{1}{6}\right) + \binom{40}{2}\left(\tfrac{5}{6}\right)^{38}\left(\tfrac{1}{6}\right)^2 + \binom{40}{3}\left(\tfrac{5}{6}\right)^{37}\left(\tfrac{1}{6}\right)^3$$
$$\simeq 0.081,$$

so we should not place much faith in this die. ∎

Example 7.26 [*A sampling technique called a 'triangular test'*]

We wished to test the performance of a change to a production process. We gave 20 people three samples – two from the old process, one from the new – and asked them to identify the "odd" one; 10 did so correctly. Does this suggest the new process has produced a noticeably different product?

We assume there is no discernible difference, so people were in effect guessing. The distribution is Bin $(20, \,^1/_3)$, since each person has a 1-in-3 chance of guessing correctly. We now calculate the probability of guessing correctly 10 or more times.

$$P(X = k) = \binom{20}{k} (^1/_3)^k \, (^2/_3)^{20-k},$$
$$P(X \geqslant 10) = \binom{20}{10} \frac{2^{10}}{3^{20}} + \binom{20}{11} \frac{2^{11}}{3^{20}} + \cdots.$$

The arithmetic is dreadful, although the terms do decrease quickly in size and soon become negligible. The first term is 0.054 and the total is 0.092, to 3 dp. Such a low probability of achieving this many correct answers by guesswork suggests that the participants were *not* guessing and that there is a discernible difference, at least to some. ∎

Example 7.27 An insurance company accepts applications from 2100 men, of the same age and health. The probability that each will still be alive 30 years later is 0.7. Find the probability that at least 1450 are still alive.

The model is Bin(2100, 0.7) and we require

$$\sum_{k=1450}^{2100} \binom{2100}{k} 0.7^k \, 0.3^{2100-k} \simeq 0.8356,$$

where the calculation has required use of a computer.   ■

These last three examples have demonstrated, with increasing force, the potential computational difficulties in using the binomial distribution. We shall later find a much simpler method, using the renowned *Normal distribution*, to calculate an *approximation* to binomial probabilities. That method gives 0.8355 for the result of Example 7.27.

Ex 7.11

(a) For a **binomial** distributed variable X, with parameters $n = 6$ and $p = 0.2$, find

    i. $P(X = 1)$ ii. $P(X = 4)$ iii. $P(X < 2)$

(b) A trial produces a success with probability $1/2$. What is the probability of exactly **four** successes in **eight** independent trials?

Ex 7.12

(a) In a ten question true/false examination, what is the probability of scoring 70% or better by guesswork?

(b) A component has a probability 0.98 of working throughout a 24 hour period. What is the probability that, out of **six** independent components, **at least five** are still working after 24 hours?

Ex 7.13

(a) A company guarantees to repair, free of charge, any car that has certain defects within one year of purchase. It is found that 15% of cars have such defects.

    i. Find the probabilities that, in a random sample of 12 cars, none will need repaired, 3 or more will need repaired.

    ii. The company sells 2500 such cars and the average cost of each repair is £400. What is the company's expected cost of repairs? You can answer this only by ignoring a flaw in the information supplied: what is it?

(b) As part of product testing of a new formulation of a household cleaner, each of a panel of 15 cleaners was given samples of the new and old formulations without being told which was which. Of these, 12 preferred the new formulation and 3 the old one. Suppose that there is no real difference between their effectiveness: what is the probability of 12 or more choosing the new one by chance?

7.7 Poisson Distribution

The approximation method just mentioned works only for values of p in $\text{Bin}(n, p)$ that are not near 0 or 1. In these cases there is an alternative approximation, using the **Poisson distribution**. This applies to cases where p is near 0. (If p is near 1, we simply reword the problem in terms of $1 - p = q$.)

The Poisson distribution is defined as follows.

Frame 7.10   *Poisson distribution with parameter μ*

$$f(k) = e^{-\mu}\frac{\mu^k}{k!} \quad (0 \leqslant k < \infty) \tag{7.20}$$

$$E(X) = \mu \tag{7.21}$$

$$\text{Var}(X) = \mu \tag{7.22}$$

Before illustrating its use, we should verify that it is indeed a valid distribution. Clearly $f(k) \geqslant 0$, as required. Also

$$\sum_{k=0}^{\infty} f(k) = e^{-\mu}\sum_{k=0}^{\infty}\frac{\mu^k}{k!} = e^{-\mu}e^{\mu} = 1.$$

The mean can be verified by

$$\mu_X = \sum_{k=0}^{\infty} k e^{-\mu}\frac{\mu^k}{k!} = \mu e^{-\mu}\sum_{k=1}^{\infty}\frac{\mu^{k-1}}{(k-1)!}$$

$$= \mu e^{-\mu}e^{\mu} = \mu,$$

where the series has had its first term removed since it has a factor $k = 0$. The variance can be verified similarly, although we shall indicate later that its value is suggested by the link to the binomial.

The Poisson distribution is the correct model for counting **independent** events that occur **entirely at random**. Such events have their occurrence controlled by a **rate of occurrence**: $R =$ so many events per unit (whatever). Examples are:

- decay of a radioactive substance: $R =$ number of detections per unit time;

- flaws in a length of material or artefact, such as a pipe: $R =$ flaws per unit distance;

- arrivals at a checkout; $R =$ number of arrivals per unit time.

To calculate the required probabilities, we first of all choose an appropriate time or space interval, T say. Then the expected number of occurrences in any such interval is

$$\mu = RT, \tag{7.23}$$

which provides the key parameter we need.

Example 7.28   A radioactive source decays at the rate of 1 detection per 20 minutes. What is the probability of **more than two** in one hour?

We have $R = \frac{1}{20}$ detection per minute and $T = 60$ minutes, so $\mu = \frac{1}{20} \times 60 = 3$. We require

$$P(X > 2) = 1 - \big[\, P(X = 0) +$$
$$P(X = 1) + P(X = 2) \,\big]$$
$$= 1 - e^{-3}\left[1 + \frac{3}{1!} + \frac{3^2}{2!}\right]$$
$$= 0.577.$$

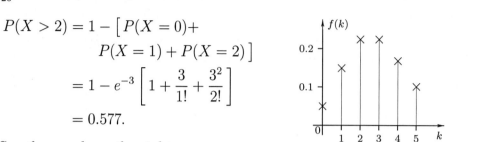

See the graph on the right.   ∎

Example 7.29   A steel sheet has an average of one flaw per 5 metres. Find the probabilities of (a) exactly one flaw in a 5 metre length, (b) at least two flaws in a 10 metre length.

(a) We have $R = \frac{1}{5}$ flaw per metre and $T = 5$ metres, so $\mu = \frac{1}{5} \times 5 = 1$. We require
$$P(X = 1) = e^{-1}\left[\tfrac{1}{1}\right] = 0.368.$$

(b) We now have $T = 10$ metres, so $\mu = \frac{1}{5} \times 10 = 2$. We require
$$P(X \geqslant 2) = 1 - \big[\, P(X = 0) + P(X = 1) \,\big]$$
$$= 1 - e^{-2}\left[1 + \frac{2}{1}\right] = 0.594.$$

∎

Although the calculations are generally easier than those for the binomial distribution – at least there are no binomial coefficients to find – the arithmetic can still be heavy, as the next example shows.

Example 7.30   Customers arrive at a checkout entirely at random, at a rate of 50 per hour. Find the probabilities of (a) no arrivals in one minute, (b) more than 10 arrivals in 6 minutes.

(a) We have $R = 50$ arrivals per hour and $T = \frac{1}{60}$ hour, so $\mu = 50 \times \frac{1}{60} = 5/6$. We require
$$P(X = 0) = e^{-5/6} = 0.435.$$

(b) We now have $T = \frac{1}{10}$ hour, so $\mu = 50 \times \frac{1}{10} = 5$. We require
$$P(X > 10) = 1 - \big[\, P(X = 0) + P(X = 1) + \cdots + P(X = 10) \,\big]$$
$$= 1 - e^{-5}\left[1 + \frac{5}{1!} + \frac{5^2}{2!} + \cdots + \frac{5^{10}}{10!}\right] = 0.014,$$

on using a computer.

∎

These examples treat the Poisson distribution in its natural form. Its other principal use is as an approximation for the binomial distribution. The link is that, in some sense, the Poisson distribution is the binomial distribution with an infinite number of trials and a zero probability, more precisely it is the limit of $\text{Bin}(n, p)$ as $n \to \infty$, $p \to 0$, $np = \mu$ (constant). Hence it should be a good approximation when:

$$n \text{ is large}, \quad p \text{ is small}, \quad \mu = np \text{ is moderate in size.}$$

It is this relationship that leads to recommendations to use the Poisson distribution for 'low probability events', although this is only an approximation.

Before examining its effectiveness, note that we take the natural step of equating the means np and μ for the two distributions. Pushing this further, for the Poisson distribution:

$$\text{Var}(X) \simeq npq = \mu q \simeq \mu,$$

since $q = 1 - p \simeq 1$. As we see in (7.22), this is in fact exact.

Example 7.31 Consider $\text{Bin}(100, 0.01)$, so $\mu = 100 \times 0.01 = 1$. The probabilities $P(X = k)$ are as follows:

r	Binomial	Poisson
0	0.366	0.368
1	0.370	0.368
2	0.185	0.184

∎

Example 7.32 Consider the three dice problem in Example 7.23. The number of sixes is given by $\text{Bin}(3, \frac{1}{6})$. Suppose we try to use Poisson with $\mu = 3 \times \frac{1}{6} = 0.5$:

$$P(X = 0) = e^{-0.5} = 0.607, \qquad \text{binomial: } 0.579,$$
$$P(X = 1) = e^{-0.5} \frac{1}{2} = 0.303, \qquad \text{binomial: } 0.347,$$
$$P(X = 2) = e^{-0.5} \frac{1}{8} = 0.076, \qquad \text{binomial: } 0.069,$$
$$P(X = 3) = e^{-0.5} \frac{1}{48} = 0.013, \qquad \text{binomial: } 0.005.$$

The probabilities are not that dissimilar, in spite of n being small. But this example makes obvious a discrepancy between the distributions that underlines the fact that it is an approximation: we can readily calculate $P(X = 4) = 0.002$ for Poisson, although this is an impossible outcome. ∎

The final example is much more realistic.

Example 7.33 Suppose that 5% of air passengers on a certain route order vegetarian meals. What is the probability that **at least four** require such a meal from a flight with 120 passengers?

The correct model is Bin(120, 0.05), which leads to a difficult calculation:

$$P(X \geqslant 4) = 1 - P(X < 4)$$

$$= 1 - \left[\binom{120}{0} 0.95^{120} + \binom{120}{1} 0.95^{119} 0.05 \right.$$

$$\left. + \binom{120}{2} 0.95^{118} 0.05^2 + \binom{120}{3} 0.95^{117} 0.05^3 \right]$$

$$= 0.8556.$$

To approximate this by a Poisson calculation, we use $\mu = 120 \times 0.05 = 6$:

$$P(X \geqslant 4) = 1 - P(X < 4)$$

$$= 1 - e^{-6} \left[1 + 6 + \frac{6^2}{2} + \frac{6^3}{6} \right]$$

$$= 1 - 61 e^{-6} = 0.8488.$$

∎

Ex 7.14 Calls coming into a telephone exchange follow a Poisson distribution. A survey, held over a long period, suggests that the average is stable at 120 per hour. Find the probabilities that:

(a) there are no calls during a one-minute period;

(b) there are less than 3 calls in a two-minute period.

Ex 7.15 A bowler has a strike rate of taking a wicket every 96 balls. Calculate the probabilities of taking one wicket and two wickets in a spell of 72 balls, using (a) Poisson with mean: $\frac{72}{96} = \frac{3}{4}$, (b) Binomial: $n = 72$, $p = \frac{1}{96}$. Which is theoretically more appropriate?

Ex 7.16 Suppose that *Sciences United* scores, on average, 1 goal every 45 minutes. Similarly, *Arts FC* scores, on average, 1 goal every 60 minutes. Assuming these are modelled by independent Poisson distributions, calculate to 3 dp the probability of a draw when they play each other in a 90 minute match.

7.8 Revision Exercises

Ex 7.17 A coin with probability of '*Heads*' of $\frac{1}{3}$ is tossed until one '*Heads*' has appeared. What is the probability that k throws are required, for $k \geqslant 1$?

A and B bet on this experiment: A pays B £1 if 1 or 2 tosses are required. B pays A £n otherwise. What value should n have to ensure neither A nor B has an advantage?

Ex 7.18 A game is played between persons A and B. A throws a fair die and B pays out (in some currency):

    0 for a throw of an odd number;   1 for a throw of 2;

    2 for a throw of 4;   3 for a throw of 6.

Find A's expected winnings. Find the variance for A's winnings.

Ex 7.19 A study of pumps in a nuclear power station shows that the probability of failure of an individual pump is 0.16 in a given time period. A system uses **eight** pumps. Assuming that failure of each pump is independent of all others, what is the appropriate distribution to model the number of pumps that fail?

Calculate, to 4 dp, the probability that **at least two pumps fail** during the period.

Ex 7.20 A person attempts a newspaper crossword every weekday (Monday to Saturday) with probability 0.6 of solving any one correctly, independent of the others. Calculate the probabilities of the following:

(a) solving all six puzzles correctly;

(b) solving exactly half correctly;

(c) solving more than half correctly.

Ex 7.21 A speed camera is activated on average three times in an hour. Assuming the **Poisson distribution** is a good model, calculate to 3 dp:

(a) The probability that no cars are photographed in an hour.

(b) The probability that more than three cars are photographed in an hour.

Ex 7.22 A proportion 0.001 of certain cells are infected. Assuming the **Poisson distribution** is a good model, calculate to 3 dp:

(a) The probability that at least one cell is infected in a sample of 2000.

(b) The probability that more than three cells are infected in a sample of 10,000.

8   CONTINUOUS DISTRIBUTIONS

We now turn attention to **continuous** random variables, where the possible values are not 'discrete' or 'isolated', but cover all of an **interval** in the real line, possibly even the entire line itself. There is an immediate complication, which must be addressed and overcome since the most important distribution of all, one that underpins most elementary statistical calculation, is a continuous one: the *Normal distribution.*

The problem is that there are so many points in an interval that it is impossible to allocate a non-zero probability to any of them and still achieve all probabilities summing to 1. (It is possible to define hybrid distributions that are discrete in parts and continuous elsewhere, but they are not natural and still throw up the same problem.) Thus, for a continuous random variable:

$$P(X = \alpha) = 0 \quad (\text{all } \alpha \text{ in } \mathbb{R}).$$

The answer to this conundrum is to group the values for X in *intervals* and to measure $P(a \leqslant X \leqslant b)$, for any chosen interval $[a, b]$. Computationally, the mathematics must change from **summation** to **integration**. Some compensation for this change is that we no longer need take care to distinguish the above probability from $P(a < X < b)$, since they have the same value: integrals are unaffected by values at isolated points, such as a and b here.

8.1   Density and Distribution Functions

There is no point in defining a probability function, like $f(x)$ in the previous chapter, since it would be zero everywhere. The replacement is suggested in the following example.

Example 8.1   Suppose that every value in $[0, 1]$ is equally likely. Then the probability of X being in any interval of width Δ is the same and must, by proportion, be Δ.

For the graph on the right, the total area enclosed between $x = 0$ and $x = 1$ is 1. Also, it is reasonable to argue that

$$P\left(\tfrac{1}{2} \leqslant X \leqslant \tfrac{2}{3}\right) = \tfrac{2}{3} - \tfrac{1}{2} = \tfrac{1}{6},$$

the area between $x = \tfrac{1}{2}$ and $\tfrac{2}{3}$. This is also $\displaystyle\int_{1/2}^{2/3} 1 \, dx.$

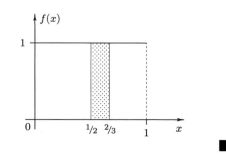

The function $f(x)$ used and graphed in this example is the key. It is called the **probability density function** for the distribution. Once it is defined we can use it to evaluate any of the probabilities we need, by calculating areas under its graph.

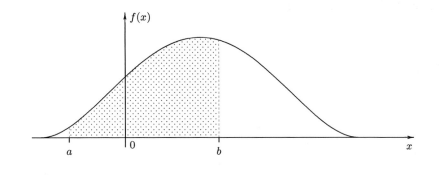

Frame 8.1   *Probability calculation for a continuous distribution*

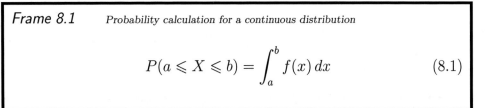

$$P(a \leqslant X \leqslant b) = \int_a^b f(x)\, dx \qquad (8.1)$$

Note that, following a comment made earlier, this is also $P(a < X \leqslant b)$, $P(a \leqslant X < b)$ and $P(a < X < b)$.

There is no concern about signs, in making the link between area and integration, since $f(x) \geqslant 0$ everywhere, due to its connection with probability. Also

$$\int_{-\infty}^{\infty} f(x)\, dx = 1, \qquad (8.2)$$

since all probability must be captured by this integral. (The infinite limits make this an *improper* integral but in all cases we encounter we can either replace them by finite numbers, or the integrations are known to be 'safe'.)

Think about it like this

The difference between discrete and continuous distributions is analogous to the difference between the physics of point masses and rigid bodies. For point masses, various formulae, such as those for momentum and torque, require the summation of their individual contributions, whereas for rigid bodies it is necessary to use integration.

The use of the word **density** in the definition of $f(x)$ is therefore no accident. The mass of a segment of a rod of uniform cross-section is calculated by integrating the function defining the density, between appropriate limits, just as we integrate in Frame 8.1.

The mass of a small section of width Δx of a body with density $\rho(x)$ is approximately $\rho(x)\,\Delta x$. This translates to perhaps the most direct interpretation of $f(x)$:

$$P(x \leqslant X \leqslant x + \Delta x) \simeq f(x)\,\Delta x \quad [\Delta x \text{ small}]. \qquad (8.3)$$

The larger $f(x)$ is, the more likely is the outcome of a statistical trial to be near x, as the probability measure in (8.3) confirms.

Example 8.2   Consider the graph shown below.

The function satisfies $f(x) \geqslant 0$ for all x, so the only requirement for it to be a probability density function is that it satisfies (8.2). It is easier to use areas:

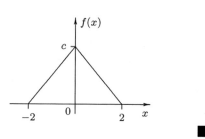

$$\tfrac{1}{2} \times 2 \times c + \tfrac{1}{2} \times 2 \times c = 1,$$

which immediately shows $c = \tfrac{1}{2}$. ∎

It is in this context that the **(cumulative) distribution function** comes into its own. It has none of the discontinuity problems we found in the discrete case and avoids the approximation in (8.3). It is defined and used as in the discrete case.

Frame 8.2   *The distribution function for a continuous distribution*

$$F(x) = P(X \leqslant x) = \int_{-\infty}^{x} f(t)\,dt \qquad (8.4)$$

$$P(a \leqslant X \leqslant b) = F(b) - F(a) \qquad (8.5)$$

Again, because $P(X = x) = 0$, we can use either $\leqslant$ or $<$ in (8.4) and (8.5).

Example 8.3   For the distribution in Example 8.1, we have the following distribution function.

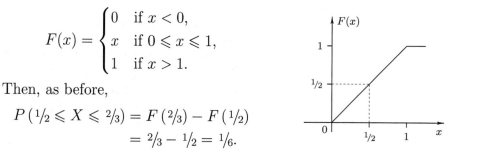

$$F(x) = \begin{cases} 0 & \text{if } x < 0, \\ x & \text{if } 0 \leqslant x \leqslant 1, \\ 1 & \text{if } x > 1. \end{cases}$$

Then, as before,

$$P\left(\tfrac{1}{2} \leqslant X \leqslant \tfrac{2}{3}\right) = F\left(\tfrac{2}{3}\right) - F\left(\tfrac{1}{2}\right)$$
$$= \tfrac{2}{3} - \tfrac{1}{2} = \tfrac{1}{6}.$$

∎

8.2   Distribution Parameters

The various parameters defined in §7.3 have direct counterparts for continuous distributions. Indeed, the **mean** and **variance** (and hence **standard deviation**) are defined in exactly the same way as in that section, provided we replace the sums by integrals. (Again there are two versions for the variance: a theoretical and a computational one.)

Frame 8.3   *Mean, variance and standard deviation for a continuous distribution*

$$E(X) = \mu_X = \int_{-\infty}^{\infty} x f(x)\, dx \qquad (8.6)$$

$$\mathrm{Var}(X) = \int_{-\infty}^{\infty} (x - \mu_X)^2 f(x)\, dx \qquad (8.7)$$

$$= \int_{-\infty}^{\infty} x^2 f(x)\, dx - \mu_X^2 \qquad (8.8)$$

$$\sigma_X = \sqrt{\mathrm{Var}(X)} \qquad (8.9)$$

Think about it like this

If $f(x)$ represents the density of a rod of uniform cross-section, then μ_X is the coordinate of the *centre of mass*, which is a natural analogue of the mean.

Example 8.4   Find the mean and variance for the distribution in Example 8.1.

The density function is zero outside $[0, 1]$, so all integrals have 0 and 1 as their limits, rather than $\pm\infty$.

$$\mu_X = \int_0^1 x \times 1\, dx = \left[\tfrac{1}{2}x^2\right]_0^1 = \tfrac{1}{2},$$

$$\mathrm{Var}(X) = \int_0^1 x^2 \times 1\, dx - (\tfrac{1}{2})^2 = \left[\tfrac{1}{3}x^3\right]_0^1 - \tfrac{1}{4} = \tfrac{1}{12}.$$

■

The **median** is defined precisely as in Frame 7.3:

$$F(m) = 0.5 \quad \Rightarrow \quad m = F^{-1}(0.5),$$

where now there is no difficulty, for 'well-behaved' distributions. (The inverse function $F^{-1}(x)$ for the distribution function is defined for all x in $(0, 1)$ if there are no 'flat' parts in the graph of $y = F(x)$ for $0 < y < 1$, which is the case for all the distributions we shall consider.)

Example 8.5   For the distribution in Example 8.1, $F(x) = x$ $(0 \leqslant x \leqslant 1)$, so $F(m) = 0.5$ when $m = \tfrac{1}{2}$, the median. ■

Calculation of the median is only one of the uses of the inverse distribution function. Much statistical work is concerned with activity near the ends of distributions, where events are unlikely to occur by chance. In such cases it is important to answer questions like the following.

- For what value of α is $P(X < \alpha) = 0.01$?

  Answer: solve $F(\alpha) = 0.01$, i.e., $\alpha = F^{-1}(0.01)$.

- For what value of β is $P(X > \beta) = 0.01$?

  Answer: solve $1 - F(\beta) = 0.01$, i.e., $\beta = F^{-1}(0.99)$.

Example 8.6 Suppose the density function for a distribution is

$$f(x) = \frac{k}{x^3} \quad (x \text{ in } [1,2]),$$

and is zero elsewhere. Then a limit $-\infty$ in any integral can be replaced by 1, and a limit ∞ by 2.

We find k using (8.2):

$$\int_1^2 \frac{k}{x^3}\, dx = k\left[-\frac{1}{2x^2}\right]_1^2 = \frac{3k}{8},$$

which is 1 if $k = 8/3$.

The **distribution function** is

$$F(x) = \int_1^x \frac{8}{3t^3}\, dt = \left[-\frac{4}{3t^2}\right]_1^x = \frac{4}{3}\left(1 - \frac{1}{x^2}\right).$$

Using this we can easily evaluate probabilities, for example:

$$P\left(4/3 \leqslant X \leqslant 5/3\right) = F\left(5/3\right) - F\left(4/3\right) = 0.27.$$

The **median** satisfies $F(m) = 0.5$, i.e.,

$$\frac{4}{3}\left(1 - \frac{1}{m^2}\right) = \frac{1}{2} \quad \Rightarrow \quad \frac{1}{m^2} = \frac{5}{8}$$

$$\Rightarrow \quad m = \sqrt{1.6} \simeq 1.26.$$

To illustrate calculations near the ends of the distribution, we find β such that $P(X > \beta) = 0.01$:

$$1 - F(\beta) = 0.01 \quad \Rightarrow \quad 1 - \frac{4}{3}\left(1 - \frac{1}{\beta^2}\right) = 0.01$$

$$\Rightarrow \quad \frac{1}{\beta^2} = 1 - 0.99 \times 0.75$$

$$\Rightarrow \quad \beta \simeq 1.97.$$

Finally, the other key parameters are:

$$\mu_X = \int_1^2 x \times \frac{8}{3x^3}\, dx = \int_1^2 \frac{8}{3x^2}\, dx$$

$$= \left[-\frac{8}{3x}\right]_1^2 = -8/6 + 8/3 = 4/3,$$

$$\mathrm{Var}(X) = \int_1^2 x^2 \times \frac{8}{3x^3}\, dx - \left(4/3\right)^2 = \int_1^2 \frac{8}{3x}\, dx - 16/9$$

$$= \left[8/3 \ln x\right]_1^2 - 16/9 = 8/3 \ln 2 - 16/9 \simeq 0.071,$$

$$\sigma_X = \sqrt{\mathrm{Var}(X)} \simeq 0.266.$$

■

Further examples will be presented in the following sections, where we consider three important practical distributions.

Ex 8.1 A random variable has density function $f(x) = 1 - \dfrac{x}{2}$ on $[0, 2]$ (and zero elsewhere). Calculate $P(0 < X < 1)$, the α where $P(X < \alpha) = 0.19$, and the median.

Ex 8.2

(a) A continuous random variable has density function $f(x) = \alpha x(2 - x)$ on $[0, 1]$ (and zero elsewhere), where α is a constant. Find the value of α.

   Calculate: $P\left(X \leqslant \tfrac{1}{4}\right)$, $P\left(X \geqslant \tfrac{1}{2}\right)$, $P\left(\tfrac{1}{4} \leqslant X \leqslant \tfrac{1}{2}\right)$.

(b) A continuous random variable has **distribution function** $F(x) = \tfrac{1}{8}x^{3/2}$ on an interval $[a, b]$, 0 for $x < a$, 1 for $x > b$. What are the values of a and b? What is the density function?

Ex 8.3 A random variable X has **density** function $f(x) = \dfrac{\alpha}{x^4}$ for $x \geqslant 1$ (and zero elsewhere). Calculate the following:

$$\alpha, \quad F(x), \quad P(2 < X < 3), \quad \mu_X, \quad \sigma_X, \quad \text{the median,}$$

where $F(x)$ is the (cumulative) distribution function.

8.3 Uniform Distribution

Like its discrete counterpart, the **uniform** distribution has all outcomes equally-likely, within some interval $[a, b]$. This means that the probability of X taking a value in any subinterval of width Δ is the same.

The density function is therefore a constant and to ensure the area under the graph is 1, that constant value must be $1/(b - a)$. Formally:

$$\int_a^b \frac{1}{b - a}\, dx = \frac{1}{b - a}\left[x\right]_a^b = 1.$$

The density and distribution functions are graphed below:

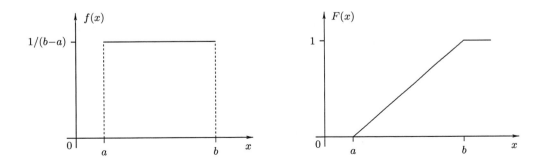

The key parameters are:

$$\mu_X = \int_a^b \frac{x}{b-a}\, dx = \frac{1}{b-a}\left[\frac{x^2}{2}\right]_a^b$$

$$= \frac{1}{2(b-a)}(b^2 - a^2) = \frac{1}{2}(a+b),$$

$$\text{Var}(X) = \int_a^b \frac{x^2}{b-a}\, dx - \mu_X^2 = \frac{1}{12}(b-a)^2,$$

after a similar calculation.

We can sum this up in the following Frame.

Frame 8.4   *Uniform distribution on* $[a,b]$

$$f(x) = \begin{cases} 0 & \text{if } x < a, \\ \frac{1}{b-a} & \text{if } a \leqslant x \leqslant b, \\ 0 & \text{if } x > b \end{cases} \tag{8.10}$$

$$\mu_X = \frac{1}{2}(a+b) \tag{8.11}$$

$$\text{Var}(x) = \frac{1}{12}(b-a)^2 \tag{8.12}$$

Example 8.7   Example 8.1 is a uniform distribution with $a = 0$, $b = 1$:

$$\mu_X = \tfrac{1}{2}(0+1) = \tfrac{1}{2}, \quad \text{Var}(X) = \tfrac{1}{12}(1-0)^2 = \tfrac{1}{12},$$

as before.   ∎

The uniform distribution is a good model for errors in individual measurements and rounding errors in individual calculations. If we know a number has been rounded to $2\,\text{dp}$, its error is somewhere in $[-0.005, 0.005]$ with equal likelihood.

Ex 8.4   Find the distribution function for the uniform distribution over $[1,6]$. Hence calculate $P(2 < X < 5)$, the α where $P(X > \alpha) = 0.1$, and the median.

Ex 8.5   A bus service leaves every 30 minutes. A person, unaware of the timetable, arrives at random. What is the distribution for the waiting time, its mean and variance?

8.4   Exponential Distribution

The **exponential** distribution has data given as follows; the mean quoted here will be verified later.

Frame 8.5 *Exponential distribution with parameter* λ

$$f(x) = \begin{cases} 0 & \text{if } x < 0, \\ \lambda e^{-\lambda x} & \text{if } x \geqslant 0 \end{cases} \qquad (8.13)$$

$$\mu_X = \sigma_X = \frac{1}{\lambda} \qquad (8.14)$$

It models the intervals (in time or space) between the occurrence of purely random events, such as radioactive decay or the occurrence of flaws in a pipeline. *More generally, X models the interval between events counted by the Poisson distribution.*

We can check that it is a genuine distribution: $f(x) \geqslant 0$ everywhere and

$$\int_0^\infty \lambda e^{-\lambda x}\, dx = \left[-e^{-\lambda x} \right]_0^\infty = -0 + 1 = 1.$$

The **distribution function** is

$$F(x) = \int_0^x \lambda e^{-\lambda t}\, dt = \left[-e^{-\lambda t} \right]_0^x = 1 - e^{-\lambda x}. \qquad (8.15)$$

The density and distribution functions are illustrated by the following graphs, where $\lambda = 1$.

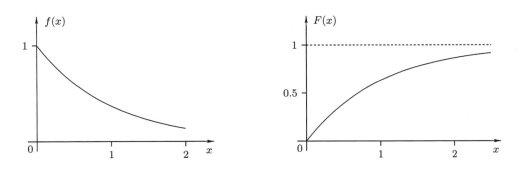

The **median** can be calculated by

$$1 - e^{-\lambda m} = {}^1\!/_2 \quad \Rightarrow \quad e^{\lambda m} = 2 \quad \Rightarrow \quad \lambda m = \ln 2$$

$$\Rightarrow \quad m = \frac{1}{\lambda} \ln 2,$$

which, not surprisingly, is the **half-life** for an exponential process, with rate constant λ.

The **mean** requires *integration by parts*:

$$\mu_X = \int_0^\infty \lambda x e^{-\lambda x}\, dx$$

$$= \left[-x e^{-\lambda x} - \frac{1}{\lambda} e^{-\lambda x} \right]_0^\infty = \frac{1}{\lambda}.$$

This gives an interpretation for λ and hence a way to estimate it: $1/\lambda$ is the **mean inter-event** measure.

Example 8.8 Suppose that a TV tube has its lifetime distributed exponentially with $\lambda = \frac{1}{8}$.

Hence the mean lifetime is 8 years. The median is $8\ln 2 \simeq 5.545$ years. What proportion is likely to lead to claims under a one-year warranty?

$$P(X \leqslant 1) = F(1) = 1 - e^{-0.125} \simeq 0.1175,$$

so 11.75% are likely to lead to such a claim.

At what time will just 10% of a batch of tubes still be working?

$$
\begin{aligned}
P(X > \alpha) = 0.1 \quad &\Rightarrow \quad F(\alpha) = P(X \leqslant \alpha) = 1 - 0.1 = 0.9 \\
&\Rightarrow \quad 1 - e^{-\alpha/8} = 0.9 \quad \Rightarrow \quad e^{-\alpha/8} = 0.1 \\
&\Rightarrow \quad \alpha = -8\ln 0.1 \simeq 18.4 \text{ years.}
\end{aligned}
$$

∎

The model used in this example is convenient but somewhat dubious, since TV tubes are likely to deteriorate with use, so the probabilities of survival decrease in time. This clashes with a striking property of the exponential distribution. It is fairly easy to prove (using integration) that

$$P(X \geqslant x + y \,|\, X \geqslant y) = P(X \geqslant x), \tag{8.16}$$

which means that the probabilities for future events do not depend on the past; the fact that an event has not occurred for some time makes it no more likely to occur in the near future. This is sometimes summed up by: *the exponential distribution has no memory.* For example, if a component has survived for $y = 20$ days, it is just as likely to survive another $x = 10$ days – and hence $x + y = 30$ days in total – as it would be to survive $x = 10$ days from new.

Ex 8.6 The time interval until a component fails has an exponential distribution with mean 50 days. Find the probability that the current component does not survive 30 days. By which time are we 90% certain to have had to replace it?

Ex 8.7 My hi-fi contains an amplifier, a CD player and a tape deck. The time between failures for these is given by exponential distributions, with means 8 years, 6 years and 4 years, respectively. I purchase a three-year guarantee. Find the probability that I do not need to make a claim under that guarantee.

8.5   Standard Normal Distribution

This final distribution is the most important of all. Like the exponential distribution it has different versions depending on parameters, in this case two: the **mean**, usually written μ, and the **variance**, usually written σ^2.

We start, however, with a very special (and important) case, where $\mu = 0$ and $\sigma^2 = 1$; the **standard normal** distribution, $N(0,1)$, with random variable Z.

Frame 8.6   *The standard normal distribution: Z is N(0,1)*

$$f(z) = \frac{1}{\sqrt{2\pi}} e^{-z^2/2} \qquad (8.17)$$

$$\mu = 0, \quad \sigma^2 = 1 \qquad (8.18)$$

In this case the density function is not helpful, since it is impossible to integrate in terms of simple functions. Hence we have no formula for the distribution function and must use computer approximations or tables. The standard normal's distribution function is, however, the key to calculations using *all* normal distributions and even has a special notation: we write it as $\Phi(z)$ [*capital phi*]:

$$\Phi(z) = P(Z \leqslant z) = \int_{-\infty}^{z} f(t)\, dt. \qquad (8.19)$$

The graphs of $f(z)$ and $\Phi(z)$ are shown below. The shape of the former explains its common name: the **bell curve**.

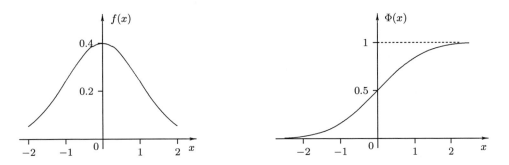

Before investigating how to use $\Phi(z)$ to deal with more general normal distributions, we must address how to extract values from a typical table, such as that presented in the *Appendix* that follows this part. A complication is that the distribution is clearly *symmetric*, which allows us to set out all the information needed in only half the space. There are various ways to do this, but the simplest is to tabulate $\Phi(z)$ only for $0 \leqslant z < \infty$.

Using the symmetry in the graph, we have

$$\Phi(-z) = P(Z \leqslant -z) = P(Z \geqslant z)$$
$$= 1 - \Phi(z).$$

It is often good policy to draw a rough sketch of this type, as a guide.

From this, we find for all z, but primarily used for $z < 0$,

$$\Phi(z) = 1 - \Phi(-z). \qquad (8.20)$$

This, together with the table, allows us to calculate $\Phi(z)$ for any value of z. (There are two further frequent cases whose formulae we shall uncover after the following example.)

Example 8.9 Consider the following probabilities related to the standard normal. We use (8.5) and (8.19); remember that there is no difference between '<' and '$\leqslant$' in this context. (8.20) is also heavily used.

$$P(0.2 < Z \leqslant 1.1) = \Phi(1.1) - \Phi(0.2) = 0.8643 - 0.5793 = 0.2850,$$
$$P(Z > 0.5) = 1 - P(Z < 0.5) = 1 - \Phi(0.5) = 1 - 0.6915 = 0.3085,$$
$$P(Z < -1) = \Phi(-1) = 1 - \Phi(1) = 1 - 0.8413 = 0.1587,$$
$$P(Z > -0.1) = 1 - P(Z < -0.1) = 1 - \Phi(-0.1)$$
$$= 1 - [1 - \Phi(0.1)] = \Phi(0.1) = 0.5398,$$
$$P(-0.7 < Z < 0.9) = \Phi(0.9) - \Phi(-0.7)$$
$$= \Phi(0.9) - [1 - \Phi(0.7)] = 0.8159 + 0.7580 - 1 = 0.5739,$$
$$P(|Z| > 2) = 1 - P(|Z| < 2) = 1 - P(-2 < Z < 2) = 1 - [\Phi(2) - \Phi(-2)]$$
$$= 1 - [\Phi(2) - (1 - \Phi(2))] = 2 - 2\Phi(2) = 2 - 2 \times 0.9772 = 0.0456.$$

∎

This last calculation, and its companion $P(|Z| < 2)$, are very common: we work at points symmetrically disposed about the mean ($\mu = 0$). It is worth noting the general formulae:

$$P(|Z| > z) = 2 - 2\Phi(z), \tag{8.21}$$
$$P(|Z| < z) = 2\Phi(z) - 1, \tag{8.22}$$

which are easily found using the diagram above.

It is common for certain key values of z to be separately tabulated, e.g.,

$$z = 1.645: \quad P(Z < z) = 0.95 \ (95\%), \quad P(|Z| < z) = 0.90 \ (90\%);$$
$$z = 1.960: \quad P(Z < z) = 0.975 \ (97.5\%), \quad P(|Z| < z) = 0.95 \ (95\%);$$
$$z = 2.576: \quad P(Z < z) = 0.995 \ (99.5\%), \quad P(|Z| < z) = 0.99 \ (99\%).$$

We shall exemplify the use of these in the next section. These values also deliver z such that $P(Z > z)$ is 5% or $P(|Z| > z)$ is 1%, etc.

One further property of these tables – which we shall encounter later – is that they are designed for the use of **linear interpolation**, to fill in between tabulated entries. By this we mean that the error in using linear interpolation is no worse than the error in rounding to 4 dp.

Ex 8.8 Calculate the following for a standard normal variate Z:
$$P(Z < 0.5), \ P(0.5 < Z \leqslant 0.6), \ P(-0.1 < Z < 0.2), \ P(Z = 0.5), \ P(|Z| > 1).$$

8.6 General Normal Distribution

We can have a normal distribution – with a similarly shaped bell curve – for any given mean μ and variance σ^2. The random variable, often called a **normal variate**, has distribution notated by $N(\mu, \sigma^2)$, consistent with $N(0, 1)$ for the standard normal distribution. We can write down a formula for its density function, but it is not particularly informative and suffers from the same integration problem as that for the standard normal.

They key to all calculations is to use the following simple and natural formulae to convert any calculation to a standard normal, and hence to $\Phi(z)$.

Frame 8.7   *Conversion to standard normal*

If X is $N(\mu, \sigma^2)$ then Z is $N(0, 1)$:

$$Z = \frac{X - \mu}{\sigma} \tag{8.23}$$

$$X = \sigma Z + \mu \tag{8.24}$$

Think about it like this

It is worth looking at the structure of (8.23). Subtracting μ effectively moves the mean to $\mu - \mu = 0$, while dividing by σ effectively rescales the measurement, to change the variance to $\sigma^2/\sigma^2 = 1$.

Example 8.10 Suppose X has distribution $N(50, 25)$, i.e., $\mu = 50$, $\sigma = 5$. We use $Z = (X - 50)/5$.

$$P(40 < X \leqslant 57) = P\left(\frac{40 - 50}{5} < Z \leqslant \frac{57 - 50}{5}\right) = P(-2 < Z \leqslant 1.4)$$

$$= \Phi(1.4) - \Phi(-2) = \Phi(1.4) - [1 - \Phi(2)] = 0.8964,$$

$$P(X > 62) = 1 - P(X \leqslant 62) = 1 - P\left(Z \leqslant \frac{62 - 50}{5}\right)$$

$$= 1 - \Phi(2.4) = 0.0082,$$

$$P(|X - 50| < 8) = P\left(|Z| < \frac{8}{5}\right) = 2\Phi(1.6) - 1 = 0.8904.$$

This last calculation is worthy of note. The final part has used (8.22). Also, the fact that 50 is the mean allowed us a shortcut; otherwise we would have had to rewrite $|X - 50| < 8$ as $42 < X < 58$. It is very common to make measurements centred at the mean, in this way. ∎

In the next example we examine the use of the special values at the 'tails' of the distribution, i.e., at large $|z|$, where little probability is located.

Example 8.11 Suppose X is distributed as $N(1, 4)$, so $\mu = 1$, $\sigma = 2$. This time we effectively use the $X \leftrightarrow Z$ conversion in reverse:

$$Z = \frac{X - 1}{2} \quad \Rightarrow \quad X = 2Z + 1.$$

If we seek α such that $P(X > \alpha) = 0.10$, then we read off, from the second last line of the table,

$$P(Z < 1.282) = 0.90 \quad \Rightarrow \quad P(Z > 1.282) = 0.10$$
$$\Rightarrow \quad \alpha = 2 \times 1.282 + 1 = 3.564.$$

If we seek β such that $P(|X - 1| > \beta) = 0.01$, then we read off, from the last line of the table,

$$P(|Z| < 2.576) = 0.99 \quad \Rightarrow \quad P(|Z| > 2.576) = 0.01$$
$$\Rightarrow \quad \beta = 2 \times 2.576 = 5.152.$$

There is no "+1" used here, since it is implicit in $|X - 1|$, 1 being the mean for X, corresponding to 0 for Z. ∎

The normal distribution is often assumed – sometimes with no justification other than convenience – to model real data. We finish with two such cases.

Example 8.12 A production line fills 1 kg bags of sugar with an amount X, distributed as $N(1.05, 0.04^2)$. What proportion of a large batch of bags are underfilled?

Here we have

$$\mu = 1.05, \quad \sigma = 0.04, \quad Z = \frac{X - 1.05}{0.04},$$

and we seek $P(X < 1.00)$, since 1 kg is the advertised content.

$$P(X < 1.00) = P\left(Z < \frac{1 - 1.05}{0.04}\right) = P(Z < -1.25)$$
$$= \Phi(-1.25) = 1 - \Phi(1.25) = 0.1056,$$

so approximately 11% are underfilled.

Suppose that we are able to adjust the mean, leaving the standard deviation unchanged. To what value should we set the mean to ensure only 1% are underfilled?

We require $P(X < 1.00) = 0.01$. From the foot of the table, we see

$$P(Z < 2.326) = 0.99 \quad \Rightarrow \quad P(Z < -2.326) = P(Z > 2.326) = 0.01,$$

Hence we set the mean to μ where

$$\frac{1 - \mu}{0.04} = -2.326 \quad \Rightarrow \quad \mu = 1.093,$$

which is the value we seek. ∎

In the next example, we are faced with a similar unsatisfactory situation, but this time it makes no sense to alter the mean; the standard deviation is the only usable parameter available.

Example 8.13 A manufacturer produces $100\,\Omega$ [*capital omega*] resistors with a stated tolerance of 5%. The actual values produced are X, distributed as $N(100, 16)$. What proportion fail to meet the tolerance?

Here we have

$$\mu = 100, \quad \sigma = 4, \quad Z = \frac{X - 100}{4},$$

and we seek $P(|X - 100| > 5)$, since 5% of 100 is 5, which is the 'absolute' tolerance. Use (8.21):

$$P(|X - 100| > 5) = P\left(|Z| > \frac{5}{4}\right) = 2\left[1 - \Phi(1.25)\right] = 0.2112,$$

so approximately 21% fail.

This is unacceptable. To what value must we reduce the standard deviation to ensure only 10% fail?

We require $P(|X - 100| > 5) = 0.10$. From the foot of the table, we see

$$P(|Z| < 1.645) = 0.90 \quad \Rightarrow \quad P(|Z| > 1.645) = 0.10,$$

Hence we set the standard deviation to σ where

$$\frac{5}{\sigma} = 1.645 \quad \Rightarrow \quad \sigma = 3.04,$$

which is the value we seek. ∎

Provided the normal model is reasonably accurate, the ability to use the table and these standard formulae for the normal distribution is convenient. But this distribution has a far more significant role in practical statistical work, to which we now turn.

Ex 8.9 For a general normal variate X, what is the probability that X takes a value within one standard deviation of its mean? What is the probability that it is larger than its mean by at least one standard deviation?

Ex 8.10

(a) A **normal variate** X has mean 8.5 and standard deviation 0.2. Calculate:

$$P(X > 8.8), \quad P(|X - 8.5| \leqslant 0.12), \quad P(8.4 < X \leqslant 8.7), \quad P(|X - 8.5| > 0.25).$$

Find values of x such that:

$$P(X > x) = 0.1, \quad P(X \leqslant x) = 0.05, \quad P(|X - 8.5| < x) = 0.99.$$

(b) Suppose that X is distributed as $N(\mu, \sigma^2)$ and that $P(X < 7.3) = 0.05$ and $P(X > 12.2) = 0.05)$. Calculate μ and σ.

Ex 8.11 The volume of beer delivered to a can on a filling line is normally distributed with mean 442 ml and standard deviation 2.5 ml. What is the probability that a randomly selected can contains less than 439 ml? What volume is exceeded by 90% of cans?

Ex 8.12 The length of a component is a normal variate with mean 5 mm and standard deviation 0.02 mm. If the length tolerance is ±1%, find the proportion of components that are out of tolerance.

8.7 Revision Exercises

Ex 8.13 The **exponential distribution** models the inter-arrival times between people arriving at random. It has density function:

$$f(t) = \lambda e^{-\lambda t} \ (t \geqslant 0), \qquad = 0 \ (t < 0),$$

and mean $1/\lambda$.

Find its **cumulative distribution function**.

People arrive to use a computer at random, with mean inter-arrival time 40 minutes. One user arrives to find the computer free, then uses it for a period of 20 minutes. Find, to 3 dp, the probability that another user will arrive before the session is completed.

Calculate the **median** inter-arrival time, to 2 dp.

Ex 8.14 The **exponential** distribution has **density** function $f(t) = \lambda e^{-\lambda t}$ and **cumulative distribution** function $F(t) = 1 - e^{-\lambda t}$, where $t \geqslant 0$ and $1/\lambda$ is the **mean**.

A series of events, whose inter-event time is thought to be exponentially distributed, is observed until 100 events have occurred, i.e., there have been 100 inter-event periods, counting from the initial time. This took 854 minutes.

(a) What value is the best estimate of λ?

(b) Using that value, what is the probability that the interval between successive events exceeds 10 minutes?

(c) How many events happen in one hour, on average?

(d) An employee takes on average 20 minutes to process an event. What is the least number of employees needed to ensure the events can be coped with in the long run?

Ex 8.15

(a) Find the probability that for Z, modelled by a **standard normal distribution**, $|Z|$ is less than 1.5.

(b) Find α such that for Z, modelled by a **standard normal distribution**, $P(Z > \alpha) = 0.2$.

(c) X is modelled by a **normal distribution** with mean 75 and variance 4. Find the probability that X lies between 74 and 76.5.

Ex 8.16

(a) Find the probability that X, modelled by a **standard normal distribution**, lies between -0.3 and 0.7.

(b) Y is modelled by a **normal distribution** with mean 2 and variance 9. Find the value of α such that $P(Y > \alpha) = 0.1$.

(c) A rod has mean diameter 3.3 cm with variance 0.04 cm^2 obeying a normal distribution. What is the probability that a rod selected at random will fit a hole of width 3.6 cm?

9 STATISTICS

Statistics can be thought of as the practical companion to *Probability*. It has four main objectives:

- The representation of sampled data, in tabular and/or graphical form, to help the reader appreciate the salient features. See §§9.1–9.3.

- The calculation, from such a sample, of key (summary) *statistics*, sometimes with an estimate of their reliability or *error*. This is useful for results calculated following a practical experiment. The *Method of Least Squares* in §2.12 is often referred to by its statistical name **regression**; in that section we stopped short of estimating the error. See §§9.4–9.9.

- The judgement of the *significance* of a particular observation or set of observations. A *statistic* is calculated and the probability of obtaining such a value is considered. We shall not pursue this application, although it was illustrated in Examples 6.5, 7.25 and 7.26.

- The design of appropriate statistical experiments. This is the domain of the professional statistician and we shall not explore it here.

9.1 Discrete Data

We consider *real data*, i.e., a **sample** found by measuring outcomes from a random process. We shall suppose that there are n values and that they have *already* been ordered:

$$x_1 \leqslant x_2 \leqslant x_3 \leqslant \cdots \leqslant x_{n-1} \leqslant x_n.$$

We seek ways to *summarise* this data. The first method is to draw up a table for the data, **grouping** it in some way to reduce the number of displayed items.

It is necessary to distinguish *discrete* and *continuous* data, just as we had to distinguish between the two types of probability distribution.

In the **discrete** case the x_k take values from only a finite set of possibilities: $v_1, \ldots, v_m$, say. Suppose our data contains f_k copies of v_k, so

$$n = f_1 + f_2 + \cdots + f_m.$$

Then f_k is the **frequency** of v_k and

$$r_k = \frac{f_k}{n} \tag{9.1}$$

is the **relative frequency**. We can construct a **line chart** to summarise the data, drawing a vertical line at $x = v_k$ of height f_k or r_k. The relative frequency case is analogous in concept to the graph of the probability function $f(k)$. For a representative sample with large n, r_k and $P(X = v_k)$ should be similar in value and therefore the line chart and the graph of the **probability function** would be similar in shape.

We can also calculate the **cumulative** relative frequency:

$$c_k = r_1 + r_2 + \cdots + r_k, \qquad (9.2)$$

giving the proportion of the sample **less than or equal to** v_k. Its graph, sometimes called an **ogive**, is analogous to that of the **distribution function**, although it is more usual to draw it as a type of line chart (without the lines) rather than the 'staircase' type of graph used for $F(x)$. The name 'ogive' is that of an architectural structure whose shape is similar to the graph of some typical cumulative frequencies.

Example 9.1   Asbestos-type fibres in air samples

The concentration of asbestos-type fibres in a workshop, which had been used for making brake linings containing asbestos, was investigated by collecting 143 one-litre samples of air. The numbers of fibres with length greater than 5 μm, width less than 3 μm and length-to-width ratio greater than 3 were automatically detected in each sample. These numbers were all equal to 0, 1, 2, 3, 4 or 5. They are summarised in the **frequency table** and the **line chart** shown below.

v_k	f_k	r_k	c_k
0	34	0.238	0.238
1	46	0.322	0.560
2	38	0.266	0.826
3	19	0.133	0.959
4	4	0.028	0.987
5	2	0.014	1.000
6 or more	0	0.000	1.000
Total	143	1.000	—

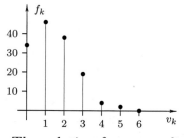

The relative frequency line chart is identical, except that the vertical scale is different.

The relative frequencies add up to 1.001. This is due to accidents of rounding and the small discrepancy is ignored.

The cumulative frequency graph (an ogive) is shown on the right; for discrete data the points are not joined up.

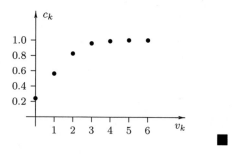

Ex 9.1   A data sample consists of 40 items with (values, frequencies):

$$(0,2), \ (1,12), \ (2,14), \ (3,8), \ (4,4).$$

Calculate the relative frequencies and display them using a line chart. Plot the cumulative frequencies.

Ex 9.2   Two 4-sided dice are thrown 100 times and their sum recorded:

(sum, frequency): $(2,5), \ (3,10), \ (4,17), \ (5,24), \ (6,20), \ (7,15), \ (8,9).$

Plot the relative frequencies using a line chart. Superimpose the probability function, assuming the dice are fair. Comment on the results.

9.2 Continuous Data

Suppose now that the data are measurements of a quantity that can take a value anywhere on the real line (or an interval in the real line), i.e., from an infinite set of possibilities. The likelihood is that the sample could consist of entirely different numbers, so all frequencies would be one. Thus, more aggressive grouping is required, collecting the x_k into different **subintervals** from the whole range of values.

> **Think about it like this**
>
> In most practical cases, the natural restriction on the measurement device would mean that only a finite number of values are actually possible, but that number is likely to be so large that it can be regarded as effectively infinite.

Hence, given a range of possible values, we split it up into subintervals:

$$[t_0 = a, t_1], \quad [t_1, t_2], \quad \ldots, \quad [t_{k-1}, t_k], \quad \ldots, \quad [t_{m-1}, t_m = b],$$

where we can have $a = -\infty$ and/or $b = \infty$. In most cases, the subintervals have equal width, except possibly for the two end ones, which often 'mop up stragglers' at the ends.

There are two decisions to make here. The first one is: how many subintervals should we use, i.e., what is m? One 'rule' is to choose $m \simeq \sqrt{n}$, where n is the size of the sample. We shall not insist on this in our examples.

The other is what to do when $x_j = t_k$ for some j, k: is it to be counted in the subinterval to the left or the right? There is no definitive rule, other than to decide on a consistent policy for the example in hand and stick to it: use either $(t_{k-1}, t_k]$ or $[t_{k-1}, t_k)$ for all k (except for one of the end intervals). We shall choose the second option, so our x_j above would lie in $[t_k, t_{k+1})$ and the extreme right hand interval will have to be a fully closed one.

We can now count the frequencies inside each subinterval and compose a table of frequencies f_k, relative frequencies r_k and cumulative relative frequencies c_k, as in §9.1.

We can also graph these, but now we use a **histogram**, where the lines in §9.1 are replaced by 'boxes', to make it clear that all values in each subinterval are contenders for inclusion in the sample. The **area** of each box is proportional to the frequency, although when all subintervals have equal width this is the same as using the **height** to reflect the frequencies. But the mention of area makes it clear that the histogram for relative frequencies should be an approximation to the **probability density function**.

Again, we can graph the cumulative relative frequency data, which should resemble the **distribution function**. But this time there is some sense in joining the points with straight lines, although any intermediate readings are only indicative. Care is needed in the definition, since using intervals $[t_{k-1}, t_k)$ means c_k gives the measure **less than** t_k, while using $(t_{k-1}, t_k]$ relates to **less than or equal to** t_k.

Example 9.2 The following values are the crushing strengths of 25 concrete specimens (in MPa), after being ordered:

27.6	30.3	32.4	34.5	35.2	36.5	37.2	37.2	37.9	37.9
38.6	38.6	38.6	39.3	39.3	39.3	40.0	40.0	40.7	40.7
41.4	42.7	44.1	46.2	49.0

The grouped table and histogram, are given below. The distribution of the crushing strengths looks roughly symmetric with a single mode at around 39 MPa. Another choice of intervals, such as 27.50–32.49, ..., 47.50–52.49, would give a slightly different histogram.

$[t_{k-1}, t_k)$	f_k	r_k	c_k
$[25.0, 30.0)$	1	.04	.04
$[30.0, 35.0)$	3	.12	.16
$[35.0, 40.0)$	12	.48	.64
$[40.0, 45.0)$	7	.28	.92
$[45.0, 50.0]$	2	.08	1.00
Total	25	1.00	—

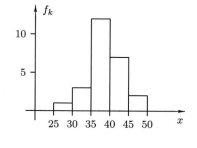

The cumulative frequency graph (an ogive) is shown on the right; this time the points are joined up. For the convention we have chosen, c_k represents the cumulative frequency up to but not including t_k.

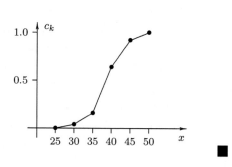

Ex 9.3 The response times by an engineer to repair a machine were as follows, in hours:

2.8	1.3	0.5	2.1	3.0	0.8	1.4	1.5	2.5	0.7	1.1	0.8	3.3
1.6	1.0	4.9	2.1	2.5	4.5	2.2	2.5	0.9	5.1	2.2	1.1

(a) Draw a histogram with equal ranges 0–0.9, 1–1.9, and so on.

(b) Make up a table showing cumulative percentages for the response times and draw a cumulative percentage plot for the data.

9.3   Five-Figure Summary and Boxplot

Often we want to compare two or more data samples corresponding, for example, to different experimental conditions, product suppliers or times of day. Line charts and histograms are not convenient for this. They tend to provide 'information overload'; a better approach is to simplify each sample by computing *summary statistics*. These can then be graphed, with each sample plotted side by side (or one above the other) on a common scale.

One commonly used plot is a **boxplot**, which is based on a so-called **five-figure summary** of each data sample.

We start again with our sample:

$$x_1 \leqslant x_2 \leqslant x_3 \leqslant \cdots \leqslant x_{n-1} \leqslant x_n,$$

assumed to be ordered as shown. The five-figure summary consists of numbers, or **statistics** derived from the data:

$$[x_1, \ Q_1, \ Q_2, \ Q_3, \ x_n]. \tag{9.3}$$

The first and last are clearly the **minimum** and **maximum**. The other three divide the data into four parts and are called, respectively, the **lower** or **first quartile**, **(sample) median** and **upper** or **third quartile**. In most cases there are no clear-cut locations for the Q_i and various conventions are used. The differences between them are usually minor. The following is one of the more logical versions.

Frame 9.1   *The five-figure summary*

$$x_1 = \textbf{minimum} \tag{9.4}$$

$$Q_1 = x_{\left(\frac{n+2}{4}\right)} \tag{9.5}$$

$$Q_2 = x_{\left(\frac{2n+2}{4}\right)} = x_{\left(\frac{n+1}{2}\right)} \tag{9.6}$$

$$Q_3 = x_{\left(\frac{3n+2}{4}\right)} \tag{9.7}$$

$$x_n = \textbf{maximum} \tag{9.8}$$

The subscripts in the Q_i are often fractions and hence do not lead to x_i values in the sequence. They depend on the following conventions, which use a *weighted average* of the values on either side of where the quartile or median falls:

$$x_{m+1/4} = \tfrac{1}{4}\left(3x_m + x_{m+1}\right), \tag{9.9}$$

$$x_{m+1/2} = \tfrac{1}{2}\left(x_m + x_{m+1}\right), \tag{9.10}$$

$$x_{m+3/4} = \tfrac{1}{4}\left(x_m + 3x_{m+1}\right). \tag{9.11}$$

Note that for the median, which should be the middle value, there are two possibilities. If n is odd, there is a clearly defined middle value and $\frac{n+1}{2}$ is a whole number, corresponding to that value. If n is even, there are two values in the middle, and (9.6) delivers their average.

The logic involved in Frame 9.1 is that each internal number x_k has to cover the patch of values from halfway towards the value on its left, to halfway towards the value on its right. We can introduce notation $x_{k-1/2}$ and $x_{k+1/2}$ to describe this and illustrate it below. (The end-points have been dealt with arbitrarily, but this is of no consequence.)

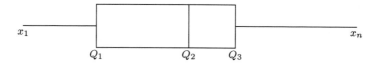

The set of values now spans from $x_{1/2}$ to $x_{n+1/2}$, a 'distance' of n. This is split into four equal distances of $n/4$, which must be added to the $1/2$ at the left, to find the quartile subscripts:

$$\tfrac{1}{2} + \tfrac{n}{4} = \tfrac{n+2}{4}, \qquad \tfrac{1}{2} + \tfrac{2n}{4} = \tfrac{n+1}{2}, \qquad \tfrac{1}{2} + \tfrac{3n}{4} = \tfrac{3n+2}{4},$$

which are precisely those in Frame 9.1.

Example 9.3   A set of $n = 7$ values is $\{17, 24, 32, 41, 55, 67, 73\}$.

The **minimum** and maximum are

$$x_1 = 17, \qquad x_7 = 73.$$

The **median** is
$$Q_2 = x_{\frac{7+1}{2}} = x_4 = 41.$$

The **lower quartile** is

$$Q_1 = x_{\frac{7+2}{4}} = x_{2^{1/4}} = \tfrac{1}{4}(3x_2 + x_3) = \tfrac{1}{4}(3 \times 24 + 32) = 26.$$

The **upper quartile** is

$$Q_3 = x_{\frac{21+2}{4}} = x_{5^{3/4}} = \tfrac{1}{4}(x_5 + 3x_6) = \tfrac{1}{4}(55 + 3 \times 67) = 64.$$

The five-figure summary is therefore: $[\,17, 26, 41, 64, 73\,]$. ■

These summary values are used pictorially in a **boxplot** or **box-and-whisker plot**. A rectangular 'box' is drawn from the lower quartile to the upper quartile, and the median is shown within this box; in the simplest form of the plot, 'whiskers' are drawn from the box to the minimum and maximum. The width of the box is not important, only its length.

Boxplots may be drawn vertically or, as below, horizontally:

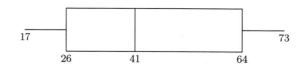

Example 9.4   For the data in Example 9.3, the boxplot is

17   26   41   64   73

■

Think about it like this

    Some statisticians restrict the length of the 'whiskers', e.g., allowing them to be no longer than $1.5(Q_3 - Q_1)$, showing any data points outside that range by dots. This is done in the example that follows, where vertical boxplots are used.

To compare several data sets, the (vertical) boxplots for the different sets are put side by side with a common scale.

Example 9.5   In an experiment into weather modification, 50 clouds were identified as suitable for seeding with silver iodide crystals, and 25 of them were chosen at random to be seeded. The following values are the summary statistics for the amounts of rainfall (in acre-feet) from the seeded and unseeded clouds, respectively.

$$[\,4.1,\ 79.45,\ 200.7,\ 358.075,\ 2745.6\,], \qquad [\,1.0, 23.725,\ 41.1,\ 183.325,\ 1202.6\,].$$

It is clear that the seeded clouds tend to produce more rainfall.

The corresponding boxplots are shown on the left below. Both distributions show that the small values are much closer together than the larger ones. As a result, the lower whiskers in the boxplot are shorter than the upper ones, and the comparison is obscured by the boxes being squashed to the bottom of the plot.

A boxplot of the (natural) logarithms of the amounts of rainfall (on the right) makes the comparison easier, showing more symmetrical distributions. (No restriction has been placed on the length of the 'whiskers' for that plot.)

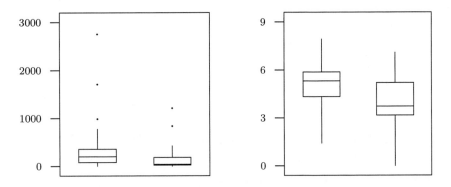

It is quite common in statistics, as in most data analysis, to try analysing or plotting the **logarithm** of the data values. This often reveals that an exponential type phenomenon is involved.   ■

Ex 9.4

(a) Find the median and quartiles for the sample in Exercise 9.1.

(b) Find the median and quartiles for the following sample and use them to draw a boxplot:

$$[\,4.8,\ 5.7,\ 6.1,\ 6.3,\ 6.6,\ 7.1,\ 7.8,\ 8.6,\ 9.8\,].$$

Ex 9.5   The table below shows the number of entries (in millions) in the UK National Lottery for each of the first 10 games in which nobody won the jackpot and the prize was 'rolled-over' to the next game. (Double 'rollovers' have been excluded.)

Game no.	3	8	19	23	27	29	33	39	43	58
Entries	48.3	57.5	62.2	63.3	62.3	64.8	63.3	63.5	64.6	67.9
Game no.	4	9	20	24	28	30	34	40	44	59
Entries	61.5	69.8	76.2	74.4	74.8	72.2	73.4	74.6	76.7	78.4

Find the five-figure summaries for each set. *Note that the data values are not in numerical order.* Draw boxplots on the same diagram and hence comment on the data. Are there any features that are not apparent from the boxplots?

9.4 Sample Statistics

If we seek a single number to summarise our data sample $\{x_1, \ldots, x_n\}$, the **median** is a possibility. There is, however, an alternative: the **(sample) mean**, which is the more familiarly called the **average**.

Frame 9.2   *The (sample) mean for a data set*

$$\overline{x} = \frac{x_1 + x_2 + \cdots + x_n}{n} = \frac{1}{n}\sum_{k=1}^{n} x_k \qquad (9.12)$$

Example 9.6 For the data in Example 9.3,

$$\overline{x} = \frac{1}{7}(17 + 24 + 32 + 41 + 55 + 67 + 73) = 44.14.$$

∎

The mean in this example is quite near the median (41). But the mean is much more sensitive to **outliers**, i.e., data values that are so different from the others that they are potentially unreliable.

Example 9.7 Find the median and mean for $\{1, 2, 3, 4, 100\}$.
We have $\overline{x} = 22$, $Q_2 = 3$. ∎

Think about it like this

In spite of this sensitivity, the sample mean lies at the heart of most statistical calculation, since it has much more elaborate theoretical support. As we shall see in later sections a great deal is known about the probabilities of the various possible values that $\overline{x}$ can take; the median has no similar support. When faced with possible outliers, the best solution is to exclude them, provided we are sure they really are unreliable.

One of the things we can achieve for the mean is an estimate of its reliability, a measure of its **error**, in a statistical sense. The key to this is the **variance**, which we often have to calculate from the sample itself. Calculators offer the facility to do this, but there is an apparent complication: they implement two different formulae.

The explanation lies in the nature of the 'sample' $\{x_1, \ldots, x_n\}$ itself: is it a *full* sample or a *representative* one, i.e., do these x_k constitute *all* the outcomes for the random event or just a *sample,* in the usual sense of the word?

Consider first the full sample, so that each x_k has the same probability $1/n$. Then Frame 7.4 gives

$$\mu_X = \frac{1}{n}(x_1 + x_2 + \cdots + x_n) = \overline{x},$$

the (sample) mean. Frame 7.5 gives

$$\text{Var}(X) = \frac{1}{n}(x_1^2 + x_2^2 + \cdot + x_n^2) - \mu_X^2,$$

which rearranges to the following computational formulae.

Frame 9.3   *Variance for a 'full' sample*

$$\text{Var}(X) = \frac{1}{n}(x_1^2 + x_2^2 + \cdots + x_n^2 - n\overline{x}^2) \qquad (9.13)$$

$$= \frac{1}{n}\left[\sum x_k^2 - \frac{1}{n}\left(\sum x_k\right)^2\right] \qquad (9.14)$$

The first version is suitable for hand calculation, while the second is often used in pre-programmed calculation.

Example 9.8 Five children in a family have heights (cm): 90, 115, 130, 145, 175.

$$\mu_X = \overline{x} = \frac{1}{5} \times 655 = 131,$$

$$\text{Var}(X) = \frac{1}{5}\left(89875 - 5 \times 131^2\right) = 814,$$

$$\sigma_X = \sqrt{814} = 28.53.$$

The units for μ and σ are cm, while those for $\text{Var}(X)$ are cm^2. ■

In this example it was clear that *all* the 'events' were covered in the data set. But in most cases we can sample only a small part, e.g., an opinion poll, a blood sample, a quality control sample.

The formulae above remain true except for two points. We must change the notation to make it clear that this is only "part of the story". Frame 9.2 holds true, but when analysing the variance we *must* use $\overline{x}$ rather than μ_X and should refer to the *sample* mean.

We also change notation from $\text{Var}(X)$ to s^2 (and hence from σ_X to s), where s^2 is the **sample variance**, and s the **sample standard deviation**. Finally, we need to make a small change in the formulae in Frame 9.3.

Frame 9.4   *Sample variance*

$$s^2 = \frac{1}{n-1}(x_1^2 + x_2^2 + \cdots + x_n^2 - n\overline{x}^2) \qquad (9.15)$$

$$= \frac{1}{n-1}\left[\sum x_k^2 - \frac{1}{n}\left(\sum x_k\right)^2\right] \qquad (9.16)$$

The change from n to $n-1$ at the final division recognises that the formula is not accurate since it uses $\overline{x}$, which is only an estimate of the true mean μ_X. A deep mathematical analysis shows that this small change is an appropriate adjustment to take account of this.

Calculators providing for statistical calculation usually offer both (9.14) and (9.16), on keys typically labelled σ_n and σ_{n-1}, respectively.

Example 9.9   Suppose that the five heights in Example 9.8 are those of a sample from a school. Then $\overline{x} = 131$ as before. But now

$$s^2 = \frac{1}{4}\left(89875 - 5 \times 131^2\right) = 1017.5,$$

$$s = \sqrt{1017.5} = 31.90.$$

These are larger than before, as we might expect: s is computed using an untrustworthy value and so we ought to err "on the safe side". ■

Example 9.10   1000 whole numbers between 1 and 100 are sampled using a random number generator. They give values:

$$\sum x_k = 50045, \qquad \sum x_k^2 = 3.38336 \times 10^6.$$

We then calculate

$$\overline{x} = \frac{50045}{10000} = 50.045,$$

$$s^2 = \frac{1}{999}\left[3.38336 \times 10^6 - 1000 \times 50.045^2\right] = 879.74.$$

By way of comparison, the exact mean and variance for this distribution are given in Frame 7.7 as:

$$\mu_X = \frac{101}{2} = 50.5, \qquad \mathrm{Var}(X) = \frac{100^2 - 1}{12} = 833.25.$$

■

Ex 9.6

(a) A sample of 1000 data values x_k gives: $\sum x_k = 6434$, $\sum x_k^2 = 75128$. Calculate the sample mean, sample variance and sample standard deviation.

(b) A coin is tossed 10 times, the results recorded (Heads = 1, Tails = 0) and added. This experiment is carried out 100 times and the data gives $\sum x_k = 542$, $\sum x_k^2 = 3180$. Show that the sample mean is 5.42 and calculate the sample variance. Is it consistent with a binomial distribution, mean 5.42?

Ex 9.7 Suppose that the time to failure of an item of equipment follows an exponential distribution with parameter λ. This parameter can be estimated from the results of a test in which items are tested to failure, by equating $1/\lambda$ to the observed mean. Estimate λ from the following table of data for 10 components:

Day of installation	0	9	11	21	40	50	50	51	52	60
Day of failure	2	128	62	98	73	77	64	75	66	97

Also, calculate the sample standard deviation. For a true exponential distribution the standard deviation and mean are equal. Comment.

9.5 Distribution of the Sample Mean

A second sample as in Example 9.10 might give $\bar{x} = 49.048$, $s^2 = 848.73$. What this suggests is that these are sample values for two **random variables**. In principle we ought to be able to assign probabilities to the various possible values or ranges of values of $\bar{x}$ and s^2. This is clearly very difficult, but we can make progress, particularly for the sample mean.

We write $\overline{X}$ as the random variable for which $\bar{x}$ is a possible value. Then key questions are

- What is $E(\overline{X})$?

- What is $\text{Var}(\overline{X})$?

- What is the distribution for $\overline{X}$, e.g., what is its probability or density function?

The first two are quite straightforward to answer, provided the individual items are sampled **independently**. The third seems intractable, but we shall be able to provide an *approximate* answer in §9.6, an answer good enough to underpin a large amount of statistical calculation.

The first two answers are simple to state and their derivation is sufficiently informative to justify a small diversion.

First, consider two random variables X and Z, where $Z = \alpha X$, with α a constant. Then the definitions of mean and variance show that

$$E(Z) = \alpha E(X), \qquad \text{Var}(Z) = \alpha^2 \text{Var}(X). \tag{9.17}$$

Indeed, there is hardly any reason to go through the calculations: Z is simply a rescaled version of X, so the mean and variance are also rescaled; recall that the unit for the mean is that of the random variable, while the unit for the variance is its square.

Second, consider a random variable Y that is the sum of n other random variables, $X_1, \ldots, X_n$. Then the definition of the mean gives

$$E(Y) = E(X_1) + \cdots + E(X_n). \tag{9.18}$$

This time the variance calculation is quite complicated, although there is a simple result *in a special but important circumstance*:

$$\text{Var}(Y) = \text{Var}(X_1) + \cdots + \text{Var}(X_n), \tag{9.19}$$

provided the probabilities for any pair are **independent**.

Example 9.11 Confirm the parameters for the binomial distribution X in Frame 7.9, which is the sum of n **independent** Bernoulli trials X_k, each with mean p and variance pq.

$$E(X) = p + p + \cdots + p = np,$$
$$\text{Var}(X) = pq + pq + \cdots + pq = npq.$$

■

We are now able to tackle $\overline{X}$. Suppose that each x_k in the calculation for $\overline{x}$ is a value of a random variable X_k, where all the X_k have the same distribution (and hence the same mean μ and variance σ^2):

$$\overline{X} = \frac{1}{n}\left(X_1 + X_2 + \cdots + X_n\right). \tag{9.20}$$

Using (9.17) with $\alpha = \frac{1}{n}$ and (9.18), we have:

$$E(\overline{X}) = \frac{1}{n}\left(\mu + \mu + \cdots + \mu\right) = \mu,$$
$$\text{Var}(\overline{X}) = \frac{1}{n^2}\left(\sigma^2 + \sigma^2 + \cdots + \sigma^2\right) = \frac{\sigma^2}{n},$$

results that are certainly worthy of being summed up in a frame.

Frame 9.5   *Mean, variance and standard error for $\overline{X}$*

$$E(\overline{X}) = \mu \tag{9.21}$$

$$\text{Var}(\overline{X}) = \frac{\sigma^2}{n} \tag{9.22}$$

$$\sigma_{\overline{X}} = \frac{\sigma}{\sqrt{n}} \qquad \textbf{[standard error]} \tag{9.23}$$

Think about it like this

These results back up our decision to use the mean – the results should be scattered round the 'true' value – and explains the commonsense judgement of the average – the larger the sample size (n), the better the answer, since the sample means are less widely scattered.

Example 9.12 A four-sided die is thrown 100 times and the results are averaged.

The base distribution is a uniform one over $\{1, 2, 3, 4\}$. We know (from Frame 7.7, with $n = 4$) that

$$E(X) = \frac{1 + 4}{2} = 5/2, \qquad \mathrm{Var}(X) = \frac{4^2 - 1}{12} = 5/4,$$

and hence

$$E(\overline{X}) = 5/2, \qquad \mathrm{Var}(\overline{X}) = \frac{1}{100}\frac{5}{4} = 1/80.$$

∎

The name **standard error** is used for both $\sigma/\sqrt{n}$ and $s/\sqrt{n}$, without the use of the word "sample" for the latter.

Example 9.13 For the sample of five children from a school, in Example 9.9, the standard error is
$$\frac{31.90}{\sqrt{5}} = 14.27.$$

∎

Think about it like this

> The standard error is not only an important quantity in calculations, but a measure of how statistical calculations perform. The 'errors' are inversely proportional to the square root of the sample size, so that to *halve* the error requires us to *quadruple* the sample size. This is a poor performance compared with what can be achieved in non-statistical calculations. Nevertheless, there are situations where the simplification offered by a statistical approach more than outweighs this. For example, the probability-based *Monte-Carlo method* is heavily used in practical calculations in Physics.

Ex 9.8

(a) The following sample is found using a die 10 times: 4, 2, 6, 1, 4, 5, 5, 2, 1, 3.

   Calculate the sample mean and variance and compare them with the corresponding values for a fair die: see Exercise 7.6. What is the standard error?

(b) Three probability experiments are held together and the results are added: a fair coin is tossed ($H = 1$, $T = 2$); a fair die is thrown; a card is selected from a deck numbered 1 to 9. Calculate the mean and variance of the sum.

Ex 9.9 If X_1 is $N\left(\mu_1, \sigma_1^2\right)$ and X_2 is $N\left(\mu_2, \sigma_2^2\right)$, with X_1 and X_2 independent, then it is known that $X_1 - X_2$ is $N\left(\mu_1 - \mu_2, \sigma_1^2 + \sigma_2^2\right)$.

Circular rods have diameters $N(1, 0.003^2)$. Washers have holes with diameters $N(1.005, 0.004^2)$. (The units are consistent.) If rods and washers are paired randomly, what proportion do not fit?

9.6   The Central Limit Theorem

Returning to the random variable $Y = X_1 + \cdots + X_n$, where the X_k have the same distribution, that of X, we know that $\mu_Y = \mu_X$ and $\mathrm{Var}(Y) = n \, \mathrm{Var}(X)$ (assuming independence). But what about the *distribution* of Y, without which we cannot calculate probabilities?

The answer is the most remarkable fact in *Statistics*: the **Central Limit Theorem** tells us that the distribution is approximately that of a **normal distribution**, $N\left(n\mu_X, n\,\mathrm{Var}(X)\right)$, irrespective of the distribution of X. We can therefore calculate all the probabilities we wish, or at least approximations to them.

There are several versions of this Theorem. The following version gives a formal statement and also sets out an immediately useful formula.

Frame 9.6   *The Central Limit Theorem when X has mean μ, variance σ^2*

$$P(X_1 + \cdots + X_n \leqslant x) \to \Phi\left(\frac{x - n\mu}{\sqrt{n}\,\sigma}\right) \quad \text{as } n \to \infty \qquad (9.24)$$

Here, $\Phi(z)$ is the distribution function for the standard normal $N(0,1)$, for which we have a table of values.

There are several comments to make about the practical interpretation of this result.

- It explains why the **normal distribution** is fundamental to much of Statistics.

- It also explains why it was so important to find the mean and variance for every distribution.

- **Independence** is essential.

- In the limit, the shape of the distribution for X is irrelevant.

- *But*, if X is already nearly normal, a small n will produce a very accurate approximation; if X is itself normal, then no limit is necessary: Y is exactly normal for all n.

- If X is far from normal, a large n may be needed to give even rudimentary accuracy; in particular, a lack of symmetry in the density function for X may necessitate a large n.

- The result holds for both **discrete** and **continuous** X distributions, although there is a small obstacle to overcome for the former; this is illustrated in the next section.

Example 9.14 Suppose X is the **uniform** distribution on $[-1, 1]$. The graphs below show the density functions for the sums of two $X_1 + X_2$ $[f_2(x)]$ and three $X_1 + X_2 + X_3$ $[f_3(x)]$ such random variables.

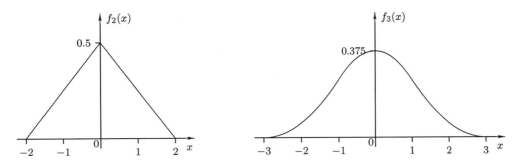

The shape is already similar to a normal density function. Although the density for X is very non-normal, it is symmetric, which speeds up the convergence. ∎

Ex 9.10 A computer, in adding numbers, rounds each off to the nearest integer. Suppose that all rounding errors are independent and uniformly distributed over the interval $(-0.5, 0.5)$. If 1500 numbers are added, what is the probability that the size (absolute value) of the total error exceeds 15?

9.7 Approximating the Binomial Distribution

Some of the examples of using the **binomial** distribution in §7.6 led to calculations that were so time-consuming that a computer was required. Some simplification was possible for p near 0 or 1, through approximating with the **Poisson** distribution. We are now able to deal with other p, and 'reasonably large' n, using the **normal** distribution, backed up by the *Central Limit Theorem*.

In Example 9.11, we noted that the binomial was the sum of n *independent* Bernoulli trials, so the Central Limit Theorem applies. We match the mean and variance and claim the following.

Frame 9.7   *Normal approximation to binomial*

$$\text{Bin}(n, p) \simeq N(np, npq) \tag{9.25}$$

This would appear to settle the issue: we merely calculate probabilities using $N(np, npq)$. But there is a fundamental problem. The binomial distribution is *discrete*, so we can talk of $P(X = k)$, while the normal is *continuous*, so we can talk only of $P(a \leqslant X \leqslant b)$. The solution is to use a simple adjustment, called the **continuity correction**.

We need to ensure that the isolated k values cover all the area under the curve, as in the graph on the right. We do this by 'smearing out' $X = k$:

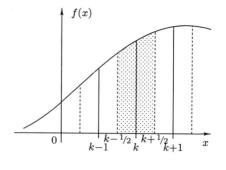

$$X_B = k \iff X_N \text{ in } [k - \tfrac{1}{2}, k + \tfrac{1}{2}].$$

Care is needed since $<$ and $\leqslant$ give different answers using X_B, but the same values using X_N.

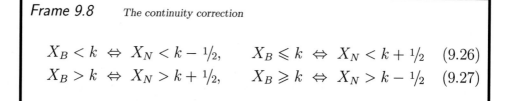

Frame 9.8   *The continuity correction*

$$X_B < k \iff X_N < k - \tfrac{1}{2}, \qquad X_B \leqslant k \iff X_N < k + \tfrac{1}{2} \quad (9.26)$$
$$X_B > k \iff X_N > k + \tfrac{1}{2}, \qquad X_B \geqslant k \iff X_N > k - \tfrac{1}{2} \quad (9.27)$$

Example 9.15 The following show the ease of calculation, but also the level of inaccuracy that may be involved: in the first case n is small, while in the second p is not near $\tfrac{1}{2}$, so the distribution is not very symmetric.

(a) Let X_B be distributed as $\mathrm{Bin}(4, 0.5)$, and estimate $P(X_B \leqslant 1)$, which is exactly 0.3125.

The distribution is approximated by $N(4 \times 0.5, 4 \times 0.5 \times 0.5)$, i.e., $N(2, 1)$. Hence use

$$P(X_N < 1 + \tfrac{1}{2}) = P\left(Z < \frac{1.5 - 2}{1}\right) = \Phi(-0.5) = 0.3085,$$

while the result ignoring the continuity correction would be

$$\Phi\left(\frac{1 - 2}{1}\right) = \Phi(-1) = 0.1587.$$

(b) Let X_B be distributed as $\mathrm{Bin}(20, 0.8)$, and estimate $P(X_B \geqslant 16)$, which is exactly 0.6296.

The distribution is approximated by $N(20 \times 0.8, 20 \times 0.8 \times 0.2)$, i.e., $N(16, 3.2)$. Hence use

$$P(X_N > 16 - \tfrac{1}{2}) = P\left(Z > \frac{15.5 - 16}{\sqrt{3.2}}\right) = 1 - \Phi(-0.28) = 0.6103,$$

while the result ignoring the continuity correction would be

$$1 - \Phi\left(\frac{16 - 16}{\sqrt{3.2}}\right) = 1 - \Phi(0) = 0.5.$$

In both cases the continuity correction significantly improved the quality of the answer. ∎

The next two examples return to those that were computationally difficult in §7.6.

Example 9.16 The *triangular test* in Example 7.26 led to the distribution Bin $(20, \frac{1}{3})$, for which we required $P(X_B \geqslant 10) = 0.092$.

We approximate this using $N\left(\frac{20}{3}, \frac{40}{9}\right)$, calculating

$$P(X_N > 9.5) = P\left(Z > \frac{9.5 - \frac{20}{3}}{\sqrt{\frac{40}{9}}}\right) = P(Z > 1.344)$$

$$= 1 - \Phi(1.344) = 1 - 0.9105 = 0.0895.$$

(Linear interpolation was used in the table of $\Phi(z)$, between the entries for $z = 1.34$ and $z = 1.35$.) ∎

Example 9.17 The insurance company's problem in Example 7.27 led to the distribution Bin$(2100, 0.7)$, for which we required $P(X_B \geqslant 1450) = 0.8356$.

We approximate this using $N(1470, 441)$ (since $np = 2100 \times 0.7 = 1470$ and $npq = 2100 \times 0.7 \times 0.3 = 441$), calculating

$$P(X_N > 1449.5) = P\left(Z > \frac{1449.5 - 1470}{\sqrt{441}}\right)$$

$$= P(Z > -0.976) = \Phi(0.976) = 0.8355.$$

(Again linear interpolation was used in the table.) ∎

Ex 9.11 15% of women have Rhesus negative blood and need special treatment during pregnancy. Use the normal approximation to the binomial distribution to find the probability that more than 27 of the 140 women attending a clinic have Rhesus negative blood.

Ex 9.12 A brewery wished to investigate whether there would be a detectable difference in aroma or taste if production were transferred from Manchester to Edinburgh. They used a *triangular test* in which 45 subjects were given three samples of the beer in random order and told (correctly) that two of the samples came from one brewery and the third from the other. The odd beer was identified correctly by 24 of the 45.

The correct model here is Bin$(45, p)$. Use the normal approximation to estimate to 4 dp the probability of achieving *at least* 24 correct selections if there were no detectable difference, so each selection is made at random with $p = \frac{1}{3}$. What conclusion would you make?

9.8 Confidence Intervals

In §9.5, we showed that $\overline{X}$ has mean μ and standard deviation $\sigma/\sqrt{n}$. The Central Limit Theorem now tells us that, approximately, the distribution is *normal*, which allows us to calculate probabilities associated with the mean.

Frame 9.9   *Distribution of $\overline{X}$*

$$\overline{X} \text{ is approximately distributed as } N\left(\mu, \frac{\sigma^2}{n}\right) \qquad (9.28)$$

$$Z = \frac{\sqrt{n}(\overline{X} - \mu)}{\sigma} \text{ is approximately } N(0,1) \qquad (9.29)$$

This result opens up a great many applications, but we shall concentrate on one. When attempting to measure a quantity, μ say, we obtain a sample of estimates, which we assume to be values of a random variable with mean μ. Then $\overline{x}$ is a good estimate of μ, but just how good is it?

Because the experiment is statistically based we cannot quote a definite error bound, as we can do when truncating a power series, for example. It is possible (with low probability, of course) for samples to be very poor.

A particularly successful approach, based on Frame 9.9, is as follows. From the table of $\Phi(z)$ we have

$$0.95 = P(|Z| \leqslant 1.960)$$

$$= P\left(\frac{\sqrt{n}|\overline{X} - \mu|}{\sigma} \leqslant 1.960\right)$$

$$= P\left(|\overline{X} - \mu| \leqslant \frac{1.960\sigma}{\sqrt{n}}\right).$$

Hence, $\overline{x}$ should lie within $\dfrac{1.960\sigma}{\sqrt{n}}$ of the true mean, with 95% probability.

Reversing this statement:

The true mean μ is within $\dfrac{1.960\sigma}{\sqrt{n}}$ of the sample mean $\overline{x}$, with 95% probability.

The range of values spanned by this statement is known as a **confidence interval** and the extremes are the **confidence limits**.

Frame 9.10   *Confidence intervals and limits*

$$\left[\overline{x} - \frac{1.960\sigma}{\sqrt{n}}, \overline{x} + \frac{1.960\sigma}{\sqrt{n}}\right] \text{ is the 95\% confidence interval for } \mu$$

$$\overline{x} \pm \frac{1.960\sigma}{\sqrt{n}} \text{ are the 95\% confidence limits for } \mu$$

Use 1.645 for 90% confidence and 2.576 for 99% confidence

Example 9.18 Suppose X is known to have distribution $N(\mu, (0.02)^2)$. A sample of 5 values is $\{3.12, 3.05, 2.83, 2.94, 3.21\}$. Find where μ may lie, with 95% confidence.

We have $\overline{x} = 3.03$. Also, noting that $\sigma = 0.02$ and $n = 5$, we have

$$\frac{1.960\sigma}{\sqrt{n}} = \frac{1.96 \times 0.02}{\sqrt{5}} \simeq 0.018,$$

so μ lies in $[\,3.012, 3.048\,]$ with 95% probability.　　　　　■

This example presupposed that we knew σ, which is often not the case. There are two approaches to this. One is to assume that historical evidence about the measurement process is extensive and has pointed to a stable value of σ. The other is to use the **sample** standard deviation, s, instead. This is safe provided n is not small. (There is a method, based on the so-called t-distribution, that compensates for small n.)

Example 9.19 A sample of 100 gives $\overline{x} = 1.72$ and $s = 0.32$. The 95% confidence limits are

$$1.72 \pm \frac{1.96 \times 0.32}{\sqrt{100}}, \quad \text{i.e., } 1.72 \pm 0.063.$$

Suppose that we require a precision 0.01 with 99% confidence. Then

$$\frac{2.576 \times 0.32}{\sqrt{n}} \leqslant 0.01 \quad \Rightarrow \quad n \geqslant \left(\frac{2.576 \times 0.32}{0.01}\right)^2 \simeq 7000.$$

This seems unrealistic, so it may be necessary to improve the process, e.g., by investing in new equipment, to reduce the standard deviation instead.

If the sample size remains at 100, we would require

$$\frac{2.576\sigma}{\sqrt{100}} \leqslant 0.01 \quad \Rightarrow \quad \sigma \leqslant \frac{0.01 \times 10}{2.576} \simeq 0.04.$$

　　　　　■

Ex 9.13 Nails of specified length 2 cm have lengths distributed with mean 2.0 and standard deviation 0.08. Find the probability that the mean of a batch of 400 will lie between 1.99 and 2.01 cm.

Ex 9.14

(a) A sample of 100 items from a population with standard deviation $\sigma = 0.32$ has sample mean $\overline{x} = 1.72$. Find a 95% confidence interval for the true mean.

(b) A large group of animals have a known standard deviation of 2.2 kg. A sample of 80 are chosen and weighed, giving an average of 8.3 kg. Construct a 90% confidence interval for the (true) mean.

9.9   Experimental Errors

The context in the previous section is similar to standard practice for quoting values determined by experimental methods. Such values are conventionally reported as

$$\text{mean} \pm \text{standard error.}$$

Since the standard error is the standard deviation for the mean, this is equivalent to using $1 \times \sigma/\sqrt{n}$ in Frame 9.10, i.e., to

$$P(|Z| \leqslant 1) = \Phi(1) - [\,1 - \Phi(1)\,] = 0.6826,$$

so quoting $\overline{x} \pm \epsilon$ is equivalent to quoting a 68% confidence interval.

This convention opens up the possibility of using the Central Limit Theorem when adding or subtracting experimental values.

Example 9.20   A quantity Q_1, determined using 50 measurements, delivers a sample mean $\overline{x}_1 = 32.7$ and sample standard deviation $s_1 = 1.4$, which we assume is a reasonable approximation to σ, since n is fairly large.

The **standard error** in $\overline{Q}_1$ is $\frac{1.4}{\sqrt{50}} \simeq 0.2$, so we quote

$$Q_1 = 32.7 \pm 0.2 \quad (68\% \text{ confidence}).$$

Suppose that a second quantity is measured *independently* from the first:

$$Q_2 = -17.3 \pm 0.15.$$

What should we quote for the sum $Q_1 + Q_2$? Clearly the only sensible value to quote is 15.4, but we need to find an error estimate.

Because of independence, we have

$$\text{Var}(\overline{Q}_1 + \overline{Q}_2) = \text{Var}(\overline{Q}_1) + \text{Var}(\overline{Q}_2) = 0.2^2 + 0.15^2 = 0.0625,$$

giving a standard error in the sum: $\sqrt{0.0625} = 0.25$. Hence, we give the final result as

$$Q_1 + Q_2 = 15.4 \pm 0.25.$$

Note that the *relative* errors have increased, from 0.6% and 0.9% to 1.6%. This is typical of the danger of error inflation inherent in subtraction.   ∎

Ex 9.15 Experiment produces $x = 7.42 \pm 0.04$ and $y = 4.13 \pm 0.02$, with the '$\pm$' indicating one standard deviation. Find an equivalent expression for $2x + 3y$.

9.10 Revision Exercises

Ex 9.16 The following values are the distances (in miles) travelled by 20 armoured personnel carriers before they failed in service:

162	200	271	320	392	508	539	629	706	778
884	1008	1081	1101	1182	1464	1603	1984	2355	2880

(a) Calculate the median and the lower and upper quartiles of these values.
$$\left(Q_1 = x_{\frac{n+2}{4}}, \ Q_3 = x_{\frac{3n+2}{4}}. \right)$$

(b) Draw an accurate boxplot for the data set.

Ex 9.17 The following values are the distribution of ages of the workforce of 19 for a small company:

19	22	22	23	25	27	31	31	34	39
41	47	48	51	55	59	61	64	65	

Note: $\sum x_k = 764$.

Calculate the mean, median, and the lower and upper quartiles of these values.

Ex 9.18 Measurements of the density of dust particles in a gas were recorded on 180 occasions:

Number of particles seen	0	1	2	3	4	5	6 or more
Number of occasions	43	59	47	23	6	2	0

Show that the mean number per occasion is 1.422 and find the probabilities for a Poisson distribution with $\mu = 1.422$, for values $0, 1, 2, 3, 4, 5, \geqslant 6$. Multiply these by 180, convert to whole numbers and compare with the values above.

Ex 9.19 The diameter of refill leads of a mechanical pencil are supposed to be 0.5 mm. Refills whose diameter are less than 0.485 mm do not stay in the pencil while those whose diameter is greater than 0.520 mm do not fit in the pencil at all. A firm makes refills with mean diameter 0.50 mm with standard deviation 0.01 mm. Find the percentage of the production that fail to fit a pencil.

Ex 9.20 A sample of 64 items produces a mean $\overline{x} = 56.8$ and sample variance $s^2 = 3.24$. Find a 95% confidence interval for the mean of the distribution from which the sample was chosen.

(You may assume that the sample size is sufficiently large for s to be an acceptable approximation for σ.)

Ex 9.21 A machine producing an item with a stipulated measurement is thought to be unreliable, although the standard deviation could be assumed to be the historically known value 0.8. A sample is to be chosen to estimate the mean measurement within 0.1. What size should this be to deliver 90% confidence in the result?

The standard normal cumulative distribution function $\Phi(z)$

$$P(Z < z) = \Phi(z), \qquad P(|Z| < z) = 2\Phi(z) - 1, \qquad \Phi(-z) = 1 - \Phi(z)$$

z	.00	.01	.02	.03	.04	.05	.06	.07	.08	.09
0.0	.5000	.5040	.5080	.5120	.5160	.5199	.5239	.5279	.5319	.5359
0.1	.5398	.5438	.5478	.5517	.5557	.5596	.5636	.5675	.5714	.5753
0.2	.5793	.5832	.5871	.5910	.5948	.5987	.6026	.6064	.6103	.6141
0.3	.6179	.6217	.6255	.6293	.6331	.6368	.6406	.6443	.6480	.6517
0.4	.6554	.6591	.6628	.6664	.6700	.6736	.6772	.6808	.6844	.6879
0.5	.6915	.6950	.6985	.7019	.7054	.7088	.7123	.7157	.7190	.7224
0.6	.7257	.7291	.7324	.7357	.7389	.7422	.7454	.7486	.7517	.7549
0.7	.7580	.7611	.7642	.7673	.7704	.7734	.7764	.7794	.7823	.7852
0.8	.7881	.7910	.7939	.7967	.7995	.8023	.8051	.8078	.8106	.8133
0.9	.8159	.8186	.8212	.8238	.8264	.8289	.8315	.8340	.8365	.8389
1.0	.8413	.8438	.8461	.8485	.8508	.8531	.8554	.8577	.8599	.8621
1.1	.8643	.8665	.8686	.8708	.8729	.8749	.8770	.8790	.8810	.8830
1.2	.8849	.8869	.8888	.8907	.8925	.8944	.8962	.8980	.8997	.9015
1.3	.9032	.9049	.9066	.9082	.9099	.9115	.9131	.9147	.9162	.9177
1.4	.9192	.9207	.9222	.9236	.9251	.9265	.9279	.9292	.9306	.9319
1.5	.9332	.9345	.9357	.9370	.9382	.9394	.9406	.9418	.9429	.9441
1.6	.9452	.9463	.9474	.9484	.9495	.9505	.9515	.9525	.9535	.9545
1.7	.9554	.9564	.9573	.9582	.9591	.9599	.9608	.9616	.9625	.9633
1.8	.9641	.9649	.9656	.9664	.9671	.9678	.9686	.9693	.9699	.9706
1.9	.9713	.9719	.9726	.9732	.9738	.9744	.9750	.9756	.9761	.9767
2.0	.9772	.9778	.9783	.9788	.9793	.9798	.9803	.9808	.9812	.9817
2.1	.9821	.9826	.9830	.9834	.9838	.9842	.9846	.9850	.9854	.9857
2.2	.9861	.9864	.9868	.9871	.9875	.9878	.9881	.9884	.9887	.9890
2.3	.9893	.9896	.9898	.9901	.9904	.9906	.9909	.9911	.9913	.9916
2.4	.9918	.9920	.9922	.9925	.9927	.9929	.9931	.9932	.9934	.9936
2.5	.9938	.9940	.9941	.9943	.9945	.9946	.9948	.9949	.9951	.9952
2.6	.9953	.9955	.9956	.9957	.9959	.9960	.9961	.9962	.9963	.9964
2.7	.9965	.9966	.9967	.9968	.9969	.9970	.9971	.9972	.9973	.9974
2.8	.9974	.9975	.9976	.9977	.9977	.9978	.9979	.9979	.9980	.9981
2.9	.9981	.9982	.9982	.9983	.9984	.9984	.9985	.9985	.9986	.9986
3.0	.9987	.9987	.9987	.9988	.9988	.9989	.9989	.9989	.9990	.9990
3.1	.9990	.9991	.9991	.9991	.9992	.9992	.9992	.9992	.9993	.9993
3.2	.9993	.9993	.9994	.9994	.9994	.9994	.9994	.9995	.9995	.9995
3.3	.9995	.9995	.9995	.9996	.9996	.9996	.9996	.9996	.9996	.9997
3.4	.9997	.9997	.9997	.9997	.9997	.9997	.9997	.9997	.9997	.9998

z	1.282	1.645	1.960	2.326	2.576	3.090	3.291	3.891
$P(Z < z)$	**0.90**	**0.95**	**0.975**	**0.99**	**0.995**	**0.999**	**0.999 5**	**0.999 95**
$P(\|Z\| < z)$	*0.80*	*0.90*	*0.95*	*0.98*	*0.99*	*0.998*	*0.999*	*0.999 9*

MATHEMATICAL

METHODS

2

1 HYPERBOLIC FUNCTIONS

In this chapter we introduce functions that are in nature exponential but have many properties that make them *appear* similar to trigonometric functions. They are not really 'new' in the sense that we can avoid their use altogether, but their enhanced symmetry makes them useful for providing speedy and neat solutions for some important problems.

One application involves their **inverse functions**. We have to address the problem involved in inverting functions that are not 'one-one', and so the chapter closes with an account of how to overcome this obstacle, applied to one of these new functions.

1.1 Definitions

The **hyperbolic cosine** $\cosh x$ and the **hyperbolic sine** $\sinh x$ are defined in terms of the exponential function as follows.

Frame 1.1   *Basic hyperbolic functions*

$$\cosh x = \frac{e^x + e^{-x}}{2}, \qquad \sinh x = \frac{e^x - e^{-x}}{2} \qquad (1.1)$$

Notation

The names are built up as, for example, 'cos' + 'h' for 'hyperbolic'. The result, in this case, is a word that is easily pronounced. There are two common resolutions to the problem of pronouncing 'sinh': either *sinsh*, by analogy with cosh, or *shine*, as a composition of sine and h.

Their values can be computed directly from (1.1), but scientific calculators almost invariably offer them through a combination of a `hyp` key and the normal `sin` and `cos` keys.

These functions are often used to replace e^x and/or e^{-x} in expressions, using the reversal of the definitions in (1.1):

$$e^x = \cosh x + \sinh x, \qquad e^{-x} = \cosh x - \sinh x. \qquad (1.2)$$

The graphs of $\cosh x$ and $\sinh x$ follow directly from (1.1) and are shown below.

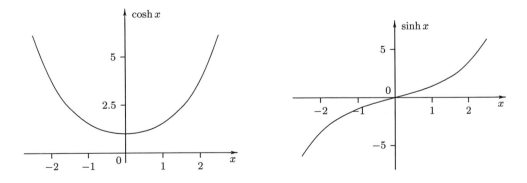

We see from these that $\cosh x$ is **even**, while $\sinh x$ is **odd**. This is one of the reasons why they are preferred to the original exponential functions in certain problems.

Other hyperbolic functions are defined by analogy with circular functions, e.g.,

$$\tanh x = \frac{\sinh x}{\cosh x}, \qquad \operatorname{sech} x = \frac{1}{\cosh x},$$

as well as $\coth x$ and $\operatorname{cosech} x$.

Notation

> In spite of their names, these functions are essentially exponential in nature. In particular, they have no periodic behaviour. But they have some other properties that are remarkably similar to those for $\cos x$ and $\sin x$ and the inclusion of 'cos' and 'sin' in their names serves both as a convenient reminder and a help in deducing these properties.

Ex 1.1 Find values of P and Q such that $5e^x - 4e^{-x} = P\sinh x + Q\cosh x$.

Is it always possible to write $ae^x + be^{-x}$ as $P\sinh x + Q\cosh x$?

1.2 Identities

We have generated six functions from just one: e^x. This suggests that, as is the case for circular functions, there will be relationships between them, i.e., we expect to find several **identities**. These can be derived using the definitions in (1.1), but there is an elegant rule that enables them to be deduced – in fact *written down* – from corresponding trigonometric identities.

Recall Euler's Formula:

$$e^{ix} = \cos x + i\sin x, \tag{1.3}$$

which gives

$$\cos x = \frac{e^{ix} + e^{-ix}}{2}, \qquad \sin x = \frac{e^{ix} - e^{-ix}}{2i}. \tag{1.4}$$

Comparing these with (1.1) suggests:

$$\cosh ix = \cos x, \qquad \cos ix = \cosh x, \tag{1.5}$$
$$\sinh ix = i\sin x, \qquad \sin ix = i\sinh x. \tag{1.6}$$

It is these relationships that allow us to convert many results in circular functions to new ones in hyperbolic functions. We can use the following 'recipe':

take any identity involving sin and cos;

replace **cos** by **cosh** and **sin** by i**sinh**.

Example 1.1 Consider the following adaptations of two familiar trigonometric identities.

$$\cos^2 x + \sin^2 x = 1 \quad \Rightarrow \quad \cosh^2 x + i^2 \sinh^2 x = 1$$
$$\Rightarrow \quad \cosh^2 x - \sinh^2 x = 1, \tag{1.7}$$
$$\sin 2x = 2 \sin x \cos x \quad \Rightarrow \quad i \sinh 2x = 2i \sinh x \cosh x$$
$$\Rightarrow \quad \sinh 2x = 2 \sinh x \cosh x. \tag{1.8}$$

■

This process can be simplified, into what is known as **Osborn's Rule**.

Frame 1.2   *Osborn's Rule*

Replace all 'sin' by 'sinh' and all 'cos' by 'cosh';
where there are two 'sin' multiplied together, change the sign

---

Note that (1.7) and (1.8) satisfy this: only the term in $\sin^2 x$ changes sign when converted.

Example 1.2   Obtain an expression for $\cosh(x + y)$ in terms of functions of x and y alone.
Start from

$$\cos(x + y) = \cos x \cos y - \sin x \sin y.$$

Translate $\cos \to \cosh$, $\sin \to \sinh$, noting the product of two sines, which forces a change of sign:

$$\cosh(x + y) = \cosh x \cosh y + \sinh x \sinh y.$$

■

Example 1.3   Express $\tanh 2x$ in terms of $\tanh x$.
Start from

$$\tan 2x = \frac{2 \tan x}{1 - \tan^2 x}.$$

Again translate, this time $\tan \to \tanh$. But the term $\tan^2 x$ hides two 'sin' terms and so forces a sign change. (The other two tan terms hide just one sin each and are on opposite sides of the identity, so there is no net effect from them.) We find

$$\tanh 2x = \frac{2 \tanh x}{1 + \tanh^2 x}.$$

■

Think about it like this

The trigonometric functions are often called **circular functions**, since $x = \cos t$, $y = \sin t$ satisfy the equation of a **circle**.

The identity (1.7) explains the name given to these new functions, since $x = \cosh t$, $y = \sinh t$ satisfy $x^2 - y^2 = 1$, the equation of a **hyperbola**.

Ex 1.2 Write down identities involving hyperbolic functions, which are counterparts to:

$$\cos 2x = 1 - 2\sin^2 x,$$
$$\sin(x + y) = \sin x \cos y + \cos x \sin y,$$
$$\sin 3x = 3 \sin x - 4 \sin^3 x.$$

Ex 1.3

(a) Given that $\sinh x = -\frac{3}{4}$, use the identity $\cosh^2 x - \sinh^2 x = 1$ to find the value of $\cosh x$. Use a calculator to verify your answer, given that $x \simeq -0.693$.

(b) Find $\sinh x$, given that $\cosh x = \frac{17}{15}$. Is the answer unique?

Ex 1.4 Explain why $\operatorname{sech}^2 x = 1 - \tanh^2 x$.
   Hence find $\cosh x$ and $\sinh x$ when $\tanh x = -\frac{7}{25}$.

1.3   Calculus Properties

Direct differentiation of the equations in (1.1), followed by reading the results in reverse, gives the basic results. For example

$$\frac{d}{dx}[\cosh x] = \frac{1}{2}\frac{d}{dx}\left[e^x + e^{-x}\right] = \frac{1}{2}\left(e^x - e^{-x}\right) = \sinh x.$$

Frame 1.3   *Calculus properties for cosh/sinh*

$$\frac{d}{dx}[\cosh x] = \sinh x, \qquad \frac{d}{dx}[\sinh x] = \cosh x,$$

$$\int \sinh x \, dx = \cosh x + C, \qquad \int \cosh x \, dx = \sinh x + C$$

Think about it like this
   Again we can make use of sin and cos to recall these results. They are identical in structure, bur rather simpler due to the absence of any minus sign.

Example 1.4   Find the values of $\sinh x$ and $\cosh x$, and their first derivatives, at $x = 0$.
   From Frames 1.1 and 1.3,

$$\sinh 0 = \tfrac{1}{2}(e^0 - e^0) = \tfrac{1}{2}(1 - 1) = \mathbf{0},$$
$$\cosh 0 = \tfrac{1}{2}(e^0 + e^0) = \tfrac{1}{2}(1 + 1) = \mathbf{1},$$
$$\frac{d}{dx}[\sinh x] = \cosh x, \text{with value } \mathbf{1} \text{ at } x = 0,$$
$$\frac{d}{dx}[\cosh x] = \sinh x, \text{with value } \mathbf{0} \text{ at } x = 0.$$

These "0/1" properties prove useful when working with certain differential equations. ∎

Example 1.5 Find the second derivative for $y = \cosh 3x$.

Using the linear composite rule,

$$y' = 3\sinh 3x, \quad y'' = 3 \times 3\cosh 3x = 9\cosh 3x.$$

This shows, incidentally, that y satisfies $y'' = 9y$, an example of a **differential equation** that is common in civil engineering calculations. ∎

Example 1.6 Differentiate $\coth x$.

From the definition, $\coth x = \dfrac{\cosh x}{\sinh x}$. Hence, use the Quotient Rule:

$$\begin{aligned}
\frac{d}{dx}[\coth x] &= \frac{\sinh x \times \sinh x - \cosh x \times \cosh x}{\sinh^2 x} \\
&= \frac{\sinh^2 x - \cosh^2 x}{\sinh^2 x} \\
&= \frac{-1}{\sinh^2 x} = -\operatorname{cosech}^2 x,
\end{aligned}$$

from (1.7). ∎

The quotient rule leads to further results of a familiar form:

$$\frac{d}{dx}[\tanh x] = \operatorname{sech}^2 x \quad \Rightarrow \quad \int \operatorname{sech}^2 x \, dx = \tanh x + C. \qquad (1.9)$$

Also, noting that $\frac{d}{dx}[\cosh x] = \sinh x$, a simple substitution rule gives

$$\int \tanh x \, dx = \int \frac{\sinh x}{\cosh x} \, dx = \ln \cosh x + C. \qquad (1.10)$$

Think about it like this

Note that this result does not use $|\cosh x|$. The reason is simple: $\cosh x > 0$ for all x, so there is no need to force the absolute value.

Example 1.7 Integrate $\sinh^2 x$, (a) directly, and (b) in terms of $e^{\pm x}$.

(a) Transcribe $\cos 2x = 1 - 2\sin^2 x$ to obtain $\cosh 2x = 1 + 2\sinh^2 x$, noting the sign change forced by the product of sin terms. Hence

$$\sinh^2 x = \tfrac{1}{2}\cosh 2x - \tfrac{1}{2}.$$

Use this as a replacement for $\sinh^2 x$:

$$\int \sinh^2 x \, dx = \int \tfrac{1}{2}\left(\cosh 2x - \tfrac{1}{2}\right) dx = \tfrac{1}{4}\sinh 2x - \tfrac{1}{2}x + C.$$

(b) The alternative calculation starts with

$$\sinh^2 x = \left[\tfrac{1}{2}(e^x - e^{-x})\right]^2 = \tfrac{1}{4}(e^{2x} - 2 + e^{-2x}).$$

Then

$$\int \sinh^2 x \, dx = \int \left(\tfrac{1}{4}e^{2x} - \tfrac{1}{2} + \tfrac{1}{4}e^{-2x}\right) dx$$
$$= \tfrac{1}{8}e^{2x} - \tfrac{1}{2}x - \tfrac{1}{8}e^{-2x} + C,$$

which is equivalent to the first form, since $\tfrac{1}{8}(e^{2x} - e^{-2x}) = \tfrac{1}{4}\sinh 2x$.

■

Ex 1.5

(a) Differentiate $3\sinh 2x - \tfrac{5}{3}\cosh 3x$.

(b) Integrate $\cosh \tfrac{x}{4}$.

Ex 1.6 Differentiate the following:

(a) $\tanh 2x$, (b) $x^2 \sinh 3x$, (c) $\ln(1 + \cosh 2x)$.

Ex 1.7 Evaluate the following:

(a) $\displaystyle\int_0^1 \sinh^2 x \, dx$ (Hint: use Exercise 1.2, or rewrite using $e^{\pm x}$),

(b) $\displaystyle\int \coth x \, dx$,

(c) $\displaystyle\int \frac{\cosh x}{\sqrt{\sinh x}} \, dx$.

Ex 1.8 Find the second derivative of $\sinh x \sin x$ and guess its fourth derivative.

1.4 Application of Hyperbolic Functions

The most far-reaching application of these functions is to a wide class of differential equation problems, like the one discovered in Example 1.5.

Here we consider a problem whose solution is expressed neatly in terms of hyperbolic functions.

An analysis of the statics of a heavy **chain**, hanging under gravity, shows that its shape in the xy-plane is given by

$$y = a + \lambda \cosh \frac{x}{\lambda},$$

where a and λ are constants that depend on the points of support and the length of the chain. Such a curve is called a **catenary**, shown in the graph below.

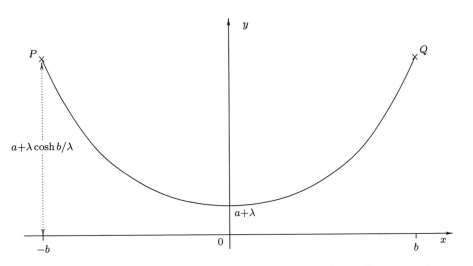

If the points of support, P and Q, are at $x = \pm b$, and are at the same height, the length of the chain is given by $L = 2\lambda \sinh \frac{b}{\lambda}$; this can be shown using the calculation in the next Example. Thus, knowledge of the length of the chain and its support points can be used to determine λ (and a).

Example 1.8 Find the length of the catenary $y = a + \cosh x$, supported at $x = \pm b$.

First, note that $y' = \sinh x$. Then, using (1.7),

$$L = \int_{-b}^{b} \left[1 + (y')^2\right]^{1/2} dx = 2 \int_{0}^{b} \left[1 + \sinh^2 x\right]^{1/2} dx \qquad \text{(evenness)}$$

$$= 2 \int_{0}^{b} \left(\cosh^2 x\right)^{1/2} dx = 2 \int_{0}^{b} \cosh x \, dx$$

$$= 2 \left[\sinh x\right]_{0}^{b} = 2 \sinh b.$$

■

1.5   Inverse Functions

Recall the key components of a **function** f: it is a process that produces, for any (input) x in its **domain**, a **unique** (output) y, where we write

$$y = f(x). \tag{1.11}$$

In some circumstances we can reverse the process: given an output, we can calculate the input required to generate it. A new function is produced, the **inverse function** for f, written f^{-1}, where

$$x = f^{-1}(y). \tag{1.12}$$

In (1.11) and (1.12) the x and y denote the same elements. It is sometimes possible to use algebraic manipulations on one to derive the other, although the more useful cases are where (1.12) defines a 'new' function, one we cannot express in terms of those in our current repertoire.

Example 1.9   Find the inverse for the function $f(x) = \dfrac{x}{x+1}$, $(x \neq -1)$.

Let $y = \dfrac{x}{x+1}$, then cross-multiply and rearrange to solve for x:

$$xy + y = x,$$
$$x(1 - y) = y,$$
$$x = \frac{y}{1-y} \quad (y \neq 1).$$

Hence $f^{-1}(y) = \dfrac{y}{1-y}$, $(y \neq 1)$, which is more usually rewritten in terms of x:

$$f^{-1}(x) = \frac{x}{1-x} \quad (x \neq 1).$$

                                                             ■

This process succeeds only when f is **one-one**, by which we mean that each output y is generated by one and only one input x. One-one nature can quickly be seen from a graph: there can be no local maximum or minimum since any line parallel to the x-axis can cut the graph no more than once. If it cuts twice, there must be two x values giving the same y value.

Hence, in the absence of the one-one property, reversing the process produces more than one x for some given y, which contradicts the key property of a function. We now turn our attention to these 'many-one' functions.

One way to get round the one-one restriction is to reduce the **domain** of the original function to a set on which the function *is* one-one.

As an example, we shall try to invert the 'square' function, $y = x^2$. The problem and its solution are illustrated below.

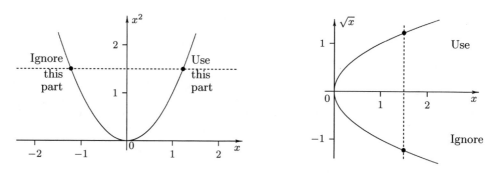

If we use the full domain $\mathbb{R}$, we cannot achieve an inverse function. For example, $4 = 2^2 = (-2)^2$, so 4 is output by two inputs: 2 and -2. Thus we cannot reverse the process to generate a valid function.

There are two solutions to this problem, both arriving at the same result, at least for this case.

Old Method: We note two possible answers, choosing one as the **principal value**, by agreed convention. In this case we choose the upper half of the right-hand graph to deliver such values.

Modern Method: We restrict the **domain** of the original function to $\mathbb{R}^+$, i.e., $\{x \,:\, x \geqslant 0\}$. This new function is **one-one**, which allows us to define its inverse function, given by the upper half of the right-hand graph, as before.

Swapping the roles of x and y, we therefore define the square root function $y = \sqrt{x}$ as follows:

$$y = \sqrt{x} \quad \text{where} \quad y^2 = x \quad \text{and} \quad y \geqslant 0, \quad (x \geqslant 0). \qquad (1.13)$$

Think about it like this

This is not the only possibility. We could have instead restricted the domain to $\{x \,:\, x \leqslant 0\}$. But for common functions like this one, there is usually a universal convention. Everyone agrees that the inverse function for the square function is defined as in (1.13). If we really need the other value for some purpose, we don't redefine the inverse but use $-\sqrt{x}$ instead.

The same approach is used to define $\sqrt[n]{x}$ for n an even number. (Note that x^n is one-one when n is odd and there is no problem in defining the inverse.)

Example 1.10 Find the inverse function for $f(x) = x^4 - 1$.

Use the right-hand part of the graph only. When replotted with x and y changing roles, we find the inverse function

$$f^{-1}(y) = \sqrt[4]{y + 1}$$

where $y \geqslant -1$.

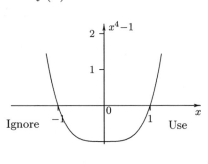

Ex 1.9 Define an inverse function for $f(x) = x^2 - 2x + 5$, appropriate for use where x must be **negative** when $f(x) = 8$.

1.6 Inverse Hyperbolic Functions

Suppose that we encounter a problem such as: "At which points is a chain at a given height?" (in §1.4). This leads to the need to solve equations such as $\cosh x = \alpha$, for a given α. We start, however, with a similar sinh problem.

Example 1.11 Find the value of x for which $\sinh x = 3/4$.

We have $\frac{1}{2}(e^x - e^{-x}) = 3/4$. Multiply by $4e^x$:

$$2e^{2x} - 2 = 3e^x.$$

Writing $u = e^x$, this becomes $2u^2 - 3u - 2 = 0$. Solve this quadratic:

$$(2u + 1)(u - 2) = 0 \quad \Rightarrow \quad u = -1/2 \text{ or } 2.$$

Hence, $x = \ln u = \ln 2$ is the required value. The other solution for u does *not* lead to a real solution since the exponential function is never negative and $\ln(-1/2)$ is undefined. ∎

Now, $\sinh x$ is **one-one** and so presumably has an inverse function. We can argue

$$\sinh(\ln 2) = {}^3\!/_4 \quad \Rightarrow \quad \sinh^{-1} {}^3\!/_4 = \ln 2.$$

Example 1.12   Find values of x for which $\cosh x = {}^{13}\!/_{12}$.
   We have $\frac{1}{2}(e^x + e^{-x}) = {}^{13}\!/_{12}$. Multiply by $12e^x$:

$$6(e^{2x} + 1) = 13e^x.$$

Writing $u = e^x$, this becomes $6u^2 - 13u + 6 = 0$. Solve this quadratic:

$$(3u - 2)(2u - 3) = 0 \quad \Rightarrow \quad u = {}^2\!/_3 \text{ or } {}^3\!/_2 \quad \Rightarrow \quad x = \ln u = \ln {}^2\!/_3 \text{ or } \ln {}^3\!/_2.$$

∎

   This time there are *two* viable answers. A brief glance at the graph of the catenary will show that we ought to expect two (or none).
   We face the same problem in inverting $\cosh x$ as we did with x^2 and the solution is the same. We restrict the domain of $\cosh x$ to $x \geqslant 0$, so that its inverse returns the positive of the two possible answers. Hence

$$\cosh\left(\ln {}^3\!/_2\right) = {}^{13}\!/_{12} \text{ and } \ln {}^3\!/_2 > 0 \quad \Rightarrow \quad \cosh^{-1} {}^{13}\!/_{12} = \ln {}^3\!/_2.$$

If we require the other value we choose $-\ln {}^3\!/_2 \ (= \ln {}^2\!/_3)$.
   A more general analysis, like those in the examples above, leads to the formulae:

$$\sinh^{-1} x = \ln\left(x + \sqrt{x^2 + 1}\right), \tag{1.14}$$

$$\cosh^{-1} x = \ln\left(x + \sqrt{x^2 - 1}\right) \quad (x \geqslant 1), \tag{1.15}$$

$$\tanh^{-1} x = \frac{1}{2}\ln\left(\frac{1 + x}{1 - x}\right) \quad (-1 < x < 1). \tag{1.16}$$

Think about it like this
   This construction has failed to generate genuinely 'new' functions for inverse hyperbolic functions. That suggests we can avoid using these, but there are two main reasons why they are sometimes encountered. Reference works often elect to use them, instead of the log versions, for three standard integrals, those of $1/\sqrt{x^2 + 1}$, $1/\sqrt{x^2 - 1}$ and $1/(1 - x^2)$. Also, scientific calculators usually offer the values of these inverse functions through a combination of the `hyp` key and the normal `sin`$^{-1}$, `cos`$^{-1}$ and `tan`$^{-1}$ keys, use of which is quicker than for the log alternatives.

Ex 1.10

(a) Explain why you cannot solve the equation $\cosh x = \frac{1}{2}$.

(b) Solve the equation $5\cosh x + 2\sinh x = 11$, to find x.

Ex 1.11   Show that $\tanh^{-1} x = \frac{1}{2}\ln\left(\frac{1 + x}{1 - x}\right)$ $(|x| < 1)$.

1.7 Revision Exercises

Ex 1.12 Derive from the definition

$$\cosh x = \frac{e^x + e^{-x}}{2}$$

an expression for $\cosh^2 x$ in terms of $\cosh(2x)$. Explain how the same result can be obtained from a trigonometric identity.

Ex 1.13 Find the second derivative, with respect to x, for: $\sin x \cosh 2x$.

Ex 1.14 Write down an identity involving hyperbolic functions, analogous to

$$\sin^2 x + \cos^2 x = 1.$$

Hence, or otherwise, compute

$$\int \cosh^3 x \, dx.$$

2   INVERSE CIRCULAR FUNCTIONS

We now investigate inverting the circular functions, $\sin x$, $\cos x$ and $\tan x$. It turns out that their inverses are very useful in calculus. Their importance lies in the fact that, unlike the situation for hyperbolic functions, these inverses are genuinely 'new' functions, ones with no formulae in terms of more basic functions. They allow us to evaluate integrals that occur frequently in practice and for which we have no other method.

In each of the three cases the original function is not **one-one** so we must identify an appropriately restricted domain.

2.1   Definitions

First, consider $y = \sin x$, which has the graph shown below. Suppose we choose a fixed output y_0 between -1 and 1 and seek corresponding inputs. These occur where the line $y = y_0$ intersects $y = \sin x$, i.e., at the x-values given by:

$$x = x_0, \ \pi - x_0, \ 2\pi + x_0, \ \ldots, \ -\pi - x_0, \ -2\pi + x_0, \ \ldots.$$

Here we have chosen x_0 to be the **unique** value between $-\frac{\pi}{2}$ and $\frac{\pi}{2}$.

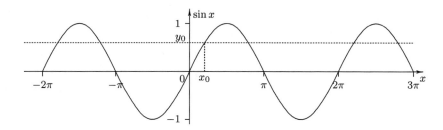

Clearly $\sin x$ is not one-one. If we wish to construct an inverse function, we must restrict its domain to allow only one solution. The most natural solution to choose is x_0 and hence we define the **inverse sine function** $y = \sin^{-1} x$ as follows.

Frame 2.1   *The inverse sine function*

$$y = \sin^{-1} x \quad \text{where} \quad \sin y = x \quad \text{and} \quad -\frac{\pi}{2} \leqslant y \leqslant \frac{\pi}{2}, \ (-1 \leqslant x \leqslant 1)$$

$$(2.1)$$

The method for finding the graph of any inverse function is to reflect the original graph in the line $y = x$. This produces the graph shown below. Note that the domain is only $[-1, 1]$, since $|\sin x| \leqslant 1$ for all x.

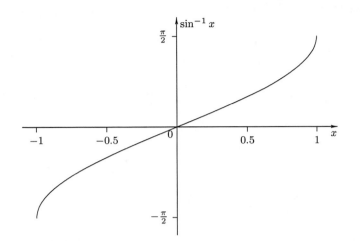

A similar consideration of the graph of $\cos x$ shows that the domain should be restricted to $[0, \pi]$ and that this will be the range of values for the inverse function $y = \cos^{-1} x$, defined as follows.

Frame 2.2   *The inverse cosine function*

$$y = \cos^{-1} x \quad \text{where} \quad \cos y = x \quad \text{and} \quad 0 \leqslant y \leqslant \pi, \quad (-1 \leqslant x \leqslant 1)$$
$$(2.2)$$

This function is less important, for our purposes, especially since it has a simple link with $\sin^{-1} x$.

Example 2.1   Find a link between the inverses of sin and cos.

Let $y = \cos^{-1} x$, so that $\cos y = x$. Using **complementary angles**, $\sin\left(\frac{\pi}{2} - y\right) = x$, which *suggests* that $\frac{\pi}{2} - y = \sin^{-1} x$. This rearranges as

$$(y =) \cos^{-1} x = \frac{\pi}{2} - \sin^{-1} x.$$

To confirm this we must check that we have used the correct range of values when using $\sin^{-1} x$.

$\frac{\pi}{2} - \sin^{-1} x$ takes values from

$$\tfrac{\pi}{2} - \left(-\tfrac{\pi}{2}\right) \quad \text{to} \quad \tfrac{\pi}{2} - \left(\tfrac{\pi}{2}\right),$$

i.e., from π to 0, exactly as required for $\cos^{-1} x$.   ■

More important is the function $y = \tan^{-1} x$. The following graphs reveal a similar situation to the sin case, in spite of the discontinuities.

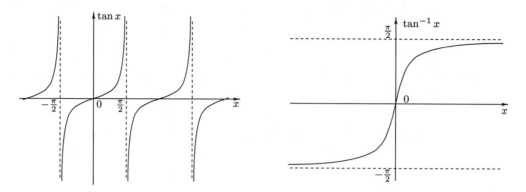

We restrict the original graph to a similar interval as that for sin, i.e., $\left(-\frac{\pi}{2}, \frac{\pi}{2}\right)$, defining the inverse tan function as follows.

Frame 2.3   *The inverse tangent function*

$$y = \tan^{-1} x \quad \text{where} \quad \tan y = x \quad \textbf{and} \quad -\frac{\pi}{2} < y < \frac{\pi}{2}, \quad (x \text{ in } \mathbb{R})$$
$$(2.3)$$

Think about it like this

We have reflected only the part of the $\tan x$ graph containing the origin. If we reflected the entire graph we would get a vertical stack of such curves, producing an infinite number of values of the function. The one we have used generates what is sometimes known as the **principal value**.

These are not the only possible conventions for restricting the domains to produce one-one functions, but there is common agreement and so they are universally used. Thus, values given by calculators conform to them.

The following show how to solve equations of the form $\sin x = c$, etc.

Frame 2.4   *Solving trigonometric equations $\sin x = c$*

If $c > 1$ or $c < -1$ there is no solution

Otherwise, find one solution: $x = \sin^{-1} c$

A second solution is $\pi - x$ (supplementary angles)

All other solutions differ from these two by multiples of 2π

Frame 2.5   *Solving trigonometric equations $\cos x = c$*

If $c > 1$ or $c < -1$ there is no solution

Otherwise, find one solution: $x = \cos^{-1} c$

A second solution is $-x$ (evenness of cos)

All other solutions differ from these two by multiples of 2π

Frame 2.6   *Solving trigonometric equations* $\tan x = c$

Find one solution: $x = \tan^{-1} c$

All other solutions differ from x by multiples of π

Example 2.2   Evaluate   (a) $\tan^{-1} 1$,   (b) $\sin^{-1} \frac{1}{2}$,   (c) $\cos^{-1}(-0.2)$.
Find all solutions for each of $\tan x = 1$, $\sin x = \frac{1}{2}$, $\cos x = -0.2$.

(a) Let $y = \tan^{-1} 1$, so that $\tan y = 1$. One solution is $y = \frac{\pi}{4}$, which is already in the correct range for y, so $\tan^{-1} 1 = \frac{\pi}{4}$.

All solutions of $\tan x = 1$ differ from $\tan^{-1} 1$ by a multiple of π, so

$$x = \tfrac{\pi}{4} + n\pi \quad (n \text{ in } \mathbb{Z}).$$

(b) Solve $\sin y = \frac{1}{2}$. One solution is $y = \frac{\pi}{6}$, which is already in the correct range for y, so $\sin^{-1} \frac{1}{2} = \frac{\pi}{6}$.

Firstly, find a second solution. Since $\sin(\pi - y) = \sin y$, this can be chosen as $\pi - \frac{\pi}{6} = \frac{5\pi}{6}$. Hence all solutions have one or other of the forms

$$x = \tfrac{\pi}{6} + 2n\pi \quad \text{and} \quad x = \tfrac{5\pi}{6} + 2n\pi \quad (n \text{ in } \mathbb{Z}).$$

(c) In this case, -0.2 is not a special value of cos, so we must use a calculator. Setting it to radians, and evaluating $\cos^{-1}$ for input `-0.2` gives $\cos^{-1}(-0.2) = 1.7722$, to 4 dp.

A second solution is found from $\cos(-y) = \cos y$. Choose -1.7722. Hence all solutions have one or other of the forms

$$x = 1.7722 + 2n\pi \quad \text{and} \quad x = -1.7722 + 2n\pi, \quad (n \text{ in } \mathbb{Z}).$$

■

Notation

It is worth repeating that the superscript '-1' is attached to f, not to $f(x)$. Do not confuse **inverse** with **reciprocal**. For example,

$$\sin^{-1} x \neq \frac{1}{\sin x} \quad \left(\text{written } (\sin x)^{-1}\right).$$

This possible confusion arises because '-1' is used in two different senses: to reciprocate a number, as in $(\sin x)^{-1}$ and to invert a function or operation, as in $\sin^{-1} x$ or A^{-1} (where A is a matrix). To avoid this confusion, ask what '-1' is attached to: if it is a symbol representing a number then it is reciprocation; if it is a symbol representing a function or an operator, it is inversion.

There is another way in which confusion may be avoided in the trigonometric function case and that is to use the alternative notation: $\arcsin x$, etc., which is somewhat old-fashioned. (It persists in computer programming for typographical reasons; there you will find `ARCSIN(x)` or `ASIN(x)` in use.)

In calculus, these functions rarely encounter the circular functions from which they are generated. But when they do, care is needed because of the ranges.

Example 2.3 Calculate $\tan\left(\tan^{-1} x\right)$ and $\tan^{-1}\left(\tan x\right)$.

Let $y = \tan^{-1} x$, so $\tan y = x$. Replacing y in this gives $\tan\left(\tan^{-1} x\right) = x$, *always*.

But the second case may differ from x. For example, choose $x = \pi$. Then $\tan x = 0$ and $\tan^{-1} 0 = 0$, *NOT* π. The problem is that we have started on the portion of the $\tan x$ graph around $x = \pi$, moved to the inverse function's graph, then back to the portion around the origin.

We can, however, state that $\tan^{-1}\left(\tan x\right) = x$, for x in $\left(-\frac{\pi}{2}, \frac{\pi}{2}\right)$. ∎

Ex 2.1

(a) Evaluate exactly $\sin^{-1}(0.5)$, and hence find both solutions of the equation $\sin x = 0.5$ in $-\pi < x < \pi$.

(b) Use a calculator to find both solutions of the equation $\sin x = 0.2$ in $-\pi < x < \pi$.

Ex 2.2 Show that, for $x > 0$, $\tan^{-1} x = \sin^{-1}\left(\dfrac{x}{\sqrt{1 + x^2}}\right)$.

(Hint: draw a right-angled triangle with sides x and 1.)

Is this result also true for $x \leqslant 0$?

Ex 2.3 *This question, for convenience, is phrased in degrees. The nature of the results also holds good for radian measure.*

Evaluate, in degrees, $\sin^{-1}(\sin x)$, for

$$x = 0,\ 30,\ 60,\ 90,\ 120,\ 180,\ 240,\ 270,\ 360,\ 450,\ 540,\ 630,\ 720.$$

Explain the results.

Draw a graph of this function for x in $[-360, 360]$.

2.2 Calculus Results

Inverting the trigonometric functions has produced 'new' functions. They are useful in solving trigonometric equations but, **for calculus their importance lies in the standard forms for integration that we obtain by reversing their derivatives.** We shall concentrate on sin and tan only, since the inverse cos occurs only rarely and, using Example 2.1, can be written in terms of the inverse sin.

In using these functions for integration, it is essential that all values are expressed using radian measure, since the calculus used to derive them relies on that measure.

First consider the derivative of the **inverse tan**. Although only the result is required, the application of the **inverse function rule** is informative. We also need one of the 'Pythagorean' identities.

$$y = \tan^{-1} x \quad \Rightarrow \quad x = \tan y \quad \Rightarrow \quad \frac{dx}{dy} = \sec^2 y = 1 + \tan^2 y = 1 + x^2.$$

Taking the reciprocal, we obtain $\frac{dy}{dx}$.

Frame 2.7   *Derivative of the inverse tan function*

$$\frac{d}{dx}\left[\tan^{-1} x\right] = \frac{1}{1 + x^2} \tag{2.4}$$

Example 2.4   Differentiate $\tan^{-1} 2x$.

Use the linear composite rule, $ax + b \equiv 2x + 0$. The derivative is

$$\frac{1}{(2x)^2 + 1} \times 2 = \frac{2}{4x^2 + 1}.$$

∎

Reversing (2.4) gives one of the standard integrals we seek:

$$\int \frac{1}{1 + x^2}\, dx = \tan^{-1} x + C. \tag{2.5}$$

This is not quite a convenient 'standard form'; we need one that is a little more flexible. Consider, then, the differentiation of $\tan^{-1} \frac{x}{a}$, using the linear composite rule:

$$\begin{aligned}
\frac{d}{dx}\left[\tan^{-1} \frac{x}{a}\right] &= \frac{1}{\left(\frac{x}{a}\right)^2 + 1} \times \frac{1}{a} \\
&= \frac{1}{\left(\frac{x}{a}\right)^2 + 1} \times \frac{a}{a^2} \\
&= \frac{a}{x^2 + a^2}.
\end{aligned}$$

Divide throughout by a factor of a and reverse the result to obtain the more useful form.

Frame 2.8   *Integration using the inverse tan*

$$\int \frac{1}{x^2 + a^2}\, dx = \frac{1}{a}\tan^{-1} \frac{x}{a} + C \tag{2.6}$$

Example 2.5   Evaluate (a) $\displaystyle\int_0^2 \frac{dx}{4 + x^2}$, (b) $\displaystyle\int \frac{dx}{2x^2 + 1}$.

(a) This is in standard form:

$$I = \left[\frac{1}{2}\tan^{-1} \frac{x}{2}\right]_0^2 = \frac{1}{2}\tan^{-1} 1 - \frac{1}{2}\tan^{-1} 0 = \frac{1}{2}\cdot\frac{\pi}{4} - 0 = \frac{\pi}{8}.$$

Note the use of radian measure! If the answer is quoted in degrees it bears no resemblance to the size of the area represented by this integral.

(b) Write $2x^2 = \left(\sqrt{2}x\right)^2$. Then use the linear composite rule, $ax + b \equiv \sqrt{2}x + 0$:

$$I = \left(\tan^{-1}\sqrt{2}x\right) \div \sqrt{2} + C = \frac{1}{\sqrt{2}}\tan^{-1}\sqrt{2}x + C.$$

■

Example 2.6   Differentiate and integrate $\dfrac{\tan^{-1}x}{1+x^2}$.

For **differentiation**, use the Quotient Rule:

$$u = \tan^{-1}x, \qquad u' = \frac{1}{1+x^2},$$
$$v = 1+x^2, \qquad v' = 2x.$$

$$\frac{dy}{dx} = \frac{(1+x^2)\frac{1}{1+x^2} - 2x\tan^{-1}x}{(1+x^2)^2} = \frac{1 - 2x\tan^{-1}x}{(1+x^2)^2}.$$

For **integration**, note the presence of

$$\frac{d}{dx}\left[\tan^{-1}x\right] = \frac{1}{1+x^2}.$$

Set $u = \tan^{-1}x$ and then use 'substitution', with $\frac{du}{dx} = \frac{1}{1+x^2}$:

$$I = \int u\frac{du}{dx}\,dx = \int u\,du$$
$$= \frac{1}{2}u^2 + C = \frac{1}{2}\left(\tan^{-1}x\right)^2 + C.$$

■

We treat the differentiation of the **inverse sin** similarly.

$$y = \sin^{-1}x \quad \Rightarrow \quad x = \sin y \quad \Rightarrow \quad \frac{dx}{dy} = \cos y = \sqrt{1 - \sin^2 y} = \sqrt{1 - x^2}.$$

Taking the reciprocal, we have the derivative we seek.

Frame 2.9   *Derivative of the inverse sin function*

$$\frac{d}{dx}\left[\sin^{-1}x\right] = \frac{1}{\sqrt{1 - x^2}} \qquad\qquad (2.7)$$

This can be reversed to give a useful integral:

$$\int \frac{1}{\sqrt{1 - x^2}}\,dx = \sin^{-1}x + C. \qquad\qquad (2.8)$$

There is one detail that did not arise in the inverse tan case. When expressing $\cos y$ in terms of $\sin y$, we took a square root and implicitly assumed that the positive version was appropriate. This is seen to be correct by examining the graph of $\sin^{-1} x$ in §2.1, which shows a **positive** gradient everywhere.

This detail is important since the equivalent differentiation for $\cos^{-1} x$ requires the choice of the *negative* square root. This is confirmed by differentiating the result of Example 2.1:

$$\frac{d}{dx}\left[\cos^{-1} x\right] = \frac{d}{dx}\left[\frac{\pi}{2} - \sin^{-1} x\right] = -\frac{1}{\sqrt{1 - x^2}}.$$

The result in (2.8) is not quite general enough to be a convenient 'standard form'. Consider, then, the differentiation of $\sin^{-1}\frac{x}{a}$, using the linear composite rule.

$$\frac{d}{dx}\left[\sin^{-1}\frac{x}{a}\right] = \frac{1}{\sqrt{1 - \left(\frac{x}{a}\right)^2}} \times \frac{1}{a}$$

$$= \frac{1}{\sqrt{a^2\left[1 - \left(\frac{x}{a}\right)^2\right]}}$$

$$= \frac{1}{\sqrt{a^2 - x^2}}.$$

This reverses to give the form we seek.

Frame 2.10   *Integration using the inverse sin*

$$\int \frac{1}{\sqrt{a^2 - x^2}}\, dx = \sin^{-1}\frac{x}{a} + C \qquad (2.9)$$

Think about it like this

Note an important difference between the standard forms in Frames 2.8 and 2.10: there is a factor $\frac{1}{a}$ in the first but not the second. This is related to *dimensionality*. Suppose that x and a are lengths, with dimension L. Then $\frac{1}{x^2+a^2}$ has dimension L^{-2}, while dx has dimension L. Hence the integral has overall dimension $L^{-2}L = L^{-1}$, which is the same as $\frac{1}{a}$; the inverse tan is a pure number.

In the other case, the square root means the integrand has dimension L^{-1} and so the integral has overall dimension $L^{-1}L$, i.e., that of a pure number; the inverse sin is a pure number.

Example 2.7   Integrate   (a) $\dfrac{1}{\sqrt{4-x^2}}$,   (b) $\dfrac{1}{\sqrt{9-4x^2}}$.

(a) This is a direct use of the standard form with $a^2 = 4$:

$$I = \sin^{-1}\frac{x}{2} + C.$$

(b) This is similar but first write $4x^2 = (2x)^2$ and then use the linear composite rule, dividing by 2:

$$I = \frac{1}{2}\sin^{-1}\frac{2x}{3} + C,$$

(where the 'a' involved is 3).

∎

Ex 2.4

(a) Differentiate: i. $\sin^{-1} 3x$,   ii. $\tan^{-1}\frac{x}{2}$.

(b) Integrate: i. $\dfrac{1}{x^2+9}$,   ii. $\dfrac{1}{\sqrt{2-x^2}}$.

Ex 2.5 Differentiate the following:
   (a) $\tan^{-1} 2x$,   (b) $\sin^{-1}(x^2)$,   (c) $x^2 \tan^{-1} x$.

Ex 2.6 Evaluate $\displaystyle\int_0^{0.1} \frac{1}{\sqrt{1-25x^2}}\, dx$.

2.3   Quadratic Denominators: Constant Numerators

At this stage in integration technique, it becomes common to refer to published tables of **standard forms**, choosing the appropriate formula and adapting it to the integral to be evaluated. We shall therefore concentrate on how to make such adaptations.

Consider the integration of

$$\frac{1}{\alpha x^2 + \beta x + \gamma} \quad \text{or} \quad \frac{1}{\sqrt{\alpha x^2 + \beta x + \gamma}}.$$

We start with the special case where $\beta = 0$, i.e., there is no 'middle' term. We can also simplify to $\alpha = \pm 1$. It will turn out that there is a great difference in behaviour according to whether $\alpha\gamma > 0$ or < 0. All of this can be encapsulated by writing the quadratic as either

$$a^2 + x^2 \quad \text{or} \quad a^2 - x^2 \quad \text{or} \quad x^2 - a^2.$$

> *Think about it like this*
>
> First of all, if α is not ± 1, we can either extract $|\alpha|$ as a common factor from the integrand, or write the squared term as $\pm\left(\sqrt{|\alpha|}\,x\right)^2$ and use the linear composite rule.
>
> The two forms $x^2 - a^2$ and $a^2 - x^2$ appear similar, but we need to make the distinction when a square root is involved, as we see in the Frame below.

When there is no square root involved, the two cases are easily dealt with. For $a^2 - x^2$ we can use **partial fractions**, although there *may* be advantages in using an inverse hyperbolic function, as set out below. For $a^2 + x^2$, we use (2.6).

For the square root case, we already have (2.9) as one standard form. The other two integrals use inverse hyperbolic functions. The full set is as follows.

Frame 2.11   *Integration for quadratic denominators*

$$\int \frac{dx}{a^2 + x^2} = \frac{1}{a} \tan^{-1} \frac{x}{a} + C \qquad (2.10)$$

$$\int \frac{dx}{a^2 - x^2} = \frac{1}{a} \tanh^{-1} \frac{x}{a} + C \qquad (2.11)$$

$$\int \frac{dx}{\sqrt{a^2 - x^2}} = \sin^{-1} \frac{x}{a} + C \qquad (2.12)$$

$$\int \frac{dx}{\sqrt{x^2 + a^2}} = \sinh^{-1} \frac{x}{a} + C \qquad (2.13)$$

$$\int \frac{dx}{\sqrt{x^2 - a^2}} = \cosh^{-1} \frac{x}{a} + C \qquad (2.14)$$

Think about it like this

You may wonder why there are not four cases to be considered when there is a square root. The missing case involves $\sqrt{-a^2 - x^2}$, which does not exist.

Before looking at examples, we first check the sinh result (2.13); the other two hyperbolic results can be checked similarly.

Example 2.8   Differentiate $\ln\left(x + \sqrt{x^2 + 1}\right)$.

This requires application of the **chain rule**, twice. The function can be broken down into

$$y = \ln u, \quad u = x + \sqrt{x^2 + 1} = x + v, \quad v = \sqrt{w}, \quad w = x^2 + 1.$$

The required derivatives are

$$\frac{dy}{du} = \frac{1}{u}, \quad \frac{du}{dx} = 1 + \frac{dv}{dx}, \quad \frac{dv}{dw} = \frac{1}{2\sqrt{w}}, \quad \frac{dw}{dx} = 2x,$$

which can be brought together to give

$$\frac{dy}{dx} = \frac{1}{u}\left[1 + \frac{x}{\sqrt{w}}\right] = \frac{1}{u}\left[1 + \frac{x}{\sqrt{x^2 + 1}}\right]$$

$$= \frac{1}{u}\frac{\sqrt{x^2 + 1} + x}{\sqrt{x^2 + 1}} = \frac{1}{\sqrt{x^2 + 1}}.$$

∎

The function in this example is the alternative expression for $\sinh^{-1} x$. Hence, reading the result backwards gives (2.13) when $a = 1$. More general values of a are treated as in the previous section: we can confirm the full version of (2.13) by differentiation using the linear composite rule.

Notation

Some tables of integrals may use the log versions directly. In practice it depends on the next step. If some algebraic manipulation is required, either version may be better. But if a number, via a definite integral, is required, the hyperbolic version will be quicker, assuming one's calculator or computer offers these functions.

Example 2.9   Evaluate $\displaystyle\int_0^1 \frac{dx}{\sqrt{x^2 + 16}}$.
Use (2.13) with $a = \sqrt{16} = 4$:

$$I = \left[\sinh^{-1} \frac{x}{4}\right]_0^1 = \sinh^{-1} \frac{1}{4} - \sinh^{-1} 0 \simeq 0.2475,$$

on using a calculator and noting $\sinh^{-1} 0 = 0$.
This is the same value as $\ln\left(0.25 + \sqrt{0.25^2 + 1}\right)$.   ∎

Example 2.10   Evaluate $\displaystyle\int_1^2 \frac{dx}{\sqrt{3x^2 - 1}}$.

Use (2.14) with $a = 1$, also writing $3x^2 = \left(\sqrt{3}x\right)^2$ and using the linear composite rule:

$$I = \left[\frac{1}{\sqrt{3}} \cosh^{-1}\left(\sqrt{3}x\right)\right]_1^2$$

$$= \frac{1}{\sqrt{3}}\left[\cosh^{-1}\left(2\sqrt{3}\right) - \cosh^{-1}\left(\sqrt{3}\right)\right] \simeq 0.4433.$$

∎

Think about it like this

When using a table of standard integrals it is essential to double-check that the correct choice is being made. It is impossible to get sensible results through, for example, trying to force the inverse sin formula to fit a problem that requires the inverse cosh: $\sqrt{a^2 - x^2}$ and $\sqrt{x^2 - a^2}$ are very different functions in calculus.

Now consider more general quadratics, those with a non-zero 'middle' term. We start without the square root.

If we can factorise the denominator, we can use **partial fractions**. Otherwise – when the quadratic is **irreducible** – we must apply **completing the square**. We can then complete the integration using (2.10) and the linear composite rule. This is best seen by means of an example.

Example 2.11   Integrate $\displaystyle\frac{1}{x^2 - 8x + 25}$.
Complete the square:

$$x^2 - 8x + 25 = (x - 4)^2 - 16 + 25 = (x - 4)^2 + 9.$$

Use the linear composite rule, $ax + b \equiv x - 4$, with an 'invisible' division by 1:

$$I = \int \frac{dx}{(x-4)^2 + 3^2} = \frac{1}{3}\tan^{-1}\frac{x-4}{3} + C.$$

If we change the constant term to 12, say, we find

$$x^2 - 8x + 12 = (x-4)^2 - 16 + 12 = (x-4)^2 - 4.$$

The minus sign is critical: we cannot use the $\tan^{-1}$ form. We could turn it round to $-[4 - (x-4)^2]$ and use (2.11), but it is simpler to use **partial fractions** directly. The quadratic can be factorised and we eventually find

$$\frac{1}{x^2 - 8x + 12} = \frac{1}{4}\left[\frac{1}{x-6} - \frac{1}{x-2}\right],$$

for which the integration is very straightforward. ∎

The same approach allows us to integrate square roots of quadratics.

Example 2.12 Integrate $\dfrac{1}{\sqrt{12 - 4x - x^2}}$ from 0 to 1.

Complete the square:

$$12 - 4x - x^2 = -\left(x^2 + 4x - 12\right) = -\left[(x+2)^2 - 4 - 12\right] = 16 - (x+2)^2.$$

Then, using the linear composite rule,

$$I = \int_0^1 \frac{dx}{\sqrt{4^2 - (x+2)^2}} = \left[\sin^{-1}\frac{x+2}{4}\right]_0^1$$

$$= \sin^{-1}\frac{3}{4} - \sin^{-1}\frac{1}{2} \simeq 0.8481 - \frac{\pi}{6} \simeq 0.3245.$$

∎

Example 2.13 Integrate $\dfrac{1}{\sqrt{6x - x^2}}$.

First of all, this *cannot* be done by using (2.12) with $a^2 = 6x$, since a must be *constant*. Instead, complete the square:

$$6x - x^2 = -\left[x^2 - 6x\right] = -\left[(x-3)^2 - 9\right] = 9 - (x-3)^2.$$

Now we can use (2.12) with $a^2 = 9$:

$$\int \frac{dx}{\sqrt{3^2 - (x-3)^2}} = \sin^{-1}\left(\frac{x-3}{3}\right) + C.$$

∎

Think about it like this

In this inverse sin case, should we find that the constant term becomes negative, in addition to the term in $-(x-\alpha)^2$, the entire quadratic can take only negative values, the square root fails and the problem is not valid!

We finish with an example involving an inverse hyperbolic function.

Example 2.14 Integrate the reciprocal of $\sqrt{x^2 + 2x + 5}$.

Start by completing the square: $x^2 + 2x + 5 = (x+1)^2 + 4$. Hence

$$\int \frac{dx}{\sqrt{x^2 + 2x + 5}} = \int \frac{dx}{\sqrt{(x+1)^2 + 2^2}} = \sinh^{-1}\left(\frac{x+1}{2}\right) + C.$$

■

Ex 2.7 Evaluate the following integrals:

(a) $\displaystyle\int_0^1 \frac{dx}{\sqrt{x^2 + 4}}$,   (a) $\displaystyle\int_5^{10} \frac{dx}{\sqrt{x^2 - 9}}$,   (c) $\displaystyle\int_0^1 \frac{dx}{\sqrt{4x^2 + 9}}$,   (d) $\displaystyle\int_1^2 \frac{dx}{\sqrt{9x^2 - 1}}$.

Ex 2.8 Evaluate the following integrals:

(a) $\displaystyle\int \frac{dx}{\sqrt{6x - x^2}}$, (b) $\displaystyle\int \frac{dx}{\sqrt{1 - 2x - x^2}}$, (c) $\displaystyle\int \frac{dx}{\sqrt{x(1 - x)}}$, (d) $\displaystyle\int_2^6 \frac{dx}{x^2 - 4x + 20}$.

2.4 Quadratic Denominators: Linear Numerators

The integration of a **rational function** – the ratio of two polynomials – is usually tackled by breaking the fraction into **partial fractions**, possibly after an initial division. The case where the denominator can be factorised into **linear factors** has already been illustrated in Example 2.11. When this is extended to deal with **irreducible** quadratic factors, new partial fractions arise, with the form:

$$\frac{Ax + B}{ax^2 + bx + c}. \tag{2.15}$$

Although the method for generating such terms is not covered here, we shall set out to integrate them.

We therefore assume that $ax^2 + bx + c$ is irreducible, which will be an essential feature of the method. We also usually have $a = 1$, since otherwise we can divide all terms – in the numerator and denominator – by a.

Such functions are integrated by **rearrangement**. They can always be split into two parts, each of which we integrate separately.

The basic idea is shown in the following example, which is simpler than the general situation since there is no 'middle' term in the denominator.

Example 2.15 Integrate $\dfrac{3x + 2}{x^2 + 9}$.

Split this into two fractions, at the '+' on the top line:

$$\int \frac{3x + 2}{x^2 + 9}\,dx = \int \left[\frac{3x}{x^2 + 9} + \frac{2}{x^2 + 9}\right] dx$$

$$= \frac{3}{2} \int \frac{2x}{x^2 + 9}\,dx + 2 \int \frac{1}{x^2 + 9}\,dx$$

$$= \frac{3}{2} \ln(x^2 + 9) + \frac{2}{3} \tan^{-1}\frac{x}{3} + C,$$

where we have used a simple substitution rule for the first integral, and (2.10) for the second. ∎

The general case is very similar, but the break in the top line is not at the '+'. This is because the x part needs to 'borrow' some of the constant term, to achieve the simple substitution form. Consider the following example.

Example 2.16 Integrate $\dfrac{2x - 3}{x^2 - 8x + 25}$.

Firstly, note that $\frac{d}{dx}\left[x^2 - 8x + 25\right] = 2x - 8$. Rewrite the numerator, absorbing all the x parts into a '$2x - 8$' term: $2x - 3 \equiv (2x - 8) + 5$. Hence

$$\frac{2x - 3}{x^2 - 8x + 25} = \frac{2x - 8}{x^2 - 8x + 25} + \frac{5}{x^2 - 8x + 25}$$

and the integral is

$$\ln(x^2 - 8x + 25) + \frac{5}{3}\tan^{-1}\left(\frac{x - 4}{3}\right) + C,$$

on reusing the result of Example 2.11 for the second part. ∎

Think about it like this

In the previous two examples we have omitted the absolute value in the log terms, e.g., writing $\ln(x^2 + 9)$. This is because the quadratics are **irreducible**, hence their graphs do not cross the x-axis and they do not change sign. They must be permanently positive or negative; in these cases they are clearly positive.

It is always possible to rearrange the numerator of (2.15) in the desired form. The following calculation shows this and is also helpful in cases that are more complicated than the previous example, when the rearrangement of the top line is not quite so easy to see.

We require $Ax + B \equiv p(2x + b) + q$ for some p and q. Hence $A = 2p$ and $B = pb + q$, giving $p = \frac{A}{2}$, $q = B - \frac{Ab}{2}$. This calculation is usually carried out whenever it is required, rather than by quoting and using these formulae.

Example 2.17 Integrate $\dfrac{5x - 13}{x^2 - 8x + 25}$.

We wish to construct an integral using $(2x - 8)/(x^2 - 8x + 25)$, as in the previous example. Let

$$5x - 13 \equiv p(2x - 8) + q \quad \Rightarrow \quad 5x - 13 \equiv 2px + (q - 8p).$$

Matching the terms gives: $2p = 5$ and $q - 8p = -13$, so $p = \frac{5}{2}$ and $q = 7$. Hence

$$I = \frac{5}{2}\int \frac{2x - 8}{x^2 - 8x + 25}\,dx + 7\int \frac{dx}{x^2 - 8x + 25}$$
$$= \frac{5}{2}\ln(x^2 - 8x + 25) + \frac{7}{3}\tan^{-1}\left(\frac{x - 4}{3}\right) + C.$$

∎

A similar method can be used when there is a square root on the bottom line. The only real difference is that a less easy substitution is required: $u = x^2 + bx + c$ leads to $\int (1/\sqrt{u})\, du$.

Example 2.18   Integrate:

$$\text{(a)}\ \ \frac{5 - 6x}{\sqrt{1 - x^2}},\quad \text{(b)}\ \ \frac{3x + 2}{\sqrt{25 - 4x^2}},\quad \text{(c)}\ \ \frac{3 - 2x}{\sqrt{7 - 6x - x^2}}.$$

(a) As in the previous case, when there is no 'middle' term a simple break on the top line can be used:

$$I = 5 \int \frac{1}{\sqrt{1 - x^2}}\, dx + 3 \int \frac{-2x}{\sqrt{1 - x^2}}\, dx.$$

The x in the numerator has been left with a coefficient of -2, anticipating the substitution $u = 1 - x^2$, where $\frac{du}{dx} = -2x$. Noting that the first integral can be written down using (2.12),

$$I = 5 \sin^{-1} x + 3 \int \frac{1}{\sqrt{u}}\, du = 5 \sin^{-1} x + 6\sqrt{u} + C$$

$$= 5 \sin^{-1} x + 6\sqrt{1 - x^2} + C.$$

(b) Again, break this at the '+', this time leaving the top of the second integral as a multiple of $-8x$, the derivative of $u = 25 - 4x^2$:

$$I = 2 \int \frac{dx}{\sqrt{25 - 4x^2}} - \frac{3}{8} \int \frac{-8x}{\sqrt{25 - 4x^2}}\, dx$$

$$= 2 \int \frac{dx}{\sqrt{5^2 - (2x)^2}} - \frac{3}{8} \int \frac{1}{\sqrt{u}}\, du$$

$$= \frac{2}{2} \sin^{-1} \frac{2x}{5} - \frac{3}{4}\sqrt{u} + C$$

$$= \sin^{-1} \frac{2x}{5} - \frac{3}{4}\sqrt{25 - 4x^2} + C.$$

(c) This requires a more complicated split on the top line. We are aiming for a substitution $u = 7 - 6x - x^2$, where $\frac{du}{dx} = -6 - 2x$. Hence write $3 - 2x \equiv 9 + (-6 - 2x)$; also complete the square $7 - 6x - x^2 = 16 - (x + 3)^2$. Putting this all together we have

$$I = 9 \int \frac{dx}{\sqrt{7 - 6x - x^2}} + \int \frac{-6 - 2x}{\sqrt{7 - 6x - x^2}}\, dx$$

$$= 9 \int \frac{dx}{\sqrt{16 - (x + 3)^2}} + \int \frac{1}{\sqrt{u}}\, du$$

$$= 9 \sin^{-1} \left(\frac{x + 3}{4} \right) + 2\sqrt{7 - 6x - x^2} + C.$$

■

Ex 2.9 Evaluate the following integrals:

(a) $\displaystyle\int \frac{x+1}{x^2+4}\,dx,$ (b) $\displaystyle\int \frac{1-2x}{\sqrt{1-x^2}}\,dx,$ (c) $\displaystyle\int \frac{x-1}{4x^2+1}\,dx,$ (d) $\displaystyle\int \frac{x-3}{\sqrt{9-x^2}}\,dx.$

Ex 2.10 Evaluate the following integrals:

(a) $\displaystyle\int \frac{5x+3}{x^2+2x+5}\,dx,$ (b) $\displaystyle\int \frac{4x+1}{\sqrt{5+4x-x^2}}\,dx,$ (c) $\displaystyle\int \frac{x}{x^2+2x+10}\,dx.$

2.5 Revision Exercises

Ex 2.11

(a) Find, **exactly**, both solutions of $\sin x = -\frac{1}{\sqrt{2}}$, where x is an angle (in radians) in the interval $-\pi < x \leqslant \pi$.

(b) Find, correct to four decimal places, both solutions of $\tan x = 1.2$, where x is an angle (in radians) in the interval $-\pi < x \leqslant \pi$.

Ex 2.12 Evaluate

$$\int_1^6 \frac{dx}{x^2-2x+26},$$

expressing your answer as an **exact** number.

Ex 2.13 Find A and B such that

$$6x - 1 \equiv A(2x - 2) + B;$$

hence integrate, with respect to x,

$$\frac{6x-1}{x^2-2x+17}.$$

Ex 2.14 Integrate $\dfrac{1-4x}{\sqrt{4-x^2}}$ with respect to x.

3   INTEGRATION BY PARTS

This chapter addresses one technique: the last of the basic 'Rules of Calculus'. The rule defines a method known as: **integration by parts**, which enables us to integrate *some* functions that are products of two simpler functions.

The method is a powerful one, but its scope is much more limited than it may appear. This often leads people to try to use it when it simply cannot work. There is also a key choice to be made when applying it, which also needs care since the wrong choice will merely make the original problem worse.

3.1   Integration by Parts

The *Product Rule* ensures we can differentiate any given product, provided we can differentiate its component functions. Unfortunately, there is no equivalent rule for integration that is *guaranteed* to integrate a product; in fact, many products have no anti-derivative.

Applying the **Fundamental Theorem of Calculus** to the **Product Rule** removes the derivative on the left and places integrals in each term on the right:

$$u(x)v(x) = \int u(x)v'(x)\,dx + \int u'(x)v(x)\,dx. \qquad (3.1)$$

This contains **two** integrals, not one, which is why the method often won't work. It is sometimes the case, however, that *one* of these integrals can be evaluated in some way. Then (3.1) provides the value of the other. This formula, rearranged to emphasise the way it is used, is the basis of the following new rule: **integration by parts**, sometimes referred to as just '**parts**'. There are two (equivalent) ways in which to write it.

Frame 3.1   Integration by parts

$$\int u(x)v'(x)\,dx = u(x)v(x) - \int u'(x)v(x)\,dx \qquad (3.2)$$

$$\int u\frac{dv}{dx}\,dx = uv - \int \frac{du}{dx}v\,dx \qquad (3.3)$$

With the exception of a few special applications, its use is reserved for products where one component is a low degree polynomial, such as x^2 in $x^2\cos x$. If that component is identified with $u(x)$ on the left, then it will generate $u'(x)$, which is one degree lower, on the right. Hence some simplification has been achieved. But this choice requires us to be able to change the other component from $v'(x)$ on the left to $v(x)$ on the right. That integration (or anti-differentiation) **may not be possible**.

Example 3.1 Evaluate $\int x \cos x \, dx$.

Aiming to differentiate 'x', choose

$$u = x, \qquad v' = \cos x,$$

then

$$u' = 1, \qquad v = \sin x.$$

Frame 3.1 gives,

$$I = x \sin x - \int 1 \times \sin x \, dx$$

$$= x \sin x - \int \sin x \, dx$$

$$= x \sin x - (-\cos x) + C$$

$$= x \sin x + \cos x + C.$$

∎

Think about it like this

The order of terms in the integrand may not correspond to the order in $u(x)v'(x)$, although it did so here. There is no serious problem if it doesn't, since we can rewrite this term as $v'(x)u(x)$; you merely have to decide for yourself which term you wish to use for $u(x)$ and which for $v'(x)$.

The version in Frame 3.1, however, has been chosen to correspond to the order for the most common type of integral for which the rule is used. The order may have to be reversed for some of the more unusual cases illustrated later.

Example 3.2 Integrate $(2x - 1)e^x$.

Again, we aim to differentiate the polynomial, choosing

$$u = 2x - 1, \qquad v' = e^x,$$

then

$$u' = 2, \qquad\qquad v = e^x.$$

Frame 3.1 gives,

$$I = (2x - 1)e^x - \int 2e^x \, dx$$

$$= (2x - 1)e^x - 2e^x + C = (2x - 3)e^x + C.$$

∎

Think about it like this

Note how, in this example, u was taken to correspond to a polynomial with more than one term. Some people would split this integral up at the start, to $\int 2xe^x \, dx - \int e^x \, dx$, but there is no gain in doing that. Indeed, it often makes the calculation longer.

Integration by parts may require several applications, reducing the degree of the polynomial by one each time, until it becomes a constant and thus effectively disappears, leaving an integrand that is *not* a product, which we hope can be integrated by some other method.

Example 3.3   Evaluate $\int x^2 \sin x \, dx$.

We aim to differentiate 'x^2', so use

$$u = x^2, \qquad\qquad v' = \sin x,$$

then

$$u' = 2x, \qquad\qquad v = -\cos x.$$

Using Frame 3.1,

$$I = -x^2 \cos x - \int -2x \cos x \, dx$$

$$= -x^2 \cos x + 2 \int x \cos x \, dx$$

$$= -x^2 \cos x + 2x \sin x + 2 \cos x + C,$$

on using the result of Example 3.1 for the new integral. By reusing the previous result we have disguised the fact that there were **two** applications of the rule used here.   ∎

Although calculation using $u(x)$ as a polynomial is the most common, there are some other procedures. One of them involves a product in which one function is difficult to deal with but has a simple derivative, e.g., $\ln x$. We can sometimes make progress by choosing this term as u, even if it means flying in the face of the advice given above, e.g., by having to *integrate* a polynomial term. The archetypal example of this is indeed the integration of $\ln x$. This also involves an unusual trick.

Write $\int \ln x \, dx = \int 1 . \ln x \, dx$ then choose $u(x) = \ln x$ and $v'(x) = 1$. We have $u'(x) = 1/x$ and $v(x) = x$, leading to the following standard form.

Frame 3.2   *Integration of $\ln x$*

$$\int \ln x \, dx = x \ln x - \int x \frac{1}{x} \, dx = x \ln x - \int 1 \, dx = x \ln x - x + C \quad (3.4)$$

Think about it like this

This unusual approach will also work successfully on $x^n \ln x$, as well as $\sin^{-1} x$ and $\tan^{-1} x$: choose the complicated function as u, with x^n or 1 as v'.

Note that, in all the above examples, there is no need to incorporate an arbitrary constant in the step of finding v from v' (and good reason not to do so). The constant should merely be added in at the very last stage, as in (3.4).

A further unusual case is that of a product of an exponential and a trigonometric function. Integration by parts appears to fail, but if applied a second time, we find an integral closely related to the original one, but with a key difference. This is best shown by an example.

Example 3.4   Find $I = \int e^x \cos x \, dx$.

In this case we can choose u and v' in either order, but the second choice must be consistent with the first. We shall choose

$$u = \cos x, \qquad v' = e^x,$$
$$u' = -\sin x, \qquad v = e^x,$$

$$I = e^x \cos x + \int e^x \sin x \, dx.$$

The new integral appears as intractable as the original, but we repeat the method, using $u = \sin x, \ v' = e^x$:

$$I = e^x \cos x + e^x \sin x - \int e^x \cos x \, dx,$$

where the integral on the right is now the original one, but with a key minus sign: this term is, in fact, $-I$. We can therefore solve for I:

$$I = \frac{1}{2} \left(e^x \cos x + e^x \sin x \right) + C.$$

■

Integrals of this type often appear in practice, with periodic (trigonometric) terms subject to exponential decay. It is therefore useful to note an alternative, much quicker, method. This uses **complex numbers**.

Example 3.5   Repeat the integration in Example 3.4.

Write $\cos x = \mathrm{Re}(\cos x + i \sin x) = \mathrm{Re}(e^{ix})$, so the integrand becomes $\mathrm{Re}(e^x e^{ix}) = \mathrm{Re}(e^{(1+i)x})$. Dropping the real part for now, we evaluate

$$\int e^{(1+i)x} \, dx = \frac{1}{1+i} e^{(1+i)x} + C = \frac{1-i}{1-i^2} e^{(1+i)x} + C$$
$$= \frac{1}{2}(1-i)e^x (\cos x + i \sin x)$$
$$= \frac{1}{2} e^x \left(\cos x + i \sin x - i \cos x + \sin x \right).$$

Now take the real part of this result:

$$I = \frac{1}{2} e^x \left(\cos x + \sin x \right) + C,$$

as before. (By taking the imaginary part we can also collect $\int e^x \sin x \, dx$, free of charge.) ■

We finish with one other example where integration by parts can be avoided, using a simpler method.

Example 3.6   Integrate $x(x+1)^9$.

Choosing $u = x$, $v' = (x+1)^9$, we have $u' = 1$, $v = \frac{1}{10}(x+1)^{10}$:

$$I = \frac{1}{10}x(x+1)^{10} - \int \frac{1}{10}(x+1)^{10}\,dx$$

$$= \frac{1}{10}(x+1)^{10} - \frac{1}{110}(x+1)^{11} + C.$$

A conceptually easier method, though arguably more difficult to spot, is **rearrangement**: replace x by $(x+1) - 1$ and so

$$I = \int \left[(x+1) - 1\right](x+1)^9\,dx = \int \left[(x+1)^{10} - (x+1)^9\right]\,dx$$

$$= \frac{1}{11}(x+1)^{11} - \frac{1}{10}(x+1)^{10} + C.$$

The two answers look different but can be reconciled by some elementary algebra. ∎

Ex 3.1   Use integration by parts to integrate $x \sin 2x$.

Ex 3.2   Evaluate the following:

(a) $\displaystyle\int x^2 \ln x\,dx$,   (b) $\displaystyle\int x \tan^{-1} x\,dx$,   (c) $\displaystyle\int (x+3)e^{2x}\,dx$.

Ex 3.3   Use integration by parts twice to evaluate $\displaystyle\int e^{4x}\sin 3x\,dx$.

An extra challenge: evaluate this integral by completing the following calculation.

$$\int e^{4x}\sin 3x\,dx = \int e^{4x}\,\mathrm{Im}\left[e^{3ix}\right]\,dx = \mathrm{Im}\left[\int e^{(4+3i)x}\,dx\right].$$

3.2   Parts or Substitution?

All the examples we have seen display a common theme: the template for the rule suggests it may be used to integrate **products** (or sometimes quotients, since $\frac{a}{b}$ can be written as $\frac{1}{b} \times a$). A further method for integrating products is to reverse the **chain rule**, since its form guarantees a result that is a product:

$$\frac{d}{dx}\left[f\big(u(x)\big)\right] = f'\big(u(x)\big)u'(x) \quad \text{or} \quad \frac{df}{du}\frac{du}{dx}.$$

This method is usually called **substitution**.

The two rules are not identical and there are few integrals that can be tackled successfully by both. The next example illustrates the difference between them.

Think about it like this

The rearrangement in Example 3.6 is equivalent to the substitution $u = x+1$, so it is an example of when both methods work. But this is not a very representative substitution.

Example 3.7 Integrate the following.

$$x \cosh(1 + x^2) \qquad\qquad (1 + x^2) \cosh x$$

We cannot integrate the cosh term on its own, suggesting that 'parts' is not an option.

We can differentiate $1 + x^2$ **and** integrate $\cosh x$, so 'parts' is viable.

Both cases contain a possible link between the two parts:

$$x = \frac{1}{2}\frac{d}{dx}\left[x^2\right].$$

Could be helpful since x is isolated and x^2 is inside cosh.

Not relevant here since it doesn't help simplify the cosh part.

Hence try a **substitution**

Hence try **parts**.

$$u = x^2.$$

$$u = 1 + x^2, \quad v' = \cosh x.$$

$$I = \frac{1}{2}\int \cosh(1 + u)\frac{du}{dx}\,dx$$

$$I = (1+x^2)\sinh x - \int 2x\sinh x\,dx,$$

$$= \frac{1}{2}\int \cosh(1 + u)\,du$$

and the integration is completed by using 'parts' again, to find

$$= \frac{1}{2}\sinh(1 + u) + C$$

$$I = (1 + x^2)\sinh x - 2x\cosh x$$

$$= \frac{1}{2}\sinh(1 + x^2) + C.$$

$$+ 2\sinh x + C.$$

■

Think about it like this

The points illustrated in the example are as follows.

In successful applications of each method, there is usually one simple term and one more complicated one.

For **integration by parts**, we must be able to integrate the more complicated one *on its own*, else we cannot proceed. For **substitution**, this is not necessary provided this term, once 'decomposed' and rewritten using u rather than x, can be integrated w.r.t. u.

For **integration by parts**, there is no need to have any link between the two terms, other than multiplication. For **substitution**, the simpler term *must* be related to the derivative of some key component of the other.

Ex 3.4 Evaluate the following:

$$\text{(a)} \int \tan^{-1}x\,dx, \qquad \text{(b)} \int_0^1 \frac{\tan^{-1}x}{1 + x^2}\,dx, \qquad \text{(c)} \int_1^9 \frac{e^{2\sqrt{x}}}{\sqrt{x}}\,dx.$$

Ex 3.5 Evaluate the integral $\displaystyle\int x^3 e^{-x^2}\, dx$.

Hint: This requires *both* a substitution and integration by parts, and these can be carried out in either order. The key is to write $x^3 = x^2 \cdot x$.

3.3 Application in Dynamics

All the examples above have used functions with known formulae. Integration by parts can be applied to cases where we have *general* functions, with no known formulae, but with derivatives involved. The following calculation illustrates this, and has been chosen because of the usefulness of its final result.

We now use time derivatives and treat a function $x(t)$. We apply integration by parts to $\displaystyle\int x' x''\, dt$. Choose

$$u = x', \qquad\qquad \frac{dv}{dt} = x'',$$
$$\frac{du}{dt} = x'', \qquad\qquad v = x',$$

leading to

$$I = (x')^2 - \int x'' x'\, dt = (x')^2 - I,$$

and so $I = \frac{1}{2}(x')^2$.

Now suppose that we are investigating the effect of a force F, with an associated **potential** V, i.e. $F = -\frac{dV}{dx}$. (Changes in potential energy are given by differences between values of V.) **Newton's second law**, relating force and acceleration, gives

$$mx'' = -\frac{dV}{dx}.$$

Multiply both sides by $x' = \frac{dx}{dt}$ and integrate with respect to t, using the above result:

$$m \int x'' x'\, dt = -\int \frac{dV}{dx}\frac{dx}{dt}\, dt,$$
$$\frac{1}{2}m(x')^2 = -\int \frac{dV}{dx}\, dx = -V + E,$$

where we have chosen to write the arbitrary constant as E.

This rearranges to give

$$\frac{1}{2}m(x')^2 + V = E, \tag{3.5}$$

which is a statement of the **conservation of energy**, since $\frac{1}{2}mv^2$ is the **kinetic energy** and $v = x'$. The fact that E is arbitrary is a reflection of the arbitrariness in V. A potential function can be given any 'zero level' since, as noted above, the energies involved are calculated as differences between its values.

3.4   Revision Exercises

Ex 3.6 Integrate $x \cosh 2x$ with respect to x.

Ex 3.7 Evaluate, as an **exact** number, $\displaystyle\int_0^{\pi/4} x \cos 4x \, dx$.

4   DIFFERENTIAL EQUATIONS

Dynamical problems often translate measures of **rates of change** immediately into **derivatives** with respect to **time**. Statical problems often translate **slopes (gradients)** or **deflections** into **derivatives** with respect to a **space** variable.

Hence, translation of a physical problem into mathematical terms – a **mathematical model** – will often relate a derivative to other quantities in the model, generating an equation such as:

$$\frac{dy}{dx} = f(x, y). \qquad (4.1)$$

Here y is the dependent variable, x is the independent variable and f encapsulates what we can deduce about the derivative. Such an expression is called a **differential equation**. It is said to be **first order**, since only a **first derivative** is involved. In real applications we are likely to choose symbols fitting the particular context, e.g., v for velocity and t for time.

Notation

> The function $f(x, y)$ in (4.1) has **two** inputs. It is a *function of two variables*, and those will form the subject of Chapter 7. For the moment, all that is required is an understanding that choosing values for x and y determines uniquely the output of the function.

4.1   Introduction

The challenge presented by (4.1) is to find a formula for y in terms of x. This means removing the $\frac{d}{dx}$, which is tantamount to anti-differentiation or **integration**.

Integration introduces an 'arbitrary constant' in the answer, which suggests that the solution to a differential equation will not be unique. This is indeed the case, but there is almost always an extra piece of information, arising naturally as part of the model, which will help us select the required solution. This information is called an **initial condition**. Usually it links the values of x and y at some special point, e.g., $y = b$ at $x = a$, written as $y(a) = b$.

Although we can ignore the arbitrary constant when performing definite integration, it is essential to include it when solving differential equations. Indeed, if we do not it is very unlikely that we can satisfy all the requirements of the model. The solution containing the arbitrary constant usually describes every possibility and is called the **General Solution (GS)**. The solution that satisfies the given initial condition is called a **Particular Solution (PS)**.

Before examining how to find these solutions, we present four examples. In two cases the modelling is straightforward; in the other two cases a considerable amount of prior analysis is required.

Populations

Primitive organisms, such as bacteria, often reproduce at a **rate** proportional to the size of the current population. Hence, the population P at time t satisfies

$$\frac{dP}{dt} = kP, \tag{4.2}$$

where k is a constant. To fix the solution, we need one further piece of information. The most natural initial condition is $P(0) = P_0$, the population size at $t = 0$.

Fall under gravity with air resistance

Consider a body of mass m, falling under gravity, but experiencing a resistive force F. Newton's law gives, for the velocity v,

$$m\frac{dv}{dt} = mg - F,$$

where the displacement (and hence the velocity) is measured **downwards** from some fixed point.

There are various methods in use for quantifying F. One simple, but approximate, model is that F is proportional to v, i.e., $F = kv$ for some k. A common initial condition states that the body is released from rest, although any initial (positive) velocity can be stipulated. These assumptions lead to the model:

$$m\frac{dv}{dt} = mg - kv, \qquad v(0) = 0. \tag{4.3}$$

Suspension bridge

A bridge of length L is supported by a collection of vertical cables, each attached to a main cable in such a way that the load is equally distributed. This cable is anchored at two points, at height h above its lowest point. Choose the origin at the left-hand end of the structure and the x-axis horizontal, passing through the lowest point of the cable, as shown in the diagram.

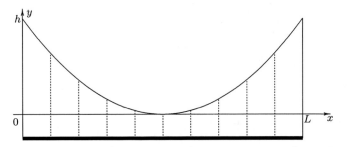

Then, using some simplifying assumptions, we can show that the height $y(x)$ of the cable, at position x, satisfies

$$\frac{dy}{dx} = \frac{2\alpha}{L}x - \alpha, \qquad y(0) = h, \tag{4.4}$$

for some constant α, related to the slope of the cable at its supports.

Fluid flow

A viscous fluid in a pipe of radius a has steady-state velocity profile $u(r)$, at distance r from the central axis of the pipe. This velocity function can be modelled as

$$\frac{d}{dr}\left(r\frac{du}{dr}\right) = -\frac{Gr}{\mu},\qquad(4.5)$$

where G and μ [mu] are constants. Using the product rule and dividing by r, we can rewrite this as

$$\frac{d^2u}{dr^2} + \frac{1}{r}\frac{du}{dr} = -\frac{G}{\mu}.$$

We see there is a **second derivative** involved and the equation is said to be **second order**. This indicates a need for two integrations and hence two arbitrary constants. (As a general rule, the order of the highest derivative matches the number of arbitrary constants needed in the General Solution.)

Thus we search for two initial conditions. One is straightforward: the fluid 'sticks' to the pipe, so the velocity at $r = a$ is zero, i.e., $u(a) = 0$. The other condition is rather unusual: it stipulates that the velocity remains finite at all places in the fluid.

4.2   Simple Examples

We can make immediate progress with a very special type of equation. This is where the function $f(x, y)$ in (4.1) depends on x alone, i.e., the equation has the form

$$\frac{dy}{dx} = f(x),\qquad y(a) = b.\qquad(4.6)$$

The right-hand side depends only on the **independent variable**, so (4.6) can be solved by anti-differentiation: the **General Solution** is the indefinite integral of the function on the right.

Before tackling the equations in the previous section – only the last two of which can be treated by anti-differentiation as they stand – we consider two simpler problems.

Example 4.1   A curve has gradient $2x$ at the point (x, y) and passes through the point $(0, 1)$. Find its equation.

This translates to the differential equation and associated initial condition:

$$\frac{dy}{dx} = 2x,\qquad y(0) = 1.$$

Integrate both sides w.r.t. x, the independent variable:

$$y = \int 2x\,dx = x^2 + C,$$

which is the **GS**. Any curve with this equation satisfies the gradient condition.

Now use the initial condition:

$$y = 1 \text{ at } x = 0 \quad \Rightarrow \quad 1 = 0 + C \quad \Rightarrow \quad C = 1,$$

leading to the **PS** $y = x^2 + 1$, the only one of the set of curves passing through the given point. ∎

The next example is a kinematics problem. This is somewhat contrived, but the context should be familiar and it exemplifies the key points.

Example 4.2 A car is travelling at $12.5 \, \text{ms}^{-1}$ (approximately 28 mph). The accelerator is then applied, providing acceleration $5 - \frac{1}{2}t$ for 10 seconds, at which time no further acceleration occurs and maximum speed is achieved. Find that maximum speed.

We have

$$\frac{dv}{dt} = 5 - \frac{1}{2}t \quad (0 \leqslant t \leqslant 10), \qquad v(0) = 12.5.$$

Since the right-hand side involves t only, anti-differentiation will solve the equation to find the **GS**:

$$v = \int \left(5 - \frac{1}{2}t\right) \, dt = 5t - \frac{1}{4}t^2 + C.$$

Now $v = 12.5$ at $t = 0$, which gives $12.5 = 0 - 0 + C$, and hence the **PS**:

$$v = 5t - \frac{1}{4}t^2 + 12.5.$$

At $t = 10$, $v(10) = 50 - \frac{1}{4} \times 100 + 12.5 = 37.5$, which is approximately 84 mph.

Note that the model terminates at $t = 10$, at which time the acceleration is zero. A larger t in the formula gives a negative acceleration, which is not valid since no braking is indicated. A more precise statement of the differential equation is:

$$\frac{dv}{dt} = \begin{cases} 5 - \frac{1}{2}t, & \text{if } 0 \leqslant t \leqslant 10, \\ 0, & \text{if } t > 10. \end{cases}$$

∎

Think about it like this

Although we can usually evaluate definite integrals without invoking an arbitrary constant, *its use in solving differential equations is indispensable.* If we omit the constant we have no way of ensuring the the solution will satisfy the specific initial condition.

Only one of the examples in the previous section can be dealt with by a single straightforward integration: the suspension bridge problem.

Example 4.3 Solve equation (4.4), to find y as a function of x.

Also, use the symmetry to find α in terms of h and L and deduce the shape in which the main cable hangs.

The right-hand side contains only the independent variable, so we can use anti-differentiation:

$$y(x) = \frac{\alpha}{L}x^2 - \alpha x + C.$$

$y = h$ at $x = 0$ gives $h = 0 - 0 + C$. Hence

$$y(x) = \frac{\alpha}{L}x^2 - \alpha x + h.$$

This is an acceptable solution, but we can do a little better for this particular problem. From symmetry – see the earlier diagram – $y = 0$ at $x = \frac{L}{2}$, so

$$0 = \frac{\alpha}{L}\frac{L^2}{4} - \alpha\frac{L}{2} + h,$$

which gives the value $\alpha = \frac{4h}{L}$. Hence

$$
\begin{aligned}
y &= \frac{4h}{L^2}x^2 - \frac{4h}{L}x + h \\
&= \frac{4h}{L^2}\left(x^2 - Lx + \frac{L^2}{4}\right) \\
&= \frac{4h}{L^2}\left(x - \tfrac{1}{2}L\right)^2,
\end{aligned}
$$

the equation of a **parabola**.   ∎

Think about it like this

> This section is very much a first look at differential equations and at present we can only make progress with a very special type of equation.
>
> Given a first order differential equation, rearrange it to isolate the derivative, i.e., write $\frac{dp}{dq} = \cdots$. Here, p and q have been used here to remind you that a variety of symbols may occur in such equations and to underline the need for vigilance about which variable is independent. Now examine the right-hand side. If this is entirely in terms of the *independent variable* (here q) we can proceed to solve it. In fact, it is just an anti-differentiation problem; the solution is the indefinite integral of the function on the right.
>
> Equations (4.4) and (4.5) are the only ones we can start to solve at present. They require only straightforward anti-differentiation, with (4.5) requiring two applications. This is because the *dependent* variable occurs only in the derivative term. Thus, (4.4) has the special form $\frac{dy}{dx} = f(x)$, with no y involved in $f(x)$. On the other hand, (4.2) contains P and (4.3) contains v on the right-hand side. This distinction is of the utmost importance since an attempt to solve such an equation by direct integration is doomed; some part of the integrand involves the (as yet unknown) solution.

To 'remove' a second derivative requires two integrations and hence should generate *two* arbitrary constants in the **GS**. If we require a **PS**, we need to identify *two* initial conditions. The following example is typical.

Example 4.4 A particle of unit mass experiences a force e^{-t} as it moves along the x-axis. Find its position as a function of t.

Newton's second law produces the differential equation

$$\frac{d^2x}{dt^2} = e^{-t}.$$

Integrate once:

$$\frac{dx}{dt} = -e^{-t} + A, \tag{4.7}$$

and again

$$x = e^{-t} + At + B, \tag{4.8}$$

which is the **GS**.

Suppose that the particle starts at $t = 0$ at position $x = 0$ with initial velocity $\frac{dx}{dt} = 1$.

$$(4.7): \quad t = 0, \ \frac{dx}{dt} = 1 \ : \quad 1 = -1 + A \quad \Rightarrow \ A = 2,$$

$$(4.8): \quad t = 0, \ x = 0 \ : \quad 0 = 1 + 0 + B \quad \Rightarrow \ B = -1,$$

giving the **PS**:

$$x = e^{-t} + 2t - 1.$$

■

Think about it like this

Some would tackle problems of this type as direct integration ones. But many scientists and engineers would first of all write them as differential equations, with initial conditions, *since that is the modelling approach they find natural,* because of its power in dealing with much more complex situations.

Now the fluid flow problem has two derivatives and the expanded form looks different from the case just considered. In its original formulation (4.5), however, two consecutive integrations deliver the solution. There appears to be only one initial condition, but we can identify an unusual second one.

Example 4.5 Find the general solution of the differential equation (4.5).

Find the particular solution for which the fluid 'sticks' to the pipe, so $u(a) = 0$ where a is the radius, assuming the velocity remains finite at all places.

Since the dependent variable u appears only inside a derivative, this problem can be solved by anti-differentiation. Integrate both sides w.r.t. r:

$$r\frac{du}{dr} = \int -\frac{Gr}{\mu}\, dr = -\frac{G}{2\mu}r^2 + A.$$

(We defer fixing the value of A for the moment.)

Now isolate $\frac{du}{dr}$:

$$\frac{du}{dr} = -\frac{G}{2\mu}r + \frac{A}{r},$$

and integrate again:

$$u = -\frac{G}{4\mu}r^2 + A\ln r + B.$$

Now u must have a value for all of $0 \leqslant r \leqslant a$, but $\ln 0$ is not defined. Hence we must choose $A = 0$, to remove that term. Otherwise, the solution will not be bounded at the centre of the pipe and that is not physically correct.

Also, $u = 0$ at $r = a$, so

$$0 = -\frac{G}{4\mu}a^2 + B,$$

which gives B and hence

$$u(r) = \frac{G}{4\mu}(a^2 - r^2).$$

∎

Ex 4.1   Find the general solution to $\dfrac{dy}{dx} = xe^{-x^2}$ and the particular solution satisfying $y(0) = 1$.

   What is the behaviour of y for $|x| \gg 1$, i.e., for x very much greater than 1?

Ex 4.2   Find the particular solution to the differential equation

$$\frac{dz}{dt} = t^2 + 1,$$

satisfying the initial condition $z(0) = 1$.

Ex 4.3   Find the general solution to the differential equation $\dfrac{dy}{dx} = \text{sech}^2 x$.

Ex 4.4   Find the particular solution to the differential equation

$$\frac{dP}{dt} = t\ln(1 + t) \quad (t \geqslant 0),$$

with initial condition $P(0) = 1$.

Ex 4.5   Solve each of the following *second-order* differential equations:

(a) $\dfrac{d^2u}{dx^2} = k, \quad u(0) = 0, \ u(1) = U; \quad (k \text{ constant}).$

(b) $\dfrac{d^2y}{dx^2} = \cos x + \sin x, \quad y(0) = 0, \ y(\pi) = 0.$

4.3   Separable Equations

We now tackle a larger class of problems, although there will remain problems that are impossible to solve by exact integration. We concentrate on two classes of equations, tackled by distinct methods, although some individual problems are susceptible to both.

   The problem, then, is to solve

$$\frac{dy}{dx} = f(x, y), \qquad y(a) = b. \tag{4.9}$$

Suppose it is possible to factorise $f(x, y)$ into the product of two **separate** functions, one of x alone and the other of y alone:

$$\frac{dy}{dx} = g(x)h(y). \qquad (4.10)$$

If this can be done, the equation is **separable** (sometimes called **variables separable**). We have 'separated' the x part from the y part.

Separable equations can be solved by performing two integrations: one w.r.t. x and one w.r.t. y. The formally correct way to do this – using the Chain Rule – can be found in many textbooks. Here, we shall examine and use a more practical approach, one that is entirely consistent with the formal method.

Separate the variables further, by moving them to different sides of the equation, treating dy as a y-term and dx as an x-term. Thus, if we collect all y references on the left and all x on the right:

$$\frac{1}{h(y)}\, dy = g(x)\, dx.$$

Think about it like this

It is essential to use only valid algebraic manipulations. There are many 'non-separable' equations, so we must resist the temptation to stray outside the permitted rules of algebra in a doomed attempt to separate such an equation.

In performing the separation, the symbols dy, dx, dt, etc. are treated as belonging to the variable included in them: dx goes on the x side of '='. Also, once we have given these freedom to exist singly, rather than in a composite term such as $\frac{dy}{dx}$, they must appear on the 'top' or main line of the expression: $\frac{1}{dx}$ has no sensible meaning.

Now integrate both sides to obtain the **General Solution (GS)**.

Frame 4.1 *General solution for a separable equation*

$$\frac{dy}{dx} = g(x)h(y) \quad \Rightarrow \quad \int \frac{1}{h(y)}\, dy = \int g(x)\, dx + C$$

Note that we require only one constant, since writing constants on each side, C_1 and C_2 say, gives nothing different. We can bring them together on one side as $C_1 - C_2$. This new constant is just as 'arbitrary' as C_1 and C_2 separately.

Suppose the indefinite integrals can be evaluated, to give

$$P(y) = Q(x) + C. \qquad (4.11)$$

The arbitrary constant is essential for obtaining the **General Solution**. Every value of C gives a valid solution. Conversely, every solution of the differential equation has this form, except that occasionally there is some extra solution not included. (Such a 'singular' solution will not concern us here.)

We still have the extra condition in (4.9) available for use: $y(a) = b$. This allows us to determine a value for C and hence find the **Particular Solution** (**PS**). Since $y = b$ when $x = a$, we have, from (4.11):

$$P(b) = Q(a) + C \quad \Rightarrow \quad C = P(b) - Q(a),$$

and hence we obtain a fully determined solution.

Notation

> Take care in the interpretation of $y(a) = b$. The equality links b with y and the brackets tell us that a is linked with x. It is a common error to think that the value of y is a, just because they are adjacent.

It is sometimes possible to rearrange the Particular Solution into the form $y = F(x)$ for some function F.

Think about it like this

> It is almost always easier and safer to use the initial condition immediately after integrating, at the stage of (4.11), rather than first trying to achieve $y = F(x)$ for the General Solution. (This is not the case for the second method, covered in §4.4.)

Example 4.6   A simplified model of a second-order chemical reaction is

$$\frac{dx}{dt} = -kx^2, \qquad x(0) = a,$$

where x measures the (matched) concentrations of the two participants in the reaction and $k > 0$. Solve this equation and sketch a graph of the solution.

Separate the x and t. The minus sign can be used on either side, but putting it on the left is neater:

$$-\frac{1}{x^2}\, dx = k\, dt.$$

Now introduce integral signs on each side:

$$\int -\frac{1}{x^2}\, dx = \int k\, dt,$$

and perform the integrations:

$$\frac{1}{x} = kt + C.$$

At $t = 0$, $x = a$: $\frac{1}{a} = 0 + C$, $C = \frac{1}{a}$. Hence

$$\frac{1}{x} = kt + \frac{1}{a} = \frac{akt + 1}{a}$$

and finally
$$x = \frac{a}{akt + 1}.$$
This rational function of t is graphed below.

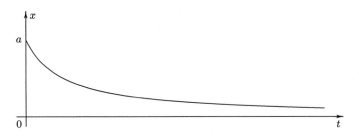

We note that $x \to 0$ as $t \to \infty$, as we would expect for such a reaction. ∎

Think about it like this

The Particular Solution, with C fixed as shown above, can be rearranged as $P(y) - P(b) = Q(x) - Q(a)$ and then each side interpreted as a definite integral, giving

$$\int_b^y \frac{1}{h(y)} \, dy = \int_a^x g(x) \, dx, \qquad (4.12)$$

which has the initial condition implicit. Although this rather neat formula has its advocates, we shall use the step-by-step derivation, as in Example 4.6. The alternative, for that example, would be to quote the solution as

$$\int_a^x -\frac{1}{x^2} \, dx = \int_0^t k \, dt,$$

then evaluate the integrals.

Example 4.7 The following differential equation models a population of bacteria, as in (4.2):
$$\frac{dP}{dt} = kP, \qquad P(0) = P_0.$$
Solve this to find t as a function of P. (Note that $k > 0$.)

Separate P and t, then integrate:

$$\int \frac{dP}{P} = \int k \, dt \quad \Rightarrow \quad \ln P = kt + C.$$

At $t = 0$, $P = P_0$ so $\ln P_0 = 0 + C$. Hence

$$\ln P = kt + \ln P_0 \quad \Rightarrow \quad kt = \ln P - \ln P_0.$$

From this, we deduce $kt = \ln \dfrac{P}{P_0}$ and hence

$$\frac{P}{P_0} = e^{kt} \quad \Rightarrow \quad P = P_0 e^{kt}.$$

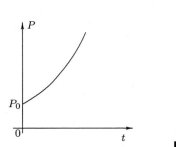

This **exponential** growth is graphed as on the right.

∎

Think about it like this

It is worth investigating why we cannot solve (4.9) by direct integration as we did for (4.6). Integrate both sides w.r.t. x:

$$y = \int f(x, y)\, dx + C.$$

The problem is that the integration is driven by x. The whole point of the differential equation is that it defines y as a function of x; suppose its solution is $y = g(x)$. Then the 'solution' above involves $\int f(x, g(x))\, dx$, which we cannot even begin to calculate, not knowing a formula for $g(x)$.

In short, when evaluating such an integral there can be only one variable in the integrand and it must be the same as that in the '$d?$' term driving the integration. Otherwise, the simple method cannot work.

The previous two examples have had just one variable in the '$f(x, y)$' part, i.e., it has been '$f(y)$' with 'y' the **dependent** variable in the derivative: $-kx^2$ for $\frac{dx}{dt}$ and kP for $\frac{dP}{dt}$. The final three examples are more general.

Example 4.8   Solve $\dfrac{dy}{dx} = \dfrac{1 + y^2}{\sqrt{x}}$, $y(0) = 1$.

Separate the variables to find $\dfrac{dy}{1 + y^2} = \dfrac{dx}{\sqrt{x}}$, then integrate:

$$\int \frac{dy}{1 + y^2} = \frac{dx}{\sqrt{x}} \quad \Rightarrow \quad \tan^{-1} y = 2\sqrt{x} + C,$$

this being the General Solution.

We have $y = 1$ when $x = 0$, giving

$$\tan^{-1} 1 = 2\sqrt{0} + C \quad \Rightarrow \quad C = \tfrac{\pi}{4}.$$

The Particular Solution is $\tan^{-1} y = 2\sqrt{x} + \tfrac{\pi}{4}$, which tidies up to give

$$y = \tan\left(2\sqrt{x} + \tfrac{\pi}{4}\right).$$

∎

Example 4.9   The **Clausius-Clapeyron** equation in thermodynamics links vapour pressure P^* and temperature T:

$$\frac{dP^*}{dT} = \frac{\Delta h\, P^*}{RT^2}.$$

This is separable if we assume that Δh and R are *constants*, which is the case for an **ideal gas**.

Separate and integrate:

$$\int \frac{dP^*}{P^*} = \int \frac{\Delta h}{R} \frac{1}{T^2}\, dT,$$

leading to the General Solution

$$\ln P^* = -\frac{\Delta h}{R} \frac{1}{T} + C.$$

∎

Example 4.10   One model of a cone and plate viscometer generates the (separable) differential equation

$$\frac{d\tau}{d\theta} = -2\tau \cot \theta, \qquad \tau\left(\tfrac{\pi}{4}\right) = 1.$$

(The initial condition here is not a natural one, but has been chosen to make the post-integration work a little easier.)

Separate τ and θ, then integrate (assuming $0 < \theta < \pi$):

$$\int -\frac{1}{2\tau}\, d\tau = \int \cot \theta\, d\theta = \int \frac{\cos \theta}{\sin \theta}\, d\theta,$$

giving

$$-\frac{1}{2} \ln \tau = \ln \sin \theta + C.$$

At $\theta = \frac{\pi}{4}$, $\tau = 1$: $-\frac{1}{2}\ln 1 = \ln \frac{1}{\sqrt{2}} + C \;\Rightarrow\; C = -\ln \frac{1}{\sqrt{2}} = \frac{1}{2}\ln 2$. Using this value of C, and the log rules, we find

$$\ln \tau = -2\ln \sin \theta - \ln 2 = -\ln \sin^2 \theta - \ln 2$$
$$= -\ln\left(2 \sin^2 \theta\right) = \ln \frac{1}{2 \sin^2 \theta}.$$

Now 'remove' the 'ln' (i.e., take the exponential of each side) to find

$$\tau = \frac{1}{2 \sin^2 \theta}.$$

■

Think about it like this

Care is needed in the algebra carried out after solving a differential equation. Suppose we have an equation of the form $X = Y$. Then it is usually permissible to subject both sides of this equation to the same operation, without affecting its validity. Thus we can write $X^2 = Y^2$ or $\frac{1}{X} = \frac{1}{Y}$ or $\ln X = \ln Y$ or $\sqrt{X} = \sqrt{Y}$, etc.

This useful technique does not extend if we treat one side as the sum of more than one piece, which tends to happen with differential equations, because of the '$+C$' part. If we work with $X = Y + Z$, say, we cannot write $\ln X = \ln Y + \ln Z$, nor can we use *any* of the operations mentioned above in such a way. Sometimes we find ourselves at a dead-end, but in other cases we can make progress in an alternative way, using some other rule. One procedure that proves particularly useful is that we can write $e^X = e^{Y+Z} = e^Y e^Z$, using an index law. This is equivalent to what was done in the previous example, but using log rules.

We finish by showing how **conservation of energy**, as modelled in §3.3, leads naturally to separable equations. Rewrite (3.5), using $\frac{dx}{dt}$ for v:

$$\frac{1}{2}m \left(\frac{dx}{dt}\right)^2 = E - V(x),$$

which can be solved to find

$$\frac{dx}{dt} = \pm\sqrt{\frac{2E - 2V(x)}{m}}.$$

This **separable** equation is solved, by integration, as

$$\int \sqrt{\frac{m}{2E - 2V(x)}}\, dx = t + C.$$

This is a powerful result, although its usefulness is often inhibited by difficulties in performing the integration. For example, a **simple pendulum** gives rise to an integral that cannot be expressed in terms of elementary functions.

Ex 4.6 Find the general solution to the equation $\dfrac{dy}{dx} = y(x^2 + 1)$.

Ex 4.7 A curve $y = f(x)$ has the property that its gradient at (x, y) satisfies the equation $\dfrac{dy}{dx} = -\dfrac{x}{y}$. Find the particular solution to this equation given that the point $(0, 1)$ lies on the curve. Interpret the solution, explaining why the gradient satisfies the given equation.

Ex 4.8 Find the general solution to the differential equation

$$\frac{dx}{dt} = ax(1 - x) \quad (a > 0).$$

Ex 4.9 The motion of a particle moving in a central potential $V = V(r)$ may be expressed in terms of the polar angle θ (i.e., the angle the line to the origin makes with the x-axis) and $u = 1/r$ via

$$\frac{du}{d\theta} = \sqrt{\frac{2E}{mh^2} - u^2 - \frac{2V(1/u)}{mh^2}},$$

where m is the mass of the particle, E its energy and h is related to the angular momentum.

Find the general solution of this equation for the attractive potentials
(a) $V(r) = -\dfrac{\mu}{r}$,   (b) $V(r) = -\dfrac{\mu}{r^2}$ [**Cote's spirals**].

4.4 Linear Equations

There is a further class of first-order equations for which we can make considerable progress. This is the class of **linear** equations. For first-order equations, we identify them using the following template.

Frame 4.2   *Template for a linear differential equation*

$$\frac{dy}{dx} + p(x)y = q(x) \tag{4.13}$$

Think about it like this

> Pay particular attention to the *only two* instances of y: these have a very simple form and occur in different terms. Note that sometimes these terms may occur on different sides of the '=', as in
>
> $$\frac{dy}{dx} = -p(x)y + q(x),$$
>
> but that does not invalidate the linearity.

There is a method for solving (4.13), in the sense of reducing the equation to an integration problem. This is set out in an optional section at the end of this chapter. There are two reasons for demoting it: the method can generate calculations that are much more complicated than the method we now examine, and it does not extend to equations of higher-orders, unlike our preferred method.

Think about it like this

> Linearity is a key mathematical idea, arising in many different contexts. We shall use a standard solution process, in the context of differential equations.
>
> These linear equations are so well understood that we can 'cheat'. Instead of solving them by integration – the normal way of removing a derivative – we shall be able to use our knowledge of the structure of the solution to solve them by the much easier technique of differentiation, allied to 'trial and error'. We shall write down what we know the solution must look like, replacing the parts we don't know by symbols, and then force this 'trial' solution to fit the equation, fixing the values of these symbols.

We now simplify (4.13), assuming that $p(x)$ is a **constant**, written as p. We also make a change to the notation, replacing variables (x, y) by (t, x).

Notation

> These are very natural choices, if we think of t as **time** and x as the **unknown quantity** we wish to determine. It is important to bear in mind the distinction between the **independent** variable t and the **dependent** variable x.

Hence, the equation we shall actually tackle is that in the following template, for the **Full Equation (FE)**.

Frame 4.3   *First-order linear differential equation with constant coefficients*

$$\textbf{FE} \qquad \frac{dx}{dt} + px = q(t) \qquad\qquad (4.14)$$

Note that, in spite of the title, $q(t)$ is *not* necessarily constant.

Our solution method requires us to consider an equation related to **FE**, but without $q(t)$, leading to the **Homogeneous Equation (HE)**.

Frame 4.4   *The Homogeneous Equation related to Frame 4.3*

$$\textbf{HE} \qquad \frac{dx}{dt} + px = 0 \qquad\qquad (4.15)$$

Think about it like this

> The term "homogeneous", which means "of the same kind", implies that all
> parts of the equation contain the dependent variable x, which means that
> $q(t)$ is not involved. Some equations have $q(t) = 0$ from the start, e.g., those
> in Examples 4.11 and 4.12.

The reason for introducing the **HE** is the following key result, which
applies to **all linear equations**, whether differential equations, or other
types.

Frame 4.5   *Solution of linear equations*

$$\textbf{GS of FE } = \textbf{ GS of HE } + \textbf{ any solution of FE}$$

The two parts are often called the **Complementary Function (CF)**
and a **Particular Integral (PI)**, respectively, so we have the simple form:

$$\textbf{GS } = \textbf{CF} + \textbf{PI}. \qquad\qquad (4.16)$$

Hence we have split the initial problem into two simpler ones. Once they have
both been solved, *and only then*, we can use Frame 4.5 or (4.16) to construct
the **GS** and then apply any initial condition to find the **Particular Solution
(PS)**.

Think about it like this

> The GS will contain an arbitrary constant, inherited from the CF. Indeed,
> that is why it is 'general'. Recall that separable equations always throw up
> such a constant, usually arising directly from an integration. The one in the
> CF is the counterpart of that. One arbitrary constant is all we need for a
> first-order equation.

> We say "**any** solution of the FE" and refer to "a PI", since in theory there are
> an infinite number of possibilities. But in practice there is only one simple
> one and that is the one we shall seek below. The full story shows that any
> two PIs differ by a part of the CF and it is better to avoid a PI containing
> some part of the CF; it will appear in the GS anyway.

> It is an unfortunate historical accident that "Particular" is used in the two
> different concepts, **PS** and **PI**.

4.4.1 Finding the CF (solving the HE)

The equation we seek to solve is (4.15):

$$\frac{dx}{dt} + px = 0,$$

which can be rewritten as

$$\frac{dx}{dt} = -px,$$

showing it to be **separable** and so susceptible to the method in §4.3.

In fact, we can write down the solution, since this equation is just a statement that x is subject to exponential growth/decay, with **rate constant** $-p$. Hence the CF is

$$x(t) = Ae^{-pt}, \tag{4.17}$$

for any constant A.

In spite of this, it is common to apply the following method, which extends straightforwardly to higher orders of linear equations. We seek a solution of the form

$$x = e^{\lambda t},$$

for some constant λ. Then

$$\frac{dx}{dt} = \lambda e^{\lambda t} \quad \Rightarrow \quad \lambda e^{\lambda t} + pe^{\lambda t} = 0.$$

Since $e^{\lambda t}$ is never zero, it can be cancelled from this equation, leaving the **auxiliary equation**

$$\lambda + p = 0.$$

This immediately gives $\lambda = -p$ and the solution in (4.17), once we attach the arbitrary constant A.

Think about it like this

> Some people use $x = Ae^{\lambda t}$ in the above, but the constant A tends to obscure the calculation. It gets cancelled at the end. (It is assumed non-zero else the solution would be the rather boring $x = 0$.)

Example 4.11   Solve (4.2), the equation for a biological population.
Try $P = e^{\lambda t}$, so $\frac{dP}{dt} = \lambda e^{\lambda t}$. Then since $\frac{dP}{dt} = kP$, we have

$$\lambda e^{\lambda t} = ke^{\lambda t}.$$

This gives $\lambda = k$ and hence $P = Ae^{kt}$, as in Example 4.7, but obtained by an easier calculation. ∎

Example 4.12   An analysis of the equilibrium of a small volume of air in the atmosphere produces the equation

$$\frac{dp}{dh} = -\frac{\rho_0 g}{p_0} p,$$

where p is atmospheric pressure (p_0 its value at sea level), h is height above sea level and ρ_0 is the density at sea level.

Trying $p = e^{\lambda h}$ leads to $\lambda = -\rho_0 g/p_0$ and the pressure distribution

$$p = A \exp\left(-\frac{\rho_0 g}{p_0} h\right).$$

This is the general solution of the differential equation. We can find the particular solution by setting $h = 0$, which should produce $p = p_0$. Doing so, we find $A = p_0$ and have a well-defined formula for p. ■

4.4.2   Finding a PI

We now seek *any* solution for

$$\frac{dx}{dt} + px = q(t). \tag{4.18}$$

We shall pursue this only for cases where $q(t)$ consists of constants, polynomials (in t), exponentials and sin/cos terms. For such cases there is always a solution $x(t)$ in the same basic form, although with different coefficients.

The method is not very different from that for the CF. We use a **trial function** of exactly the same form but with (currently) **undetermined coefficients**. When we force this trial function to fit the differential equation (4.18), we obtain equations that fix the values of these coefficients.

Think about it like this

The reason why this works is as follows. Polynomial, exponential and trigonometric terms all have the property that a member of such a class remains in the same class after differentiation. Hence we can argue that a function of this kind appearing in $q(t)$, on the right of (4.18), must have arisen from a similar one contained as part of $x(t)$, on the left.

The table below gives, with examples, the rules for choosing the trial function.

right-hand side: $q(t)$	example	trial function: $x(t)$
constant	3	$x = a$ (constant)
linear	$4 - 3t$	$x = a + bt$
exponential (rate constant k)	e^{-5t}	$x = ae^{kt}$
sinusoidal (angular frequency ω)	$\sin t - 3\cos t$	$x = a\cos\omega t + b\sin\omega t$

Notation

In the last column of this table the symbols k and ω are not to be regarded as undetermined. They are not simple coefficients, being inside the function arguments. They should be placed in the trial solution with exactly the values they have in $q(t)$. For example, if $q(t)$ contains $\cos 3t - 2\sin 3t$ you should use $a\cos 3t + b\sin 3t$.

Also, the *full* version in the final column must be used at all times, even if $q(t)$ is simpler, e.g., for $q(t) = t$ we must use $x = a + bt$, and for $x = \sin t$, the full cos/sin form is needed.

Example 4.13 Solve $\dfrac{dx}{dt} - 3x = 9$.

This $q(t)$ is a **constant** and so we use a trial function where x is also a constant, currently unknown. Try $x(t) = 1$, so $\frac{dx}{dt} = 0$ since a is constant. Hence

$$0 - 3a = 9 \quad \Rightarrow \quad a = -3$$

and the PI is $x(t) = -3$. ∎

Think about it like this

The method used to find a PI may appear strange, but it is an example of a commonly used problem-solving technique of considerable power: the 'method of undetermined coefficients'. It has the advantage of placing less reliance on memory. Most mathematical methods you have seen to date are 'direct' in the sense of having a set of operations to carry out on some given data to produce an answer. This method is a 'reverse' one. We know (or can make a good guess at) the form of the answer, but do not know the values of some of the factors involved in it. We replace those by symbols – the undetermined coefficients – and then force this 'trial' answer to fit the problem, thereby deriving equations for the values we need.

The following example illustrates the method in a familiar context. Suppose we want to find the equation of the line passing through $(1, 5)$ and $(4, -1)$. The (direct) method is to find the gradient $(-1 - 5)/(4 - 1) = -2$ and then use the formula $y - 5 = -2(x - 1)$ to get $y = -2x + 7$. The alternative (reverse) method is to conjecture that the equation is $y = mx + c$ with m and c representing values to be determined. Since the line passes through $y = 5$, $x = 1$ we have $5 = m + c$. Similarly we have $-1 = 4m + c$. These two simultaneous equations can be solved to find $m = -2$, $c = 7$. This requires recall of neither the formula for the gradient nor that for a line through a known point.

The situation in experimental science is similar: we often cannot measure directly what we wish, so we must measure something else and deduce the result from it.

In some of the examples that follow, we shall proceed to write down the GS, then to use an initial condition to fix the constant in the CF. *Note that this can only be done when both CF and PI have been found.*

Example 4.14 Solve $\dfrac{dx}{dt} - 2x = 3e^{-t}, \quad x(0) = 1$.

We use the trial function $x = ae^{-t}$ for the PI. Unlike the situation for the CF, there is no need to use 'λ' as a rate constant, since differentiation never changes the rate constant, which will be -1 throughout finding this PI. We have $\frac{dx}{dt} = -ae^{-t}$ and, using the differential equation, we find

$$-ae^{-t} - 2ae^{-t} = 3e^{-t} \quad \Rightarrow \quad a = -1.$$

The PI is therefore $x(t) = -e^{-t}$. The CF is found, as in the previous subsection, to be $x = Ae^{2t}$, so the GS is

$$x(t) = Ae^{2t} - e^{-t}.$$

The initial condition gives $x = 1$ when $t = 0$, so $1 = A - 1$ and the PS is

$$x(t) = 2e^{2t} - e^{-t}.$$

■

Example 4.15   Solve $\dfrac{dx}{dt} + 2x = 3 - 2t$.

Using $x = e^{\lambda t}$ in the HE leads to $\lambda + 2 = 0$, so the CF is $x = Ae^{-2t}$.

The required trial function for the PI is a **linear** polynomial: $x = a + bt$, which gives $\frac{dx}{dt} = b$. Substitute these into the differential equation:

$$b + 2(a + bt) = 3 - 2t.$$

This is an **identity**, which means that the constant parts and the coefficients of t must separately agree, on both sides:

$$b + 2a = 3, \quad 2b = -2 \quad \Rightarrow \quad b = -1, \quad a = 2,$$

giving the PI $x = 2 - t$. The GS is therefore

$$x(t) = Ae^{-2t} + 2 - t.$$

■

The final two examples are 'real' applications.

Example 4.16   Solve (4.3), the differential equation describing fall with air resistance proportional to velocity.

This equation is, in fact, *separable*, but the solution below, which takes advantage of its linearity, is much easier than that obtained by separation, integration and subsequent rearrangement to find v.

The HE is

$$\frac{dv}{dt} + \frac{k}{m}v = 0 \quad \Rightarrow \quad v = Ae^{-\frac{k}{m}t}.$$

The right-hand side is a constant, so use the trial function $v = a$, $\frac{dv}{dt} = 0$:

$$0 + ka = mg \quad \Rightarrow \quad a = \frac{mg}{k}.$$

Hence the GS is

$$v = Ae^{-\frac{k}{m}t} + \frac{mg}{k},$$

and the initial condition gives

$$0 = A + \frac{mg}{k},$$

so the PS is

$$v = \frac{mg}{k} - \frac{mg}{k}e^{-\frac{k}{m}t}.$$

As t increases, the body speeds up as the exponential term decreases. But that term tends to zero, so the body's speed approaches but never reaches $\frac{mg}{k}$, the **terminal velocity**. (If the fall starts at a speed greater than this, the body slows down, approaching the terminal velocity.)   ■

Example 4.17 An L-R electrical circuit with AC input has current i given by

$$L\frac{di}{dt} + Ri = V\sin\omega t,$$

where L is the inductance, R is the resistance and V is the maximum amplitude of the AC voltage, which has period $2\pi/\omega$.

Although this equation is not separable, it is **linear**. The CF is

$$i = Ae^{-\frac{R}{L}t},$$

which dies away as t increases. It is known as a **transient** and plays no part in the current in the long-term. Hence we shall ignore it and concentrate on the PI.

To simplify the calculations, we now use the values $\omega = 1$, $L = 5$, $R = 35$ and $V = 250$; this does not influence the method used. The equation is

$$\frac{di}{dt} + 7i = 50\sin t.$$

The table suggests a trial function using $\sin t$ and $\cos t$, choosing the same angular frequency as on the right-hand side:

$$i = a\cos t + b\sin t,$$
$$\frac{di}{dt} = -a\sin t + b\cos t.$$

Substitution into the differential equation gives

$$-a\sin t + b\cos t + 7a\cos t + 7b\sin t = 50\sin t,$$

which is an **identity**, valid only if the sin and cos terms separately match:

$$7a + b = 0, \quad -a + 7b = 50.$$

Simple elimination leads to the solution $a = -1$, $b = 7$, so the PI is

$$i = -\cos t + 7\sin t.$$

This formula is not immediately useful and it is usually converted to the form $i = I\sin(t + \phi)$. Here we have **amplitude**

$$I = \sqrt{(-1)^2 + 7^2} = \sqrt{50} \simeq 7.07,$$

and $\phi < 0$, so there is a **phase lag**. Note that this is in line with the simple measure from Ohm's Law, ignoring the inductance: $\frac{V}{R} = \frac{50}{7} \simeq 7.14$. ∎

Ex 4.10 Find the general solution to the linear equation $\dfrac{dz}{dt} + 8z = 24e^{-2t}$.

Ex 4.11 Find the general solution to each of the following differential equations:

(a) $\dfrac{du}{dt} + 0.1u = 1$,

(b) $\dfrac{dy}{dx} - y = 3\cos x + \sin x$.

Ex 4.12 The current $i(t)$, measured in amps, in a particular electric circuit satisfies the equation

$$0.25\frac{di}{dt} + 20i = 40,$$

with the initial condition $i(0) = 0$. Find i as a function of t.

Ex 4.13 Find the general solution, and hence the particular solution, to each of the following differential equations:

(a) $\dfrac{dy}{dt} + 2y = 1 - 2t$, $y(1) = 0$;

(b) $\dfrac{dz}{dx} - 5z = 8e^x$, $z(0) = 2$.

4.5 Integrating Factors (Optional)

Now return to the full version of a linear first-order equation:

$$\frac{dy}{dx} + p(x)y = q(x). \tag{4.19}$$

The method we use is to multiply (4.19) by a function $I(x)$, called an **integrating factor**. With a suitable $I(x)$, the new equation,

$$I(x)\frac{dy}{dx} + I(x)p(x)y = I(x)q(x), \tag{4.20}$$

has a left-hand side that can be written as the derivative of a product. Then integration of both sides allows us to solve the equation.

Rather than derive a suitable I from first principles, we simply check that the following formula works.

Frame 4.6   *Integration factor for a linear differential equation*

$$I(x) = e^{\int p(x)\,dx} = \exp\left(\int p(x)\,dx\right) \tag{4.21}$$

(There is no need for a constant of integration here.)

If it does work, then (4.20) should become

$$\frac{d}{dx}[I(x)y] = I(x)q(x). \tag{4.22}$$

This is seen to be the case because

$$\frac{d}{dx}[I(x)y] = I(x)y' + I'(x)y,$$

by the Product Rule, and we have

$$I'(x) = p(x)e^{\int p(x)\,dx} = p(x)I(x),$$

using the Chain Rule.

Integration of (4.22) gives the solution

$$I(x)y = \int I(x)q(x)\,dx + C, \tag{4.23}$$

from which y is easily found.

Example 4.18   Solve $x\dfrac{dy}{dx} + y = x^2.$

Firstly, divide throughout by the coefficient of $\frac{dy}{dx}$:

$$\frac{dy}{dx} + \frac{1}{x}y = x.$$

The integrating factor is therefore

$$I(x) = \exp\left(\int \frac{1}{x}\,dx\right) = \exp\left(\ln x\right) = x.$$

Multiply throughout by x:

$$x\frac{dy}{dx} + y = x^2,$$

which is the version we started with. But now we can confidently identify the solution method. This equation must have the form

$$\frac{d}{dx}[xy] = x^2.$$

(It is worth expanding the left-hand side to check this: $x\frac{dy}{dx} + \frac{dx}{dx}y = x\frac{dy}{dx} + y$, as required.) Integrate both sides:

$$xy = \int x^2\,dx = \tfrac{1}{3}x^3 + C,$$

from which we obtain the final (general) solution

$$y = \frac{1}{3}x^2 + \frac{C}{x}.$$

■

Think about it like this

It is very common for the integration involved in $I(x)$ to contain a logarithm, as in the previous example. Care is needed in dealing with it, so as to take advantage of the exponential to 'cancel' that logarithm. The following example also illustrates this.

Example 4.19   Solve $t\dfrac{dx}{dt} - 2x = t$.

Firstly, divide throughout by the coefficient of $\frac{dx}{dt}$:

$$\frac{dx}{dt} - \frac{2}{t}x = 1. \tag{4.24}$$

The integrating factor is therefore

$$I(t) = \exp\left(\int -\frac{2}{t}\,dt\right) = \exp\left(-2\ln t\right) = \exp\left(\ln t^{-2}\right) = t^{-2}.$$

Multiply throughout (4.24) – **not** the original equation – by $1/t^2$:

$$\frac{1}{t^2}\frac{dx}{dt} - \frac{2}{t^3}x = \frac{1}{t^2}.$$

This must have the form

$$\frac{d}{dt}\left[\frac{1}{t^2}x\right] = \frac{1}{t^2}.$$

(It is worth expanding the left-hand side to check this.) Integrate both sides:

$$\frac{1}{t^2}x = \int \frac{1}{t^2}\,dt = -\frac{1}{t} + C,$$

from which we obtain the final (general) solution

$$x = -t + Ct^2.$$

∎

Finally, we consider an example in which the coefficients of both y and $\frac{dy}{dx}$ are **constants**. This is the type of equation we considered in the previous section.

Example 4.20   Solve $\dfrac{dQ}{dt} + 5Q = e^{-2t}$.

There is no need for a preliminary division. Hence we move directly to the integrating factor

$$I(t) = \exp\left(\int 5\,dt\right) = \exp(5t) = e^{5t}.$$

Multiply throughout by this:

$$e^{5t}\frac{dQ}{dt} + 5e^{5t}Q = e^{5t}e^{-2t} \quad \Rightarrow \quad \frac{d}{dt}\left[e^{5t}Q\right] = e^{3t}.$$

Integrate both sides:

$$e^{5t}Q = \frac{1}{3}e^{3t} + C \quad \Rightarrow \quad Q = \frac{1}{3}e^{-2t} + Ce^{-5t}.$$

∎

Think about it like this

The general solution in this example – like those for the others in this section – is in two parts, one of which contains an arbitrary constant. This is consistent with what was assumed in §4.4.

What is different here, in this constant coefficient case, is that one term is a pure exponential, with a rate constant given by the negative of the coefficient of Q, while the other term has precisely the same form as the original right-hand side, but with a different coefficient. These properties persist for all constant coefficient problems and even extend to second and higher-order problems.

The integrating factor method appears to be powerful in its ability to solve any linear equation – whether with constant or variable coefficients – by reducing it to an integration problem. But there are two drawbacks.

One is that the method cannot be extended to higher orders of derivatives, unlike the method in §4.4.

The other is that the integrations can turn out to be intimidating. Thus, for the equation in Example 4.17, we would have to integrate

$$e^{\frac{R}{L}t} \sin \omega t,$$

which requires either a double integration by parts or the use of complex numbers. The earlier method used simple differentiation.

Ex 4.14 Find the general solution to each of the following linear equations:

$$\text{(a) } t\frac{dx}{dt} + 2x = t; \qquad \text{(b) } \frac{dQ}{dt} + 5Q = e^{3t}.$$

In the case of (b), verify the answer by using the constant coefficients solution method.

Ex 4.15 Find the particular solution to each of the following linear equations:

$$\text{(a) } x\frac{dy}{dx} - 3y = 1, \ \ y(1) = \tfrac{1}{6}; \qquad \text{(b) } \frac{dQ}{dt} - 2Q = 1, \ \ Q(0) = 1.$$

In the case of (b), verify the answer by using the constant coefficients solution method.

4.6 Revision Exercises

Ex 4.16 Find the particular solution to the differential equation

$$\frac{dy}{dx} = \frac{2x}{1 + x^2}$$

that satisfies $y(0) = 2$.

Ex 4.17 Solve the differential equation

$$y\frac{dy}{dx} = x\left(1 + y^2\right), \qquad y(0) = -2.$$

Express your answer in the form $y = f(x)$.

Ex 4.18 A conical tank is positioned with its axis vertical and its point at the bottom. The angle between its axis and its sloping side is α. It is filled with liquid. Use the formula for the volume of a cone ($\frac{1}{3}\pi r^2 h$) to show that when the depth is x m, the volume of liquid is $V = \frac{1}{3}\pi x^3 \tan^2 \alpha \, \mathrm{m}^3$.

Torricelli's Law tells us that, when a tap at the bottom is opened, the liquid flows out at a rate $-\frac{dV}{dt}$ equal to $k\sqrt{x}$, where k is a constant and x is the 'head' of liquid above the tap. Use the chain rule to show that

$$\frac{dx}{dt} = \frac{-k}{\pi \tan^2 \alpha} \frac{1}{x^{3/2}}.$$

Hence find the time taken for a full tank to empty, when it is filled to depth h m and the tap is opened.

Ex 4.19 Find the general solution to the differential equation

$$\frac{dx}{dt} + 2x = 1 + 10e^{3t}.$$

Ex 4.20 A tank is initially filled with 1000 litres of brine, containing 0.25 kg of salt per litre. Fresh brine containing 0.50 kg of salt per litre runs into the tank at a rate of 2 litres per second and the mixture (kept uniform by constant stirring) runs out at the same rate. Show that, if Q kg is the amount of salt in the tank at time t seconds, then

$$\frac{dQ}{dt} + \frac{Q}{500} = 1, \qquad Q(0) = 250.$$

Find the *equilibrium* value for Q, i.e., the value when Q would become constant.

The equation above is a linear one and the coefficients are constant. Find its solution.

Verify that Q never actually achieves its equilibrium value, but tends to it as $t \to \infty$.

5 NUMERICAL CALCULUS

Calculus was born out of the need to avoid lengthy approximate calculations using small non-zero quantities. In this chapter we appear to reverse the procedure: we shall replace calculus-type calculations using arithmetic ones.

There are several situations in which this is either essential or advisable. These include the following.

- It is only too easy to write down a differential equation that has a solution (in theory) but for which there is no method for deriving a formula for that solution. The numerical solution of such equations is a huge topic, with many software packages available. In §5.1 we look at a graphical method that delivers qualitative information, while in §5.2 we look at **Euler's method**, the simplest of computational schemes for quantitative estimates.

- Similarly, it is often a challenge to find anti-derivatives. There are many functions whose integrals cannot be expressed in terms of 'known' functions, for example, $\int e^{-x^2}\, dx$ plays a central role in statistics and 'exists' in the sense that there is a well-defined area under the graph of e^{-x^2}, no matter what limits we choose, but we cannot express this indefinite integral in terms of familiar functions. In §§5.3, 5.4 and 5.5 we explore **numerical integration**, which delivers methods for finding approximate values for definite integrals, to any desired accuracy.

- In some other contexts we may be aware that there is a function involved but have no formula for it. The best we can do is to find a finite set of values, e.g., by experiment. We may wish to integrate this function, as above, or even to differentiate it; §5.6 investigates **numerical differentiation**.

The methods we examine are much more accurate than the simple-minded approach of truncating the limits in the definitions of $f'(a)$ and $\int_a^b f(x)\, dx$. Ironically, the analysis that justifies this claim uses calculus.

5.1 Direction Fields

Consider the **differential equation**

$$\frac{dx}{dt} = f(t, x). \qquad (5.1)$$

It is often the case that we cannot solve equations in the form (5.1) to find a formula $x(t)$. The best we can do is to seek a graphical or tabular **approximation** to the solution.

The equation (5.1) tells us that, at the point $P(t, x)$, the **gradient** of any solution curve through P, which must be the value of the derivative, is $f(t, x)$. For this reason $f(t, x)$ is often called the **gradient function** for the differential equation. This observation is the basis for the following (approximate) graphical method.

1. The aim is to draw a graph of x against t. Select a set of grid points in the (t, x) plane – t horizontal, x vertical – usually with equal spacing in t and in x.

2. At each of these points, say (α, β), calculate the **gradient**, $m = f(\alpha, \beta)$.

3. Draw, through (α, β), a short line of gradient m. The full set of such lines is a **direction field**.

4. Select a starting point, e.g., using (a, b), corresponding to an initial condition $x(a) = b$. Move in the direction of its short line, bridging the gap to a nearby one and continuing in its direction, and so on. It may also be permissible to move backwards, in the negative t direction.

Example 5.1   A part of the direction field for the equation

$$\frac{dx}{dt} = \frac{2x}{1+t}$$

is shown below.

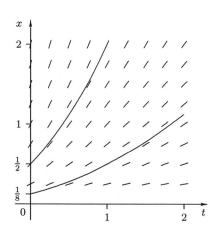

The particular solutions for which $x(0) = \frac{1}{8}$ and $x(0) = \frac{1}{2}$ have been superimposed. These are (exactly)

$$x(t) = A(1+t)^2, \quad A = \tfrac{1}{8}, \tfrac{1}{2}.$$

■

Example 5.2   (Logistic population growth.) A part of the direction field for the equation

$$\frac{dP}{dt} = P(1.75 - P)$$

is shown below.

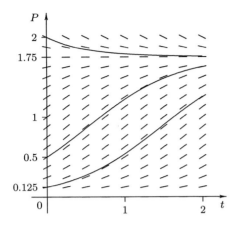

This attempts to model growth that is exponential for small population size, when P' is assumed to be approximately proportional to P. It takes into account, however, that there are limited resources for larger populations. Here, 1.75 (in the chosen unit) is the maximum sustainable population.

Three solutions have been superimposed. The lowest starts exponentially but tapers off as the 'ceiling' is approached, while the highest – initially larger than 1.75 – decreases towards that value. ∎

Ex 5.1 A certain body falling under air resistance has its velocity given by the differential equation

$$\frac{dv}{dt} = 1 - 0.8v.$$

Construct a direction field using values of v from 0 to 2 in steps of $1/4$, and values of t from 0 to 4 in steps of 1. *Note that the gradient function does not contain t, so that the elements drawn for $t = 0$ can be reused for all the other t values.*

Trace approximate solutions for the initial conditions $v(0) = 0$, 1.25, 2. Discuss these, noting that the exact solution is $v(t) = 1.25 + Ae^{-0.8t}$.

5.2 Euler's Method

The graphical method in the previous section is easily quantified, to produce a **numerical** method suitable for large-scale computation.

We consider the same differential equation, but this time we include an **initial condition**.

$$\frac{dx}{dt} = f(t, x), \qquad x(a) = b, \tag{5.2}$$

where a is the value of t at which we know the initial value b of x.

The aim is to construct a sequence of points:

$$(t_0, x_0) \, [= (a, b)], \ (t_1, x_1), \ (t_2, x_2), \ \ldots, \ (t_n, x_n),$$

where $x_n \simeq x(t_n)$, the true value for the solution $x(t)$ at $t = t_n$.

Think about it like this

> These points should be approximately those at the centres of the lines joined up in the direction field.

The key question is: how do we get from (t_k, x_k) to the next point (t_{k+1}, x_{k+1})? Consider the diagram below:

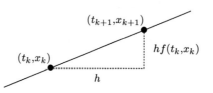

The only simple option we have at (t_k, x_k) is to follow the line drawn there, with gradient $m = f(t_k, x_k)$, which we write for convenience as f_k. The diagram shows the computation needed, which defines **Euler's method**.

Frame 5.1   *Euler's method*

$$t_{k+1} = t_k + h, \qquad\qquad t_0 = a \qquad\qquad (5.3)$$
$$x_{k+1} = x_k + hf(t_k, x_k), \qquad x_0 = b \qquad\qquad (5.4)$$
$$k = 0, 1, 2, \ldots, \qquad\qquad x_k \simeq x(t_k)$$

The quantity h here is a flexible parameter and can be adjusted as the solution progresses. A good implementation will reduce h if x starts to change more rapidly, so that it is less well approximated by long straight lines. Similarly, it will increase h if x becomes more constant. In examples and exercises we usually keep h fixed, at a specified value.

This process is particularly well-suited for tabular calculation, as we see in the next example.

Example 5.3   Use Euler's method, with $h = 0.1$, to approximate $x(1.4)$ where

$$\frac{dx}{dt} = t + x, \qquad x(1) = 5.$$

We enter $t_0 = 1$ and $x_0 = 5$. Then complete the table using Frame 5.1, choosing the most up-to-date values of t_k and x_k at each stage.

k	t_k	x_k	f_k	h	Euler calculation
0	1.0	5.0000	$1 + 5 = 6$	0.1	$5 + 0.1 \times 6 = 5.6$
1	1.1	5.6000	$1.1 + 5.6 = 6.7$	0.1	$5.6 + 0.1 \times 6.7 = 6.27$
2	1.2	6.2700	$1.2 + 6.27 = 7.47$	0.1	$6.27 + 0.1 \times 7.47 = 7.017$
3	1.3	7.0170	$1.3 + 7.017 = 8.317$	0.1	$7.017 + 0.1 \times 8.317 = 7.8487$
4	1.4	7.8487	—	—	—

The result of the calculation in "Euler calculation" is written in the next row, in the x_k column. The values in the f_k column are found using the t_k and x_k values immediately to the left

This equation is **linear** with constant coefficients and so can be solved using the method in Chapter 4. The true solution is

$$x(t) = \frac{7}{e}e^t - 1 - t \quad \Rightarrow \quad x(1.4) = 8.0428.$$

Hence the size of the error is 0.1941.

Using $h = 0.2$ gives $x(1.4) \simeq x_2 = 7.68$, with error 0.3628. This suggests that halving h approximately halves the error in each corresponding value. (The values have to be aligned correctly, since $x(1.4)$ is approximated by x_4 when $h = 0.1$ and x_2 when $h = 0.2$.)

That would mean that the error is approximately proportional to h. In principle, the sort of extrapolation device to be considered in §5.5 could be used (with some adjustment), but this is seldom cost-effective in this context.

∎

Think about it like this

The method is one of a type known as a **step-by-step** method. If the points in the table are graphed, you can think of them as *stepping stones* along the solution path, or rather along a path that we hope is near the solution path.

You are strongly recommended to use a table to control the calculation, such as that in the example above. In this simple method, all the data needed to start the new row is to be found **only** in the current row. Once you have done the calculation to find the new t_k and x_k, you need never consult that row again, but merely work with the row you have just started.

Think about driving along a road in which the gradient is varying and we seek to keep a record of our height above sea-level. We could do so by intermittently measuring the current gradient and using it to estimate the change in height associated with the distance travelled. That is effectively Euler's method: we find the slope of the curve (road), multiply it by the step-length h (horizontal distance to be travelled for the next part of the journey), to get the change in the height of the curve (road). This is added to the height above the x-axis (sea level) at the start of **this step** (not the start of the whole 'journey') to estimate the height at the end of this step (current height above sea level).

There is an important point to note about these tables. We start each row with 'known' information, use it to compute the rest of the row and then produce the new t_k and x_k numbers at the start of the next row. This means that a step of the process stops midway through the row: there is no need to complete it unless it is intended to start another step. The table in Example 5.3 uses '—' to show where to stop.

This also means that care is needed in reading the approximation required from the table. The x_k at the **start** of the row approximates $x(t_k)$ for the t_k **adjacent to it**.

Notation

Recall the need to take care in interpreting an initial condition $x(a) = b$, i.e., $x = b$ when $t = a$. This means that a is entered in the t-column and b in the x-column. *Failure to do this step correctly means that every subsequent calculation is worthless.*

For our second example, we choose a practical one, namely the **logistic growth** equation.

Example 5.4 Use Euler's method to calculate approximations for the differential equation

$$\frac{dP}{dt} = P(1.75 - P), \qquad P(0) = 0.125,$$

which corresponds to the lowest of the solutions in Example 5.2.

We choose $h = 0.25$ and work to 4 dp. The gradient function is $f(t, P) = P(1.75 - P)$, which happens to be independent of t in this case, but this is of no consequence. Also, $t_0 = 0$, $P_0 = 0.125$, which seeds the first row of the table.

k	t_k	P_k	f_k	h	Euler calculation
0	0	0.1250	0.2031	0.25	$0.1250 + 0.25 \times 0.2031$
1	0.25	0.1758	0.2767	0.25	$0.1758 + 0.25 \times 0.2767$
2	0.50	0.2450	0.3687	0.25	$0.2450 + 0.25 \times 0.3687$
3	0.75	0.3371	0.4763	0.25	$0.3371 + 0.25 \times 0.4763$
4	1.00	0.4562	—	—	—

The values in the f_k column are found using the P_k values immediately to the left, e.g.,

$$f_0 = P_0(1.75 - P_0) = 0.125 \times (1.75 - 0.125) = 0.2031.$$

The pairs (t_k, P_k) can now be compared with values read from the graph in Example 5.2. We stopped at $P(1) \simeq 0.4562$. Using more steps would give $P(5) \simeq 1.7488$, which is almost the maximum value achieved; indeed the gradient there is approximately $1.7488 \times (1.75 - 1.7488) = 0.0021$, which is quite small.   ∎

Euler's method is very rudimentary and is rarely used in its own right. But almost all the very powerful methods in use today stem from it. Indeed, an Euler calculation is often a first step in providing an input to the more accurate formulae that are available.

Ex 5.2 Use Euler's method, with $h = 0.1$, to estimate $x(0.5)$, where

$$\frac{dx}{dt} = t + x, \qquad x(0) = 1.$$

You may extend and complete the table below, in which the first step has been entered.

n	t_n	x_n	f_n	h	Euler calculation
0	0	1	$f(0, 1) = 0 + 1 = 1$	0.1	$x = 1 + 0.1 \times 1 = 1.1$
1	0.1	1.1			

Ex 5.3 Estimate the value of $x(0.5)$ for the initial-value problem

$$\frac{dx}{dt} = 2t\sqrt{1 - x^2}, \qquad x(0) = \frac{1}{\sqrt{2}},$$

using Euler's method with step size $h = 0.1$. Work to 5 dp.

Determine the exact solution of this equation and compare your results.

Ex 5.4 Use Euler's method with step size $h = 0.04$ to estimate $x(0.2)$, where

$$\frac{dx}{dt} = t - 2x, \qquad x(0) = 0.5.$$

Determine the exact solution of this equation and compare your results.

5.3   The Trapezium Rule

Suppose that we need to evaluate a definite integral $I = \int_a^b f(x)\,dx$, but we do not have a formula for an anti-derivative of $f(x)$. There are two (linked) ideas that we could use: the interpretation of the integral as the limit of a **sum**, and the link to **area**.

We could simply stop short of taking the limit (of the sum) and approximate the integral as a **finite** sum. We would not expect very good results if we do this in an unimaginative way, so we start by looking at the simplest **practical** method, whose formula has a structure common in this context. We choose a set of 'sample' points, find the function values and add them, suitably 'weighted'. Here we use weights $\tfrac{1}{2}h$ and h:

$$\int_a^b f(x)\,dx \simeq h\left[\tfrac{1}{2}f_0 + f_1 + f_2 + \cdots + f_{n-2} + f_{n-1} + \tfrac{1}{2}f_n\right]. \qquad (5.5)$$

The x_k points are equally-spaced between a and b, with $x_0 = a$, $x_n = b$ and $nh = b - a$. The term f_k is shorthand for $f(x_k) = f(a + kh)$; it is the **height** of the graph of the function at $x = x_k$.

> ### Think about it like this
> Thinking of the x_k as 'sample' points makes this seem reasonable, but why the factors of $1/2$ at the ends? A careful count will show that we have n intervals, but we are using $n + 1$ points. The two factors of $1/2$ reduce the 'weight' of the values at the end, so we effectively use the 'weight' of n points. But there is a deeper reason, one associated with enhancing the accuracy.

To derive this formula, we think of area, assuming for now that the function's graph lies entirely above the x-axis, although this is unnecessary. We divide $[a, b]$ into n equal subintervals using the points x_k. Then we approximate the curve between a and b using a sequence of straight lines joining the points $\big(x_k, f(x_k)\big)$: the dashed lines in the graph below. We *approximate* the area under the curve by the area under the straight lines.

Now this area can be broken into a collection of **trapezia**, where a trapezium is a four-sided figure with two of its sides parallel, as shown below.

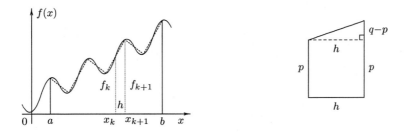

Consider the trapezium shown in the diagram, of width h and with sides p and q. Break it in two, using the dashed line, to find the area as:

$$hp + \tfrac{1}{2}h(q - p) = \tfrac{1}{2}h(p + q),$$

i.e., the area is the average of the parallel sides multiplied by the distance between them. This is true for any trapezium, even one without right angles.

Apply this to the trapezium selected in the left-hand diagram, where $p = f(x_k) = f_k$ and $q = f(x_{k+1}) = f_{k+1}$:

$$\int_{x_k}^{x_{k+1}} f(x)\, dx \simeq \tfrac{1}{2} h\left(f_k + f_{k+1}\right). \tag{5.6}$$

Then the integral from a to b is approximated by the sum of the estimates of each sub-integral:

$$
\begin{aligned}
I &= \int_a^b f(x)\, dx \\
&= \int_{x_0}^{x_1} f(x)\, dx + \int_{x_1}^{x_2} f(x)\, dx + \cdots + \int_{x_{n-1}}^{x_n} f(x)\, dx \\
&\simeq \tfrac{1}{2} h\left[f_0 + f_1\right] + \tfrac{1}{2} h\left[f_1 + f_2\right] + \cdots + \tfrac{1}{2} h\left[f_{n-2} + f_{n-1}\right] + \tfrac{1}{2} h\left[f_{n-1} + f_n\right] \\
&= h\left[\tfrac{1}{2} f_0 + f_1 + f_2 + \cdots + f_{n-2} + f_{n-1} + \tfrac{1}{2} f_n\right].
\end{aligned}
$$

This last result is the one already quoted as (5.5). It is the **(composite) trapezium rule**.

Strictly speaking, the term 'trapezium rule' refers to the 'basic' form in (5.6), which we now investigate briefly. We can rewrite this as

$$\int_a^b f(x)\, dx \simeq \tfrac{1}{2} h\left[f(a) + f(b)\right]. \tag{5.7}$$

Think about it like this

> The basic trapezium rule for integrating over the interval $[a, b]$ is easy to remember: the integral is approximated by the interval width $h = (b - a)$ times the average of the values of the function at the end-points $\frac{1}{2}[f(a)+f(b)]$. This is natural: recall that the (precise) mean value is the integral divided by $(b - a)$. This is a rearrangement of that result, using the average at the ends as an approximation to the true mean.

Example 5.5   The basic trapezium rule, applied to $I = \displaystyle\int_1^3 \frac{1}{1 + x}\, dx = \ln 2$, gives

$$I \simeq T(2) = \frac{1}{2}\left[\frac{1}{1 + 1} + \frac{1}{1 + 3}\right] \times (3 - 1) = \frac{3}{4},$$

i.e., a value of 0.75 compared to the exact value, 0.693 to 3 dp.   ■

Clearly, this is a very coarse estimate. If we wish high precision we need to find some way to improve the method and a good approach is to *compose* many copies of (5.7), as we did above, to obtain the **(composite) trapezium rule** in (5.5), repeated in the following frame.

Frame 5.2   *Composite trapezium rule*

$$\int_{x_0}^{x_n} f(x)\,dx \simeq T(h) = h\left[\frac{1}{2}f(x_0) + f(x_1) + f(x_2) + \cdots\right.$$

$$\left.\cdots + f(x_{n-1}) + \frac{1}{2}f(x_n)\right] \quad (5.8)$$

$$\text{where } nh = x_n - x_0,\ h = \frac{x_n - x_0}{n}$$

Before looking at a numerical example of the composite rule, we must address a very important issue in all numerical methods: how to estimate the accuracy of the result. There are formulae for the error in the trapezium rule, based on values of derivatives of $f(x)$, which can sometimes be informative. This is not always viable and the **composite** rule again provides an alternative approach.

One of the most commonly used practical methods for error estimation is to perform the calculation several times, using the composite form with decreasing values of h, and then compare the results. There are risks involved, e.g., this cannot detect a **systematic** error affecting all the estimates. Nonetheless, it may be the only realistic option and is acceptable if used with care.

A glance at an earlier diagram suggests that the smaller h is, the better is the answer. This can be confirmed using the error formulae mentioned above. The **rounding error**, however, increases as h gets smaller, since more calculations are needed. Fortunately, this usually has little effect for the sizes of h used in practice.

The usual method for improving the accuracy of the trapezium rule is to *halve* the size of h at each step, a process called **interval-halving**. This is used in the following Example.

Example 5.6   The values below are for the function $f(x) = xe^{-x}$.

x	1.0	1.5	2.0	2.5	3.0
$f(x)$	0.36788	0.33470	0.27067	0.20521	0.14936

Let $I = \displaystyle\int_1^3 f(x)\,dx$, for which the exact value is 0.536 61 to 5 dp.

The basic trapezium rule, with $h = 2$, gives the estimate

$$T(2) = \tfrac{1}{2}\left[f(1) + f(3)\right] \times (3 - 1) = \tfrac{1}{2}\left[0.36788 + 0.14936\right] \times 2 = \mathbf{0.517\,24}.$$

Dividing the interval into two, so that $h = 1$, we find

$$T(1) = 1 \times \left[\tfrac{1}{2}f(1) + f(2) + \tfrac{1}{2}f(3)\right]$$
$$= \tfrac{1}{2} \times 0.36788 + 0.27067 + \tfrac{1}{2} \times 0.14936 = \mathbf{0.529\,29}.$$

Dividing the interval into four, so that $h = 0.5$, we find

$$T(0.5) = 0.5 \times \left[\tfrac{1}{2} f(1) + f(1.5) + f(2) + f(2.5) + \tfrac{1}{2} f(3) \right] = \mathbf{0.534\,60}.$$

The results are still quite inaccurate but are approaching the correct value increasingly fast.   ∎

Think about it like this

Computing more than one estimate involves extra work so the efficiency must be considered. In practice, it is the computation of the f_k values that dominates the workload, since the calculations associated with using the rule itself involve nothing more than additions and a few multiplications. There is a particularly efficient implementation when interval-halving is used, but we shall not pursue this here.

In most exercises you will be given a table pre-computed using the formula for the function. This is not a reflection of standard practice; rather it means you can concentrate your effort on the fundamental objective of the exercise. In practice, f_k values are not usually available free of charge!

Ex 5.5 Use the trapezium rule three times, with $h = 1$, 0.5, 0.25, to estimate $\displaystyle\int_1^2 f(x)\, dx$, where values of $f(x)$ are given in the table below.

x	1.00	1.25	1.50	1.75	2.00
$f(x)$	0.7071	0.6247	0.5547	0.4961	0.4472

5.4   Simpson's Rule

An alternative approach to better accuracy is to use a more accurate replacement for the graph of the function. It is always possible to find a **quadratic function** passing through the three points $\big(a, f(a)\big)$, $\big(c, f(c)\big)$ and $\big(b, f(b)\big)$, where c is the mid-point of the interval $[a, b]$, i.e., $c = \frac{a+b}{2}$. This quadratic coincides with $f(x)$ at these three points, so we hope it remains near $f(x)$ at other places.

We then integrate this quadratic and use the answer as an approximation to the target integral. The calculation is an elementary one, but is long and technical. It results in the basic **Simpson's rule**:

$$I \simeq \frac{b - a}{6} \left[f(a) + 4f\left(\tfrac{1}{2}(a + b)\right) + f(b) \right]. \tag{5.9}$$

Example 5.7   Reworking Example 5.5 (integrating $1/(1+x)$ from 1 to 3), we have

$$I \simeq \frac{3 - 1}{6} \left[\frac{1}{1 + 1} + 4 \times \frac{1}{1 + 2} + \frac{1}{1 + 3} \right] = \frac{25}{36}.$$

This is, to 3 dp, 0.694, a much better approximation to $\ln 2 \simeq 0.693$.   ∎

In spite of this significant improvement, the basic version of the rule is not always capable of producing the desired precision. One possibility is to try fitting a cubic or higher degree polynomial to the points passed through by the graph, but this proves to be ill-advised, for theoretical and practical reasons.

Instead, we implement a **composite** method, just as was done in the previous section for the trapezium rule. We fit quadratics to consecutive triples of data points. This means we estimate the area of two subintervals at a time, so there is a need for an *even number of subintervals*, i.e., an *odd number of values*. We have:

$$
\begin{aligned}
I &= \int_a^b f(x)\, dx \\
&= \int_{x_0}^{x_2} f(x)\, dx + \int_{x_2}^{x_4} f(x)\, dx + \cdots + \int_{x_{n-2}}^{x_n} f(x)\, dx \\
&\simeq \frac{2h}{6}\left[f_0 + 4f_1 + f_2\right] + \frac{2h}{6}\left[f_2 + 4f_3 + f_4\right] + \cdots + \frac{2h}{6}\left[f_{n-2} + 4f_{n-1} + f_n\right] \\
&= \frac{h}{3}\left[f_0 + 4f_1 + 2f_2 + 4f_3 + 2f_4 + \cdots + 2f_{n-2} + 4f_{n-1} + f_n\right].
\end{aligned}
$$

The result is a formula similar in structure to (5.8), but with different 'weights', i.e., coefficients for the f_k values.

Frame 5.3   *Composite Simpson's rule*

$$
\int_{x_0}^{x_n} f(x)\, dx \simeq S(h) = \frac{h}{3}\Big[f_0 + 4f_1 + 2f_2 + 4f_3 + 2f_4 + 4f_5 + \cdots
$$

$$
\cdots + 2f_{n-2} + 4f_{n-1} + f_n \Big] \quad (5.10)
$$

$$
\text{where } nh = x_n - x_0, \quad h = \frac{x_n - x_0}{n}
$$

Example 5.8   Rework Example 5.6, i.e., integrate xe^{-x} from 1 to 3.

The basic Simpson's rule, with $h = 1$, gives the estimate

$$
\begin{aligned}
S(1) &= \frac{3-1}{6}\left[f(1) + 4f(2) + f(3)\right] \\
&= \frac{1}{3}\left[0.36788 + 4 \times 0.27067 + 0.14936\right] = \mathbf{0.533\,31}.
\end{aligned}
$$

This is better than the trapezium rule estimate using the same data.

Dividing the interval into two groups of two, so that $h = 0.5$, we find

$$
S(0.5) = \frac{0.5}{3}\left[f(1) + 4f(1.5) + 2f(2) + 4f(2.5) + f(3)\right] = \mathbf{0.536\,37}.
$$

This is much better than any of the earlier estimates.   ∎

The variety of weights in Simpson's rule (1, 2 and 4) means that care is needed to make sure the calculations are carried out efficiently. One good method is to sum the various groups of values separately:

$$
\begin{array}{lll}
f_0 + f_n & \times 1 & \text{ADD} \\
f_1 + f_3 + f_5 + \cdots & \times 4 & \text{THE} \\
f_2 + f_4 + f_6 + \cdots & \times 2 & \text{RESULTS}
\end{array}
$$

The value obtained is then multiplied by $h/3$ to obtain the final result.

It is easy to jump to the conclusion that Simpson's rule is much better than the trapezium rule, making the latter redundant. This is *not* the case:

- The trapezium rule, with interval-halving, can be implemented in a very efficient way, so that only new f_k values are used at each stage; the real costs in all such methods is the evaluation of these. There is no such implementation for Simpson's rule. Recall that interval reduction, and the comparison of results, is the simplest way to estimate the error.

- If the Simpson's rule results are really needed, they can be calculated from the trapezium rule results at virtually no cost, as we see in the next section.

- The trapezium rule can even out-perform Simpson's rule in some cases, e.g., when the function is strongly **periodic**. See the example that follows.

Example 5.9   Estimate $\int_0^{\pi/2} \sin^2 x\, dx$ using the basic trapezium rule.

Choose $h = \pi/2$ and hence points $x_0 = 0$, $x_1 = \pi/2$.

$$
I \simeq \frac{1}{2}\left[\sin^2 0 + \sin^2 \frac{\pi}{2}\right] \times \left(\frac{\pi}{2} - 0\right) = \frac{1}{2}(0+1) \times \frac{\pi}{2} = \frac{\pi}{4},
$$

which is **exact**! In this case, Simpson's rule is also exact but at greater computational cost. ∎

Ex 5.6 Use both the trapezium rule and Simpson's rule, with $h = 0.5$, to estimate $\int_0^2 f(x)\, dx$, where values of $f(x)$ are given in the table below.

x	0.0	0.5	1.0	1.5	2.0
$f(x)$	0.0000	0.1951	0.3828	0.5556	0.7072

5.5 Richardson's Extrapolation

There is an unexpected bonus to interval-halving. When the function is well-behaved the results exhibit a trend that is far from random. It is possible to quantify the changes that are happening as we halve h and then **extrapolate** (forecast) what would happen if h were further reduced. This method, known as **Richardson's extrapolation** involves trivially easy calculation and so can jump forward in the sequence at a fraction of the cost of direct calculation.

Experimentation with cases where the exact answer is known shows that in almost all applications of the trapezium rule, when the interval h is **halved**, the error is approximately **quartered**. This suggests that the error satisfies

$$T(h) - I \simeq Ah^2, \tag{5.11}$$

for some constant, but unknown, A. This can be justified by a difficult analysis, provided the function is 'well-behaved'.

This discovery can be put to use as follows: choose an interval of width $2h$ and also one of half that width, i.e., h. Then from (5.11):

$$T(2h) - I \simeq A(2h)^2 = 4Ah^2, \tag{5.12}$$
$$T(h) - I \simeq Ah^2. \tag{5.13}$$

Now, $4 \times (5.13) - (5.12)$ eliminates the unknown A and gives

$$4T(h) - T(2h) - 4I + I \simeq 0,$$

which produces the following formula.

Frame 5.4   *Richardson's extrapolation for the trapezium rule*

$$I \simeq \frac{1}{3}\left[\,4T(h) - T(2h)\,\right] \tag{5.14}$$

Although this new estimate is still not exact, it is usually very much better than either $T(h)$ or $T(2h)$ and is obtained by an easy calculation.

Think about it like this

Observe that this calculation is a sort of *weighted average*. The two values are given weights $4/3$ and $-1/3$, which add up to 1. This means that the result should be a similar size to the input values. Note, too, that the greater weight is given to the better estimate, i.e., that associated with the smaller h value.

Example 5.10 Apply Richardson's extrapolation to the trapezium rule results found in Example 5.6.

Using the results in the earlier example:

$$\frac{4T(0.5) - T(1)}{3} = \frac{4 \times 0.53460 - 0.52929}{3} = \mathbf{0.536\,37}.$$

(Note that this is the same as $S(0.5)$.)

This trivial calculation is all that is required to use the method. In this case, however, we happen to know the exact answer and it is worth taking the time to inspect the errors in these estimates. They are:

$$0.01937, \qquad 0.00732, \qquad 0.00201,$$

whose successive ratios (0.38 and 0.27) are approaching $\frac{1}{4}$ ($= 0.25$), as claimed above. ■

Think about it like this

The observation about $S(0.5)$ is no accident. Application of this extrapolation method to $T(2h)$ and $T(h)$ is exactly equivalent to calculating $S(h)$.

Recall that there are efficient methods for going from $T(2h)$ to $T(h)$ and that the extrapolation calculation is trivial. This confirms the claim made earlier that using the trapezium rule to implement Simpson's rule is particularly efficient.

The same approach can be used for Simpson's rule, but this time the errors usually decrease by a factor of 16, when h is halved. This implies the error is approximately of the form

$$S(h) - I \simeq Ah^4. \tag{5.15}$$

A similar analysis produces the following version of Richardson's extrapolation.

Frame 5.5   *Richardson's extrapolation for Simpson's rule*

$$I \simeq \frac{1}{15} \left[16S(h) - S(2h) \right] \tag{5.16}$$

Think about it like this

Again take note of the format: this is a weighted average with the larger weight given to be better input answer, i.e., that associated with the smaller h value.

Example 5.11   Apply Richardson's extrapolation to the Simpson's rule results found in Example 5.8.

As in the trapezium case, we have the extrapolation:

$$\frac{16S(0.5) - S(1)}{15} = \frac{16 \times 0.53637 - 0.53331}{15} = \mathbf{0.536\,57}.$$

This is the best estimate we have computed to date; the exact answer is **0.536 61**.

Again we can calculate the errors in this case:

$$0.000330, \qquad 0.000024,$$

whose ratio (0.073) is fairly near to $\frac{1}{16}$ ($= 0.062$). ■

Think about it like this

These rules usually work better than illustrated above. The function xe^x is a tricky one for numerical integration, since it increases rapidly at the right of the interval, where its derivative is large. It has been chosen for that reason, to bring out the differences in performance.

Ex 5.7 Use the values calculated in Exercise 5.5 to obtain improved estimates of the integral.

Ex 5.8 Use Simpson's rule, with $h = 0.5$, to estimate $\int_1^3 f(x)\,dx$, where values of $f(x)$ are given in the table below.

x	1.0	1.5	2.0	2.5	3.0
$f(x)$	0.70711	0.63246	0.57735	0.53452	0.50000

Given that Simpson's rule with $h = 1.0$ leads to the estimate 1.17217, find an improved estimate using Richardson's extrapolation.

Ex 5.9 Investigate numerical integration applied to the following integral

$$\int_0^1 f(x)\,dx = \int_0^1 \frac{1}{1+x^2}\,dx = \tfrac{\pi}{4} = 0.785\,398.$$

The appropriate values for $f(x)$ (at x values spaced by 0.25) are given by

x	0.00	0.25	0.50	0.75	1.00
$f(x)$	1.000 000	0.941 176	0.800 000	0.640 000	0.500 000

(a) Apply the trapezium rule using $h = 1$, 0.5, 0.25 and use Richardson's extrapolation on the last two.

(b) Let the first trapezium rule estimate be $T(1)$. Then calculate $T(0.5) = \frac{1}{2}T(1) + 0.5f(0.5)$ and $\frac{1}{2}T(0.5) + 0.25[f(0.25) + f(0.75)]$.

(c) Apply Simpson's rule using $h = 0.5$ and 0.25.

(d) Identify any of the above numbers that match and discuss what this suggests about an *efficient* calculation process, if we assume that each value of $f(x)$ must be calculated when needed – rather than read from a table – and that this is very time-consuming.

5.6 Numerical Differentiation (Optional)

The value of a derivative is defined as a limit 'as $h \to 0$'. This suggests that **approximate** values may be obtained by halting the limiting process, i.e., using a non-zero value of h in the definition. To estimate the derivative of $f(x)$ at a **fixed** point a, we could choose a (small) non-zero value h and use:

$$f'(a) \simeq \frac{f(a+h) - f(a)}{h}. \tag{5.17}$$

This quantity is the gradient of the (dashed) line in the left-hand graph below, joining the two points at $x = a$ and $x = a + h$. That line is an approximation to the tangent at a. Hence its gradient is an approximation to that of the tangent, which is the derivative we seek. We would expect that the smaller h is, the more accurate should be the formula.

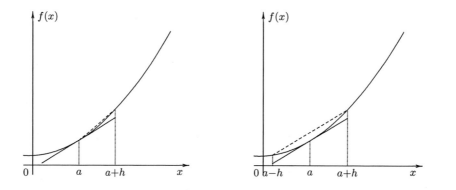

This **one-sided** estimate – it uses information either to the left or the right of the given point – can give reasonable values, but it is more usual to apply the so-called **central difference formula**. This is similar, but is more symmetric and, as is often the case in numerical calculations, is more accurate as a result.

Frame 5.6   *Central-difference estimate for $f'(a)$*

$$f'(a) \simeq D(h) = \frac{f(a + h) - f(a - h)}{2h} \qquad (5.18)$$

This is illustrated in the right-hand graph, where the gradient of the (dashed) line is the approximation found. The greater accuracy of (5.18) is clear.

Example 5.12   Differentiate $\sin x°$ at $x = 10$, using a numerical estimate with $h = 1$.

$$f'(10) \simeq \frac{1}{2 \times 1} [\sin 11° - \sin 9°] = \mathbf{0.017\,187}.$$

Note that $\frac{\pi}{180} \cos 10° = 0.017\,188$.   ∎

Notation

> The formula for numerical differentiation uses $f(a + h)$ and $f(a - h)$. You need to be aware of what these mean. We are using the function $f(x)$ with 'arguments' $a + h$ and $a - h$. Note the values of a and h to be used, calculate $a + h$ and $a - h$, then look up the given table (or use the given function formula) with these numbers as inputs, to find the required output values.

The error involved in using (5.18) turns out to be almost proportional to h^2 and hence it is possible to consider use of **Richardson's extrapolation**, if interval-halving is used. Suppose we have found two estimates $D(2h)$ and $D(h)$, using intervals $2h$ and h, respectively. A better value is usually obtained by the same weighted average as for the trapezium rule.

Frame 5.7 *Richardson's extrapolation for numerical differentiation*

$$f'(a) \simeq \frac{1}{3}\left[4D(h) - D(2h)\right] \tag{5.19}$$

Example 5.13 Differentiate $\ln x$ at $x = 4$, using a numerical estimate with $h = 1$, 0.5 and Richardson's extrapolation (RE).

Use the formulae in Frames 5.6 and 5.7.

$$h = 1 \qquad f'(4) \simeq \tfrac{1}{2}[\ln 5 - \ln 3] = \mathbf{0.255\,413},$$
$$h = 0.5 \qquad f'(4) \simeq [\ln 4.5 - \ln 3.5] = \mathbf{0.251\,314},$$

$$\text{RE} = \frac{1}{3}\left[4 \times 0.251\,314 - 0.255\,413\right] = \mathbf{0.249\,948}.$$

The exact answer is $\frac{1}{x} = 0.25$ at $x = 4$. ∎

Think about it like this

A straightforward application of the **Taylor series** justifies this extrapolation:

$$f(a + h) = f(a) + hf'(a) + \tfrac{1}{2}h^2 f''(a) + \tfrac{1}{6}h^3 f'''(a) + \cdots,$$
$$f(a - h) = f(a) - hf'(a) + \tfrac{1}{2}h^2 f''(a) - \tfrac{1}{6}h^3 f'''(a) + \cdots.$$

Subtract these to find

$$f(a + h) - f(a - h) = 2hf'(a) + \tfrac{1}{3}h^3 f'''(a) + \cdots,$$

then divide by $2h$,

$$\frac{f(a + h) - f(a - h)}{2h} = f'(a) + \tfrac{1}{6}h^2 f'''(a) + \cdots,$$

which confirms the approximate formula and shows the *principal error term* is proportional to h^2.

Unlike the trapezium rule, the central difference approximation is often unreliable. It may give bad results if h is chosen to be very small, since the rounding error becomes disproportionately large. Yet choosing a larger h may give poor results since the formula is inaccurate for large h.

Finally, note that the method can give an 'answer' in cases where there is none! Thus, for the absolute value function $|x|$ at $x = 0$, we have

$$f'(0) \simeq \frac{|0 + h| - |0 - h|}{2h} = \frac{h - h}{2h} = 0,$$

no matter what is the value of h. But the graph has no tangent at $x = 0$ and hence no gradient; there is no derivative to evaluate. (The **one-sided** formula produces values $+1$ when $h > 0$ and -1 when $h < 0$, consistent with the gradient of the graph on each side of $x = 0$.)

Ex 5.10 Switch your calculator to radian measure and consider the estimation of derivatives of $f(x) = \sin x$, using various values h in the formula

$$f'(a) \simeq \frac{f(a + h) - f(a - h)}{2h}.$$

The answers should be $\cos x$ (approximately).

First choose $a = 0.5$ and $h = 0.02$ and compare the answer with $\cos 0.5$. Find the error: approx. value $- \cos 0.5$.

Repeat these calculations using $h = 0.01$, and check that the ratio of the errors for the two different h values is approximately 0.25. Use a Richardson extrapolation to improve the second value.

Ex 5.11 Numerical differentiation is a potentially unstable calculation. Significantly different answers can be obtained from different calculators due to different rounding accuracy and conventions being inflated by the process. To fix attention on this, we set out with data deliberately rounded to 4 dp.

The following table represents a function $f(x)$. Use it to estimate $f'(1.0)$ by means of the central difference formula, accelerated by Richardson's extrapolation. Use $h = 0.8$, 0.4, 0.2.

x	0.2	0.6	0.8	1.2	1.4	1.8
$f(x)$	0.2013	0.6367	0.8881	1.5095	1.9043	2.9422

The function $f(x)$ is in fact $f(x) = \sinh x$. Compute $f'(1.0)$ exactly and compare it with the result above.

5.7 Revision Exercises

Ex 5.12 Use **Euler's method** with $h = 0.1$ to complete the following table, in order to estimate $x(0.7)$, where

$$\frac{dx}{dt} = 2xt, \qquad x(0.5) = 1.$$

n	t_n	x_n	f_n	h	Euler calculation
0				0.1	
1					
2					

Ex 5.13 Consider the differential equation

$$\frac{dx}{dt} = x\sqrt{1 + x^3}, \quad x(1) = 1.$$

Use Euler's method with step size $h = 0.1$ to find an approximate value for $x(1.2)$, expressing your answer to 4 dp.

Ex 5.14 Use both the trapezium rule and Simpson's rule with $h = 0.5$ to estimate $\int_0^2 f(x)\,dx$, where $f(x)$ is given in the table below.

x	0.0	0.5	1.0	1.5	2.0
$f(x)$	0.6931	0.6419	0.5878	0.5306	0.4700

Ex 5.15 Use Simpson's rule with $h = 0.5$ to estimate $\int_0^2 f(x)\,dx$, where $f(x)$ is given in the table below.

x	0.0	0.5	1.0	1.5	2.0
$f(x)$	0.0000	0.1516	0.3679	0.5020	0.5413

Given that Simpson's rule with $h = 0.25$ leads to the estimate 0.6468, find an improved estimate using Richardson's extrapolation.

6   FUNCTIONS and GRAPHS

Functions have, until now, been specified by formulae of the form $y = f(x)$, which have in turn been used to draw **graphs**. This formulation is sometimes too strict. It does not reflect any **symmetry** that may be present in the graph, since x and y have very different roles in the formula. Also, the key property that each x leads to a single y is not consistent with the properties of some useful curves. The **circle** $x^2 + y^2 = a^2$ is an example of both issues. We shall examine three alternatives that do not suffer these disadvantages.

6.1   Implicit Functions

We have specified a functional relationship between x and y using an **explicit** formula of the form

$$y = f(x). \tag{6.1}$$

There are situations where it is impossible to find such a formula, e.g., the solutions of some separable differential equations. There are also situations where there is a better option.

A function may be specified **implicitly** by an equation linking x and y:

$$F(x, y) = 0. \tag{6.2}$$

Choosing a value of x, say $x = a$, will generate an equation $F(a, y) = 0$, which can be solved, at least in theory, for y, e.g., giving $y = b$. This provides one of the key features of a function: a value for x determines a value for y. The point (a, b) can be plotted in a graph.

Example 6.1   Consider $y^3 + (y - 2)x^2 = 0$.
Suppose we choose $x = a$. Then the cubic equation

$$f(y) = y^3 + a^2 y - 2a^2 = 0$$

gives possible values of y to correspond with that value of x. In this case there is **at least one** such y, since every cubic equation has a real root. Indeed, there is only one root and hence **precisely one** y value for each x, as needed for a function.

Applying this to a selection of x values
will produce an outline graph, e.g.,

$$x = 1 \quad \Rightarrow \quad y^3 + y - 2 = 0$$
$$\Rightarrow \quad y = 1.$$

We can also use symmetry: x and $-x$ lead
to the same equation for y, so points on the
graph appear in (x, y) and $(-x, y)$ pairs.
Therefore the function is **even**.

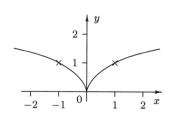

■

There may be a problem in some cases. There is no guarantee that the equation $F(a, y) = 0$ has only **one** solution for y, as required for a true function. The resolution of this problem is like that for inverse functions: we stipulate precisely which of the possible values of y we wish, whenever there is a choice.

In fact this 'problem' may be an advantage. Consider one of the most familiar implicit definitions, that for a **circle** radius a:

$$x^2 + y^2 = a^2.$$

The alternative formula $y = \sqrt{a^2 - x^2}$ is clearly less attractive. The square root offers two values. We may choose either, but that will give only half the graph: choosing $y \geqslant 0$ gives the upper semicircle and $y \leqslant 0$ the lower semicircle. Also, the fact that each value of x gives rise to **two** possible values of y shows this is not a true functional relationship.

Implicit definitions are popular for specifying symmetric curves like the circle, which do not treat either the x or y axis as more fundamental than the other. This makes an implicit relationship more natural: it leaves open the choice of which variable we may wish to regard as independent.

The curve-function relationship is summed up as follows. A curve (or curves) may be specified **implicitly** by an equation linking x and y, of the form in (6.2). The curve is a **union** – a combination – of the graphs of several **functions**. A circle is the union of the graphs of $y = \sqrt{a^2 - x^2}$ and $y = -\sqrt{a^2 - x^2}$.

Example 6.2 The equation $\dfrac{x^2}{a^2} + \dfrac{y^2}{b^2} = 1$, $(a, b > 0)$, defines an **ellipse**.

Changing x to $-x$ does not change the equation, since $(-x)^2 = x^2$, nor does changing y to $-y$. Hence the graph is symmetric about both axes. This means we need only investigate it in the first quadrant, using the symmetry to draw the rest.

Suppose $x > a$. Then $\dfrac{y^2}{b^2} = 1 - \dfrac{x^2}{a^2} < 0$, which is impossible. So also is $y > b$. The ellipse is therefore confined within a rectangle, $-a \leqslant x \leqslant a$, $-b \leqslant y \leqslant b$. At the boundary of the rectangle:

$$x = \pm a \quad \Rightarrow \quad y^2 = 0, \quad \Rightarrow \quad y = 0,$$
$$y = \pm b \quad \Rightarrow \quad x^2 = 0, \quad \Rightarrow \quad x = 0.$$

Calculate a few other values, e.g.,

$$x = \frac{a}{2} \quad \Rightarrow \quad \frac{y^2}{b^2} = \frac{3}{4} \quad \Rightarrow \quad y = \pm\frac{\sqrt{3}}{2}b.$$

Sketch this information in the first quadrant, then extend it to the others using the double symmetry. The **axes** are $2a$ and $2b$:

$\max(a, b)$ is the **semi-major** axis,
$\min(a, b)$ is the **semi-minor** axis.

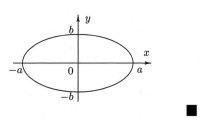

■

Further analysis of these functions requires access to derivatives. There are ways to find $\frac{dy}{dx}$ (or $\frac{dx}{dy}$) using the Chain Rule, but we shall defer this until the next two chapters, where we will find more straightforward methods.

Ex 6.1 A **hyperbola** can be defined by

$$\frac{x^2}{a^2} - \frac{y^2}{b^2} = 1.$$

(There is a similar, but different, hyperbola that uses '$= -1$'.)

Explain why the hyperbola is symmetric about both the x and y axes. In fact, if (x, y) lies on the curve, so do $(x, -y)$, $(-x, y)$ and $(-x, -y)$.

Initially, assume that $x \geqslant 0$ and $y \geqslant 0$, concentrating on the properties in the first quadrant only. Explain why we can have no points in the interval $0 \leqslant x < a$. Further, explain why we can have no points with $y \geqslant \frac{b}{a}x$.

Show that, as $x \to \infty$, $\frac{y}{x} \to \frac{b}{a}$, which means that the line $y = \frac{b}{a}x$ is an **asymptote**: a line the curve approaches but never meets.

Use this information to sketch that part of the curve $\dfrac{x^2}{4} - \dfrac{y^2}{1} = 1$ in the first quadrant. Then use symmetry to extend this to the other three quadrants.

Ex 6.2 The aim is to draw the graph defined by

$$x^{2/3} + y^{2/3} = 1.$$

Explain why the graph lies inside the square $-1 \leqslant x \leqslant 1$, $-1 \leqslant y \leqslant 1$ and is symmetric about both axes. Note that interchanging x and y does not change the equation, so the graph is also symmetric about the line $x = y$.

Find the point on the graph, in Quadrant 1, where $x = y$. Find y when $x = 0.5,\ 0.75,\ 0.9,\ 1$. Hence sketch the graph in all four quadrants.

6.2   Parametric Representation

It is possible to define a functional relationship between x and y through a third-party or 'proxy' variable, say t. If we know functions

$$x = f(t), \qquad y = g(t), \tag{6.3}$$

then choosing a specific value of t, say T, gives values $X = f(T)$ and $Y = g(T)$ and (X, Y) can be plotted as part of a graph. (6.3) is called a **parametric representation** of the curve.

Notation

We can use any variable, u, θ, etc. We can even use x: $y = f(x)$ can be interpreted, parametrically, as $(x, y(x))$.

Think about it like this

There is a natural occurrence of such a representation: where t measures **time**. Indeed, that is why the symbol t is often used. Suppose we walk along a curve and at each time t we measure and record our x and y coordinates. These are then **functions of time** and the point is $(x(t), y(t))$. The functions $x(t)$ and $y(t)$ completely determine the curve. A similar example is a 'tracer' placed on a vehicle; it transmits data giving, for each value of time, the x (east) and y (north) coordinates so that its path can be traced on a map.

Example 6.3   An electron, charge e, mass m, when injected into an electric field E with velocity u has position:

$$x = ut, \quad y = -\frac{1}{2}\frac{eE}{m}t^2.$$

From the first equation, $t = \dfrac{x}{u}$. Hence

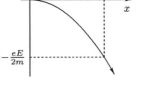

$$y = -\frac{1}{2}\frac{eE}{m}\frac{x^2}{u^2} = -\left(\frac{eE}{2mu^2}\right)x^2,$$

a **parabola**. In the graph here, the point corresponding to $t = 1$ has been indicated. ∎

Example 6.4   Find parametric representations for the **circle** $x^2 + y^2 = a^2$, the **hyperbola** $x^2 - y^2 = a^2$ and the **parabola** $y^2 = x$.

From the diagram, using t as the angle of rotation about the centre of the circle,

$$x = a\cos t, \quad y = a\sin t,$$

gives a parametric representation. Note that

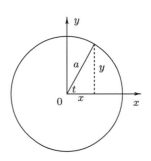

$$x^2 + y^2 = a^2\cos^2 t + a^2\sin^2 t = a^2,$$

as required.

Recall that $\cos t$ and $\sin t$ are often referred to as *circular* functions. Following that up, we find the *hyperbolic* functions deliver a similar parametric representation for the hyperbola:

$$x = a\cosh t, \; y = a\sinh t \quad \Rightarrow \quad x^2 - y^2 = a^2(\cosh^2 t - \sinh^2 t) = a^2,$$

using (1.7).

For the parabola, a common parametrisation is $x = t^2$, $y = t$. Then $y^2 = t^2 = x$, as required. ∎

We may encounter the same problem as in §6.1: the possibility of more than one value of y for some x. If we choose a desired value of x, we must solve $x = f(t)$ to find a suitable t to use in $y = g(t)$ to calculate y. But this equation may give more than one t and hence more than one y, contradicting the requirements for a function. Like implicit curves, a parametric curve is in general the union of the graphs of more than one function.

Example 6.5   Consider the curve $x = t^3 - t$, $y = t^2$, particularly at the point $(0, 1)$.

Start by exploring some simple points:

$$y = 1 \quad \Rightarrow \quad t^2 = 1 \quad \Rightarrow \quad t = \pm 1,$$
$$t = 1 \quad \Rightarrow \quad x = 0,$$
$$t = -1 \quad \Rightarrow \quad x = 0.$$

Hence $(0, 1)$ appears to be visited twice.

Also, $t = 0 \ \Rightarrow \ x = y = 0$, and

$$-1 < t < 0 \quad \Rightarrow \quad x > 0,$$
$$0 < t < 1 \quad \Rightarrow \quad x < 0.$$

This parametrisation generates a **loop** as shown in the graph, where the arrow indicates increasing t.

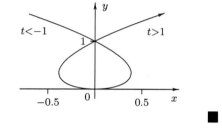

■

Ex 6.3

(a) A circle of radius $a > 0$ has a parametric representation $x = a \cos t$, $y = a \sin t$. What curve would you expect to be represented by

$$x = a \cos t, \qquad y = b \sin t,$$

where $a, b > 0$? Draw a rough sketch of the curve when $a = 2$ and $b = 1$.

(b) What curve would you expect to be represented by

$$x = t \cos t, \qquad y = t \sin t?$$

(Tabulate x and y for $t = 0$ to 3π in steps of $\frac{\pi}{2}$, and for $t = \frac{\pi}{4}$; then draw a rough sketch of the curve.)

Ex 6.4 Show that the curve in Exercise 6.2 $\left(x^{2/3} + y^{2/3} = 1\right)$ may also be expressed parametrically by

$$(x, y) = (\cos^3 t, \sin^3 t).$$

6.3   Calculus for Parametric Representations

Finding $\frac{dy}{dx}$ for a parametric curve is straightforward, but first we introduce another notation for a derivative, a notation that provides particularly neat formulae in this context. We write

$$\frac{dx}{dt} = \dot{x}, \qquad \frac{d^2x}{dt^2} = \ddot{x}.$$

Notation

This notation was invented by Newton. Although it is normally reserved for *time* differentiation, there is nothing to stop us using it here, especially since t is our default parameter. We shall not require the second derivative in this chapter, but the double-dot notation is very common in second-order differential equations, with time as the driving variable.

We differentiate (6.3):

$$\frac{dx}{dt} = f'(t), \qquad \frac{dy}{dt} = g'(t),$$

leading to the required rule.

Frame 6.1   *Differentiation using a parametric representation*

$$\frac{dy}{dx} = \frac{dy/dt}{dx/dt} = \frac{g'(t)}{f'(t)} = \frac{\dot{y}}{\dot{x}} \qquad (6.4)$$

Think about it like this

The rule for finding the first derivative for a parametrically defined function is straightforward and very natural. The last version above, i.e., $\dot{y}/\dot{x}$, is analogous to the definition of *gradient*, i.e., change in y ÷ change in x.

Example 6.6   Find an expression for $\frac{dy}{dx}$ when (x, y) lies on the circle in Example 6.4.

Differentiating $x = a\cos t$ and $y = a\sin t$ gives

$$\dot{x} = -a\sin t, \qquad \dot{y} = a\cos t$$

and hence

$$\frac{dy}{dx} = \frac{\dot{y}}{\dot{x}} = \frac{a\cos t}{-a\sin t} = -\cot t.$$

Note that

$$(-\cot t) \times \tan t = -\frac{\cos t}{\sin t} \cdot \frac{\sin t}{\cos t} = -1,$$

as we would expect, since $\tan t$ is the gradient of the radius from O to (x, y), which must be perpendicular to the tangent, whose gradient is $\frac{dy}{dx}$.   ∎

For the **arc-length** s of the portion of the curve between the values α and β of t, as in the explicit formula case, we start with $ds^2 = dx^2 + dy^2$ and convert it to a more usable form:

$$s = \int_{t=\alpha}^{t=\beta} ds = \int_{\alpha}^{\beta} \frac{ds}{dt}\, dt = \int_{\alpha}^{\beta} \sqrt{\frac{dx^2 + dy^2}{dt^2}}\, dt,$$

which rearranges to give the desired result.

Frame 6.2   *Arc-length for a curve defined parametrically*

$$s = \int_{\alpha}^{\beta} \sqrt{\dot{x}^2 + \dot{y}^2}\, dt \qquad (6.5)$$

This formula is more symmetrical than that for an explicitly defined function, and thereby easier to recall.

Consider the **area** under the graph of y, between x values determined by $t = \alpha$ and β, i.e., between $x = a$ and $x = b$ where:

$$a = f(\alpha), \qquad b = f(\beta).$$

We can use the normal integral measure of area, with a 'substitution' to get a formula in terms of t.

Frame 6.3   *Area under a curve defined parametrically*

$$A = \int_{x=a}^{x=b} y\, dx = \int_{t=\alpha}^{t=\beta} y\, \frac{dx}{dt}\, dt = \int_{\alpha}^{\beta} g(t) f'(t)\, dt \qquad (6.6)$$

Example 6.7   A **cycloid** is the curve traced by a point P on the rim of a wheel, as the wheel rolls without slipping, along a horizontal line. Choose a coordinate system in which this line is the x-axis and the origin is at the initial position of P. Suppose the wheel has radius a. The coordinates of P are given by

$$x = a(t - \sin t), \quad y = a(1 - \cos t),$$

where t measures the angle rotated through by the wheel.

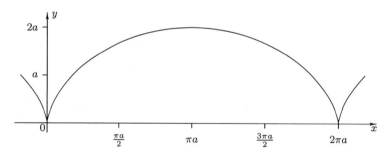

The corresponding function is **periodic**, with period $2\pi a$, which is the circumference of the wheel. Once it has rolled through an angle 2π it will be back to its initial position and will have travelled through a distance $2\pi a$.

We shall concentrate on the central arch of the graph. First of all, calculate

$$\dot{x} = a - a\cos t, \qquad \dot{y} = a\sin t.$$

The following calculations are good illustrations of the usefulness of the double- and half-angle formulae.

$$\left(\frac{ds}{dt}\right)^2 = \dot{x}^2 + \dot{y}^2 = a^2(1 - \cos t)^2 + a^2 \sin^2 t$$
$$= a^2 \left[1 - 2\cos t + \cos^2 t + \sin^2 t\right]$$
$$= a^2 \left[2 - 2\cos t\right]$$
$$= 2a^2 \left[1 - (1 - 2\sin^2 \tfrac{t}{2})\right]$$
$$= 4a^2 \sin^2 \tfrac{t}{2}.$$

Hence the length of the arch is

$$L = \int_0^{2\pi} \frac{ds}{dt}\, dt = \int_0^{2\pi} 2a \sin \tfrac{t}{2}\, dt$$
$$= \left[-4a \cos \tfrac{t}{2}\right]_0^{2\pi} = -4a(-1 - 1) = 8a.$$

The area of the arch is

$$A = \int_{x=0}^{x=2\pi a} y\, dx = \int_{t=0}^{t=2\pi} y \frac{dx}{dt}\, dt$$
$$= \int_0^{2\pi} a(1 - \cos t)a(1 - \cos t)\, dt$$
$$= a^2 \int_0^{2\pi} \left(1 - 2\cos t + \cos^2 t\right) dt$$
$$= a^2 \int_0^{2\pi} \left(1 - 2\cos t + \tfrac{1}{2} + \tfrac{1}{2}\cos 2t\right) dt$$
$$= a^2 \left[\tfrac{3}{2}t - 2\sin t + \tfrac{1}{4}\sin 2t\right]_0^{2\pi}$$
$$= a^2(3\pi - 0 + 0) = 3\pi a^2.$$

∎

Ex 6.5 If $x = 3\cos\theta - \cos^3\theta$ and $y = 3\sin\theta - \sin^3\theta$, show that $\frac{dy}{dx} = -\cot^3\theta$.

Ex 6.6 A **rectangular hyperbola** $xy = c^2$ may be represented parametrically by

$$x = ct, \qquad y = \frac{c}{t}.$$

(A rectangular hyperbola has its asymptotes perpendicular: here they are the coordinate axes.)

Suppose we wish to find the equation of a tangent to such a curve at a point given by t. We would require the gradient at the point. Find $\dot{x}$ and $\dot{y}$ and hence a formula for $\frac{dy}{dx} = \frac{\dot{y}}{\dot{x}}$ in terms of t. Apply this to the hyperbola that passes through $(4, 1)$, given the parametric representation above. You must first find values of c and t that will fix the particular hyperbola and point involved. Then find the gradient and tangent at $(4, 1)$.

Ex 6.7 Consider the curve defined by

$$x = t^3, \qquad y = t^2.$$

Find an expression for $\frac{dy}{dx}$ in terms of t.

Tabulate x, y and $\frac{dy}{dx}$ for $t = 0$, $\pm^1/_2$, ± 1, ± 2, and sketch the curve. Take note of the derivative when $t = 0$, which implies unusual behaviour at that point: the curve has a **cusp**.

Compute the area under the curve from $x = 0$ to $x = 8$, i.e., from $t = 0$ to $t = 2$.

Construct an integral giving the length of that portion of the curve from $x = 0$ to $x = 1$, i.e., from $t = 0$ to $t = 1$. Evaluate this integral using a substitution.

6.4   Polar Coordinates

It is found useful, when working with complex numbers, to interpret them as points in the Argand diagram in two different ways: the **cartesian form** $x + iy$ and the **polar form** $r(\cos\theta + i\sin\theta)$. The latter idea is commonly used as an alternative coordinate system for the (real) xy-plane, without the complex numbers.

Choose an origin O and a reference line L extending from O. Then a point P in the plane can be fixed by specifying its distance r from O and the angle OP makes with L, as shown in the diagram below. We call (r, θ) the **polar coordinates** of P.

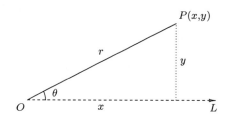

Notation

The **polar coordinate** system requires only the use of a point O and a line L. It is only when we want to convert between that system and the cartesian one that we have to introduce x and y axes. Then the almost universal convention is that the x-axis is chosen to be L.

We can easily pass from the polar form to the cartesian form (x, y).

Frame 6.4   Conversion from polar to cartesian coordinates

$$x = r\cos\theta, \qquad y = r\sin\theta \qquad\qquad (6.7)$$

We can also move in the opposite direction, but great care is needed in finding θ, just as for finding the direction of a vector or the polar form for a complex number.

Frame 6.5 *Conversion from cartesian to polar coordinates*

$$r = \sqrt{x^2 + y^2}, \qquad \theta = \tan^{-1}\frac{y}{x}, \text{ possibly } +\pi \text{ or } -\pi \qquad (6.8)$$

Example 6.8 Find the polar coordinates for the point $(-2\sqrt{2}, 2\sqrt{2})$.

First of all, $r = \sqrt{(-2\sqrt{2})^2 + (2\sqrt{2})^2} = \sqrt{8 + 8} = 4$.

Then $\tan\theta = (2\sqrt{2})/(-2\sqrt{2}) = -1$.

This does not, of itself, fix θ; $\tan^{-1}(-1) = -\frac{\pi}{4}$, but θ lies in the 2nd quadrant, since we see that $x < 0$ and $y > 0$. Hence we must adjust this value and choose $\theta = -\frac{\pi}{4} + \pi = \frac{3\pi}{4}$. ∎

Example 6.9 Convert the equation $x^2 + y^2 = a^2$ to polar coordinates and interpret the result.

Let $x = r\cos\theta$ and $y = r\sin\theta$:

$$x^2 + y^2 = r^2\cos^2\theta + r^2\sin^2\theta = r^2.$$

Hence $r^2 = a^2$, i.e., $r = a$.

The equation $r = a$ shows that the curve consists of all points distant a from the origin irrespective of θ, i.e., a **circle** radius a, consistent with the cartesian equation. ∎

This example shows that some curves may be expressed much more simply by using polar coordinates than cartesian ones. Indeed the expression

$$r = f(\theta)$$

is referred to as the **polar equation** of a curve or simply a **polar curve**.

Example 6.10 Convert the polar equation $r = 2a\cos\theta$ to cartesian coordinates and interpret the result.

Multiply by r: $r^2 = 2ar\cos\theta$, which translates to

$$x^2 + y^2 = 2ax \quad \Rightarrow \quad (x - a)^2 + y^2 = a^2.$$

This is a circle centre $(a, 0)$, radius a.
We can verify this from the diagram. OPQ
is a right-angle, so

$$r = OP = OQ\cos\theta = 2a\cos\theta.$$

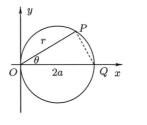

∎

Notation

It is a common convention that $r \geqslant 0$, but you may encounter the use of negative r. It is easy to convert to this: you merely travel along the line in the given θ direction, but in the negative sense, i.e., backwards. Polar coordinates are implemented in this way in some graphics calculators.

This functional form is particularly suited to the representation of curves with some sort of rotational symmetry, such as closed loops and spirals.

When considering such curves, we may wish to loosen the restrictions on θ, allowing it to venture outside the usual interval of $(-\pi, \pi]$. This is useful for functions $f(\theta)$ that are not **periodic** in θ, such as those that involve elements other than $\cos\theta$, $\sin\theta$, etc.

Example 6.11   Investigate the curve: $r = e^{-\frac{\theta}{\pi}}$.

Construct a table of r against θ:

θ	0	$\frac{\pi}{2}$	π	$\frac{3\pi}{2}$	2π	$\frac{5\pi}{2}$	3π	$\to \infty$
r	1	0.607	0.368	0.223	0.135	0.082	0.050	$\to$ 0

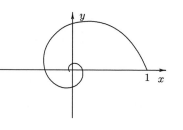

As θ increases indefinitely, r gets smaller and smaller, tending to 0. Plot this data. The curve is a **spiral**, heading towards the origin, but never reaching it. There are many spirals; this one is an **exponential spiral** and approaches O very quickly.

■

In sketching curves defined in polar form, we can use many of the devices for cartesian forms, such as looking for symmetry and using a table of values of r at convenient angles θ.

Example 6.12   The curve known as a **cardioid** is defined by $r = 1 + \cos\theta$.

Since $\cos(-\theta) = \cos\theta$, the r values for $0 \leqslant \theta \leqslant \pi$ will be the same as those for $-\pi \leqslant \theta \leqslant 0$. Hence we need only sketch the top half and reflect it in the x-axis.

Compute, and plot, some values.

θ	0	$\frac{\pi}{6}$	$\frac{\pi}{3}$	$\frac{\pi}{2}$	$\frac{2\pi}{3}$	$\frac{5\pi}{6}$	π
r	2	$1 + \frac{\sqrt{3}}{2}$	$\frac{3}{2}$	1	$\frac{1}{2}$	$1 - \frac{\sqrt{3}}{2}$	0

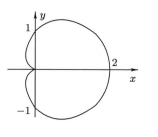

The curve is heart-shaped, which explains its name. An analysis of the gradient shows the tangent is vertical at $(2,0)$, when $\theta = 0$, and horizontal at $(0,0)$, when $\theta = \pi$. The point at $(0,0)$ is a **cusp**. (The cycloid also contains cusps.)

■

Finally, it is possible to calculate arc-lengths and areas for polar curves. The relevant formulae are given below, for reference.

Frame 6.6   Arc-length for a polar curve

$$s = \int ds = \int \left\{ r^2 (d\theta)^2 + (dr)^2 \right\}^{1/2} = \int_\alpha^\beta \left\{ r^2 + \left(\frac{dr}{d\theta} \right)^2 \right\}^{1/2} d\theta$$

Frame 6.7   Area of a sector of a polar curve

$$A = \int_\alpha^\beta \tfrac{1}{2} r^2 \, d\theta = \int_\alpha^\beta \tfrac{1}{2} [f(\theta)]^2 \, d\theta$$

Example 6.13   For the cardioid in the previous example, find its length and the the area it encloses.

Using symmetry to simplify a little, the two values are:

$$s = 2 \int_0^\pi [2 + 2 \cos \theta]^{1/2} \, d\theta = 8,$$

$$A = 2 \int_0^\pi \tfrac{1}{2} (1 + \cos \theta)^2 \, d\theta = \frac{3\pi}{2}.$$

The details for the evaluation of these integrals are similar to those for the cycloid in Example 6.7.   ∎

Ex 6.8   What are the polar coordinates of the points:

$$(x, y) = (1, 1), \quad (-2, 0), \quad (1, 2)?$$

What are the cartesian coordinates of the points:

$$(r, \theta) = (2, \pi/6), \quad (5, -\pi/4), \quad (3, 2\pi/3)?$$

Ex 6.9   Consider the curve $r = \frac{1}{\pi}\theta$. Construct a table of r, using values of θ from 0 to 3π in steps of $\frac{\pi}{4}$. Plot these points and identify the type of curve this function defines.

Ex 6.10   Consider the function defined by

$$r = \sin \theta + \cos \theta.$$

Multiply throughout by r and hence convert this to a cartesian equation. Show that this represents a circle, finding its centre and radius.

6.5   Revision Exercises

Ex 6.11 Find the equation of the tangent to the curve defined parametrically by

$$x = t^2, \qquad y = t + \sin(\pi t),$$

at the point given by $t = 1/2$.

Ex 6.12 A curve is defined parametrically by

$$\begin{cases} x = t - \frac{1}{2}t^2; \\ y = \frac{4}{3}t^{3/2}; \end{cases} \quad \text{with } 0 \leqslant t \leqslant 1.$$

Compute the area A under the curve and the length L of the curve.

Ex 6.13 A spiral is given by the polar equation

$$r(\theta) = e^\theta.$$

Find the cartesian coordinates of the point on the curve given by $\theta = \frac{\pi}{2}$.

7 PARTIAL DIFFERENTIATION

Hitherto, almost every function we have encountered has had **one** (input) variable. This is a severe limitation, if only because space has three dimensions, and physical processes often evolve in time as well. Hence, a straightforward mathematical model of a physical situation could involve **four** variables. Complicated models may use many more variables.

Think about it like this

> In complicated models with a large collection of inter-related objects there may be many variables. Thus, analysing gravitational attractions between 100 masses would require 300 variables: three space coordinates for each mass.
>
> But even a single factor in a real context can require **four** variables. An example we shall find useful later is atmospheric temperature. This depends on the position in the atmosphere and on time, the variables x, y, z and t.

7.1 Functions of Two or More Variables

A function of one variable may be defined by:

$$z = f(x) \qquad (x \text{ in } X),$$

and is often written as $z(x)$ or $f(x)$. Here x is the **independent** variable and z is the **dependent** variable. The set X is the **domain**.

A function with **two independent** (input) variables can be written

$$z = f(x, y). \tag{7.1}$$

A function of one variable can be represented as an input-output **process** and this readily extends to more variables. We simply have more inputs:

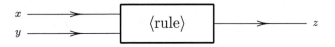

The **domain** is now a set of **pairs** of numbers. We must define the set of (x, y) values that lead to a valid function value. This can be thought of as a subset in the xy-plane. For example,

$$\{(x, y) \ : \ x \geqslant 0, \ y \geqslant 0\}$$

would define the domain to be the **first quadrant**. In most cases we will not have any restriction and, unless otherwise stated, the domain can be taken to be the entire xy-plane or all of xyz-space, etc.

Extension to more than two variables introduces no significant new ideas.

Example 7.1 Euler's method uses a **gradient function**, $f(t, x)$. We now see that this is a function of two variables. In Example 5.12, we had $f(t, x) = t + x$. There is no need for any restriction on its domain.

A full analysis of convergence and error bounds for this method makes heavy use of the type of differentiation we soon embark upon. ∎

One problem is how to visualise these functions, since we do not have available that most useful of tools: a simple graph. There are several possible devices, some of which are described in what follows. When considering these, it is useful to think of the function as representing a topographic terrain or landscape; z is the height (above 'sea-level') at a point with 'grid reference' (x, y) on a 'map'.

Notation

This topographic analogy is the best one for grasping the ideas that follow. We shall sometimes refer directly to N(orth) and E(ast), which can be taken to correspond to y and x, respectively. Having taken this step, we shall not hold back from references to NW, SE, etc.

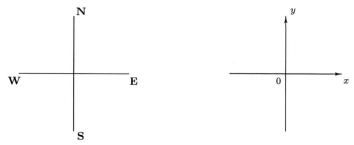

- We may construct a 'plaster cast' model, where z is the height of the surface above the base, at position (x, y). This is expensive and time-consuming and is rarely done except for very special functions.

- We may attempt to project a 'virtual' plaster model onto a flat surface, like a photograph of our landscape. This requires sophisticated artwork, although there are computer packages to help. The outcome, however, depends on the viewpoint and a significant feature may remain hidden from some viewpoints, a problem well-known to sightseers.

- We may construct a series of 'cross-sections', typically using horizontal or vertical cutting planes. The functions that result from vertical cross-sections are **section functions**. If we set $y = b$ (constant), then our function (7.1) becomes $f(x, b)$, a function of just one variable. It represents the shape we would get if we sliced through a plaster model with a knife, cutting parallel to the x-axis, at position $y = b$. Similarly $f(a, y)$ is a section function parallel to the y-axis. These section functions are similar to some geological diagrams.

- We may draw a **contour map**. This is similar to a set of horizontal cross-sections, but they are all projected vertically downwards to the xy-plane. We now pursue this in detail.

A **contour** or **level curve** is a (joined-up) set of points on a map where the terrain is at the same height. In the function context, it is a curve in the xy-plane where each (x, y) point gives the same value of z. Thus, for any fixed C, a contour is defined by

$$f(x, y) = C. \tag{7.2}$$

Varying the value of C gives different contours.

All (x, y) pairs on the contour have the same value of $f(x, y)$, i.e., C. Note that (7.2) is the kind of **implicit function** covered in the previous chapter.

Example 7.2   Analyse the function $z = 4 - x^2 - y^2$.

The first thing to note is that x^2 and y^2 are never negative, so the largest possible value of z is 4, attained at the origin. Hence this could represent some sort of 'hill'.

To obtain a vertical cross-section in the 'easterly' direction, we set $y = 0$ to obtain $z = 4 - x^2$. In the z-x plane this represents a parabola, a cross-section of our hill. This is shown in the left-hand figure below, together with section functions for $y = 1$ and $y = 2$.

The contours are the curves $4 - x^2 - y^2 = C$, i.e. $x^2 + y^2 = 4 - C$. For any $C < 4$ this represents a circle of radius $\sqrt{4 - C}$, centred at the origin. Some are shown in the right-hand figure below. The contours represent heights 3, 2, 1, 0, -1, with that for height 0 emphasised; it has radius 2.

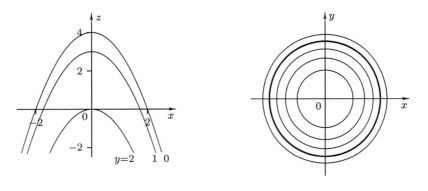

Example 7.3   Analyse the function $z = xy$.

The section functions are $z = bx$, $z = ay$, i.e., they are all straight lines. Those for $b = -2$, -1, 0, 1, 2 are shown below (left). This does not mean that the surface is composed of flat patches. Indeed, the contours show how curved it is. They are $xy = C$, which are **rectangular hyperbolae**, i.e., they are hyperbolae with asymptotes at right angles to each both. The equation looks rather different from that in Example 6.4, but that is because the hyperbola has been rotated. Some contours are shown in the graph below (right), with $C = \pm 1$. Each is in two parts; the one with $C = -1$ is shown as dashed lines.

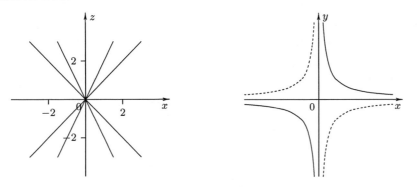

This surface is an important one, since general surfaces often have patches that resemble its shape near the origin. It exhibits a **saddle point** there. Imagine you are sitting astride the surface, looking NE. It slopes up in front of and behind you, as does the part of a saddle that gives support to the body. But in the SE–NW direction it slopes down, as a saddle does to accommodate your legs.

The **parametric** method of Chapter 6 helps here. The SW–NE direction is defined by $x = t$, $y = t$. On that line, $z = t^2$, i.e., we have a parabola with a **minimum** value 0 at the origin. The SE–NW direction is defined by $x = t$, $y = -t$. On that line, $z = -t^2$, i.e., we have a parabola with a **maximum** value 0 at the origin. ∎

For functions of more than two variables, the 'process' model is easily adapted. The visualisation problem, however, becomes worse and we shall not pursue it further.

Ex 7.1 Find the contours for the function defined by $z = x - 2y$ and draw some of them. What kind of surface does this function represent?

7.2 Partial Differentiation

An important application of a **derivative** in modelling is to specify a **rate of change** or **gradient**. In the one-variable case we already know how to find this; for the function $y = f(x)$ it is

$$\pm \frac{dy}{dx}, \qquad \text{or} \qquad \pm f'(x),$$

the $\pm$ depending on whether we move in the positive x-direction $(+)$ or in the negative direction $(-)$.

For the two-variable case, $z = f(x, y)$, we have much more freedom. Imagine you are hill walking; as you stand at one place (a, b) you have an infinite number of possible gradients facing you as you decide in which direction to walk. You will, however, have well-determined gradients if you decide that you will walk only due East or due North, say.

This decision is equivalent to deciding that you will only consider rates of change along the x-direction or the y-direction. In effect, you have decided to follow one of the **section functions**, $z = f(x, b)$ (East) or $z = f(a, y)$ (North). It will turn out that these two measures are sufficient to answer all sensible questions about rates of change for these functions, *whatever direction we choose*. The rate of change in a general direction is pursued in the next section.

Example 7.4 Find derivatives for the functions in Examples 7.2 and 7.3, in the x-direction. Choose a specific value and a general value for where the cross-section is positioned.

For $z = 4 - x^2 - y^2$:

$$\text{fix } y = 1 \;:\; z = 3 - x^2, \qquad \frac{dz}{dx} = -2x,$$

$$\text{fix } y = b \;:\; z = 4 - x^2 - b^2, \;\; \frac{dz}{dx} = -2x.$$

For $z = xy$:

$$\text{fix } y = -2 \;:\; z = -2x, \;\; \frac{dz}{dx} = -2,$$

$$\text{fix } y = b \;:\; z = bx, \qquad \frac{dz}{dx} = b.$$

∎

The results usually depend on which section function is used, as we see in the second case above. There we controlled the section function by b and the answer depended on b. The key to what follows is that using b now turns out to be rather irrelevant, indeed it lengthens the calculation. We may as well have used the original y, but treating it as we treated b, i.e., *regarding y as if it is constant, when differentiating w.r.t. x.*

We therefore define the **partial derivative** of f (or z) w.r.t. x as the one-variable derivative when all occurrences of y are treated as if y is a constant. The partial derivative w.r.t. y is defined likewise: we treat x as if it is a constant.

Before exemplifying this, we need some new notation, to distinguish the results from the derivatives we have used to date. We write:

$$\frac{\partial f}{\partial x} \qquad \text{(N.B. } \partial \textbf{ not } \delta\text{)}.$$

The result is usually read as "partial d f by d x". (The old notation $\frac{dy}{dx}$ is the **ordinary derivative**.)

There are other notations in common use, e.g.,

$$\frac{\partial z}{\partial x}, \qquad \frac{\partial}{\partial x}[f(x,y)], \qquad f_x(x,y), \qquad D_x f,$$

and the notation for differentiation w.r.t. y (or any other variable) is similar.

Example 7.5   Differentiate, partially, the functions in Example 7.4:

$$\text{(a) } z = 4 - x^2 - y^2, \qquad \text{(b) } z = xy.$$

(a) First, hold y constant and differentiate w.r.t. x:

$$\frac{\partial z}{\partial x} = \frac{\partial}{\partial x}[4] - \frac{\partial}{\partial x}\left[x^2\right] - \frac{\partial}{\partial x}\left[y^2\right] = 0 - 2x - 0.$$

Similarly, $\dfrac{\partial z}{\partial y} = -2y$.

(b) In the same way,

$$\frac{\partial z}{\partial x} = y \quad (x \text{ treated as constant}), \quad \frac{\partial z}{\partial y} = x \quad (y \text{ treated as constant}).$$

∎

All the rules of differentiation for one variable still apply; we merely treat y (or x) as constant, just as we would 2, -1, α, etc. Note the following important consequences:

$$\frac{\partial}{\partial x}[f(y)] = 0, \qquad \frac{\partial}{\partial y}[g(x)] = 0, \tag{7.3}$$

for **any** functions $f(y)$ and $g(x)$.

Example 7.6   Differentiate $f(x, y) = x^2 - y^3 + 2xy^2$ and evaluate the results at $(2, -1)$.

For the x-derivative, the $-y^3$ is a constant and hence has zero derivative. The y^2 is regarded as constant just like the 2 in that term:

$$\frac{\partial f}{\partial x} = 2x - 0 + 2y^2 \times 1 = 2x + 2y^2.$$

Similarly,

$$\frac{\partial f}{\partial y} = -3y^2 + 4xy.$$

At the given point, we have values $f_x(2, -1) = 6$ and $f_y(2, -1) = -11$. Looking in the direction of the positive x-axis at this point, we would see a gradient of 6, while looking in the direction of the y-axis, we would see a gradient of -11. ∎

Notation

Note the way that the notation shifted in the previous example, from $\frac{\partial f}{\partial x}$ to $f_x(2, -1)$. This is analogous to the way we tend to use $\frac{df}{dx}$ for a general formula and $f'(a)$ for a specific value.

The more complicated differentiation rules apply without change.

Example 7.7   Find f_x and f_y for $f(x, y) = e^{-4x} \sin(2x + 3y)$.

Here we need to use the product and linear argument rules for the x-derivative, but only the latter for the y-derivative.

$$\begin{aligned}
\frac{\partial f}{\partial x} &= e^{-4x} \frac{\partial}{\partial x}[\sin(2x + 3y)] + \frac{\partial}{\partial x}\left[e^{-4x}\right]\sin(2x + 3y) \\
&= 2e^{-4x}\cos(2x + 3y) - 4e^{-4x}\sin(2x + 3y) \\
&= e^{-4x}\left[2\cos(2x + 3y) - 4\sin(2x + 3y)\right], \\
\frac{\partial f}{\partial y} &= 3e^{-4x}\cos(2x + 3y).
\end{aligned}$$

∎

The final example illustrates the situation with **three** independent variables.

Example 7.8 Find all partial derivatives for

$$h(x, y, t) = x^2 y^3 t^4 + 2xy + 4t^2 x^2 + y.$$

There are three variables here, but that raises no new issue: we treat **both** y and t as constant when finding the x-derivative:

$$\frac{\partial h}{\partial x} = 2xy^3 t^4 + 2y + 8t^2 x.$$

Similarly,

$$\frac{\partial h}{\partial y} = 3x^2 y^2 t^4 + 2x + 1,$$

$$\frac{\partial h}{\partial t} = 4x^2 y^3 t^3 + 8tx^2.$$

Note that $\dfrac{\partial}{\partial y}\left[4t^2 x^2\right] = 0$, $\dfrac{\partial}{\partial t}\left[2xy\right] = 0$, since both functions are effectively constant when the differentiation is carried out.

∎

Sometimes these partial derivatives have a direct modelling role. A good example is the concept of **specific heat**. This represents a rate of change of a heat quantity, X say, with respect to temperature, and so could be written as $\frac{dX}{dT}$. But, in thermodynamics, it is found that this is ambiguous since there are other variables involved. For a gas, we talk of specific heat **at constant volume**, or **at constant pressure**. These extra phrases reflect the idea behind partial differentiation involving two independent variables: one independent variable is held constant while the other drives the differentiation.

Ex 7.2 Calculate $\dfrac{\partial f}{\partial x}$, $\dfrac{\partial f}{\partial y}$ and $\dfrac{\partial f}{\partial z}$, when $f(x, y, z)$ is each of:

$$2x^3 - 3xy + 5y^2, \qquad e^{xyz}, \qquad x\ln(x+y), \qquad \frac{1}{x+y+z}.$$

Ex 7.3 Calculate $\dfrac{\partial f}{\partial x}$, $\dfrac{\partial f}{\partial y}$ and $\dfrac{\partial f}{\partial z}$, when $f(x, y, z)$ is each of:

$$2x^3 + 6xy^2 + 2zx + z^2, \qquad \left(x^2 + 2y^2 + 3z^2\right)^{1/2}, \qquad \left(x^2 + y^2\right)^{1/2}\sin(xyz).$$

Ex 7.4 Draw contours for the function $f(x, y) = \exp\left(-x^2 - 2y^2\right)$. Find f_x and f_y.

7.3   Directional Derivative and Gradient

The previous section enabled us to find gradients in the directions North and East, as well as South and West by taking their negatives. We now ask how we can find the gradient in a general direction.

Suppose that we are at a point (a, b) and wish to know the gradient we perceive in a direction at angle α to the x-axis, as shown in the diagram. This direction is defined by a (unit) vector $\mathbf{u} = (\cos \alpha, \sin \alpha)$.

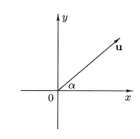

A shrewd guess for the gradient would be a kind of proportion based on the resolution of vectors:

$$\cos \alpha \frac{\partial f}{\partial x} + \sin \alpha \frac{\partial f}{\partial y}.$$

(We shall justify this later.)

Thus we talk of the **rate of change in the direction u** (with **u** a unit vector), or a **directional derivative**, which is the quantity given by

$$D_{\mathbf{u}} f = \mathbf{u} \bullet \big(f_x(a, b), f_y(a, b) \big), \tag{7.4}$$

the '$\bullet$' signifying the 'dot' or 'inner' product of the two vectors.

The vector dotted with **u** here is exceptionally important and has a special notation: ∇f, pronounced 'grad f'; it is called the **gradient** of f. It is defined as a function of x and y (and z, etc.). When applied to a problem like that above, those variables are replaced by the specific coordinate values.

Frame 7.1   *Definition of the gradient vector for two and three variables*

$$\nabla f = \left(\frac{\partial f}{\partial x}, \frac{\partial f}{\partial y} \right), \qquad \nabla f = \left(\frac{\partial f}{\partial x}, \frac{\partial f}{\partial y}, \frac{\partial f}{\partial z} \right)$$

The gradient is important because it stores all we need to know about f from the point of view of its rate of change (first derivative). When we apply extra information defining the direction in which we are interested, we are able to extract the rate of change from ∇f, using the following Frame.

Frame 7.2   *Directional derivative for a function of two variables*

$$D_{\mathbf{u}} f = \mathbf{u} \bullet \nabla f(a, b) \tag{7.5}$$

The three variable case is a simple extension of this, using (a, b, c) as the argument.

Think about it like this

Note the special cases:

$$D_{(1,0)} = \frac{\partial f}{\partial x} \quad (\alpha = 0), \qquad D_{(0,1)} = \frac{\partial f}{\partial y} \quad (\alpha = 90°).$$

In other words, the directional derivative along the x-axis is the partial derivative f_x and that along the y-axis is the partial derivative f_y, as we would expect.

Example 7.9   Let $f(x, y) = x^2 y$ and consider the point $(2, 1)$. Determine the rate of change in direction $(\frac{\sqrt{3}}{2}, \frac{1}{2})$, where $\alpha = 30°$.

The partial derivatives are $f_x = 2xy, \ f_y = x^2$. Hence

$$\begin{aligned} D_{\mathbf{u}}f &= \left(\tfrac{\sqrt{3}}{2}, \tfrac{1}{2}\right) \bullet \left(2xy, x^2\right) = \sqrt{3}xy + \tfrac{1}{2}x^2 \\ &= 2\sqrt{3} + 2 \quad \text{at } (2, 1). \end{aligned}$$

∎

The formula we have developed tells us more about f than its rate of change in given directions. From the property of the dot product, we know that $\mathbf{u} \bullet \nabla f$ has its largest size when $\mathbf{u}$ is parallel to ∇f. Hence $\mathbf{u} = k\nabla f$ for some k, calculated to make $\mathbf{u}$ a unit vector. When this occurs we have $|D_{\mathbf{u}}| = |\nabla f|$, since the dot product is the product of the magnitudes.

This important situation is summed up in the following Frame.

Frame 7.3   *Steepest ascent and descent*

∇f is the direction of **steepest ascent**

$-\nabla f$ is the direction of **steepest descent**

$|\nabla f|$ is the magnitude of the steepest ascent/descent rate

---

Example 7.10   Consider $f(x, y) = x^2 - xy + 2y^2$, at $(2, 1)$.

Calculate the partial derivatives at the given point:

$$\frac{\partial f}{\partial x} = 2x - y = 3, \quad \text{at } (2, 1),$$

$$\frac{\partial f}{\partial y} = -x + 4y = 2, \quad \text{at } (2, 1),$$

Hence $\nabla f(2, 1) = (3, 2)$, which is the direction of steepest ascent. A unit vector in this direction is $\mathbf{u} = (3/\sqrt{13}, 2/\sqrt{13})$, while this maximum rate of ascent is $|(3, 2)| = \sqrt{13}$. The direction of steepest descent is $-\mathbf{u}$. ∎

Think about it like this

> These directions are sometimes used in practical optimisation methods. If
> you seek to make a function of several variables as large as possible, choose a
> starting point and explore in the steepest ascent direction, which will initially
> have the function increasing as fast as possible.

Now consider the case of a direction $\mathbf{v} \perp \nabla f$. Then, in the two variable case,

$$\mathbf{v} = k\left(-\frac{\partial f}{\partial y}, \frac{\partial f}{\partial x}\right),$$

since $\mathbf{v} \cdot \nabla f = 0$. There is therefore no change in f in this direction, so we must be looking along a direction related to a **contour**, the set of points giving the same value of f.

The gradient of the vector $\mathbf{v}$ is the ratio of its y and x components, i.e.,

$$\frac{dy}{dx} = -\frac{f_x}{f_y}$$

for points on a contour. We shall confirm this directly in §7.5.3.

Example 7.11   Consider $f(x,y) = x^2 + y^2$.
    The gradient vector is

$$\nabla f = (2x, 2y) \quad \perp \quad (-2y, 2x).$$

Hence the gradient of the contour at (x,y) is $-\frac{2x}{2y}$.

The contours are $x^2 + y^2 = C$, i.e., they are circles centred at the origin. The tangent to a circle is perpendicular to the radius it intersects with. The radius to (x,y) has gradient $\frac{y}{x}$, so that of the tangent is $-\frac{x}{y}$, consistent with the above.   ∎

Think about it like this

> From the above, we see that the directions of the steepest ascent $\mathbf{u}$ and the
> contour $\mathbf{v}$ satisfy $\mathbf{u} \cdot \mathbf{v} = 0$. Hence, the directions of steepest ascent/descent
> are perpendicular to the contours. This fact is well-known to map-readers.
> The steepest rate of climb is perpendicular to the contours.

We finish with a three-variable example.

Example 7.12   Consider $f(x,y,z) = xy + yz + zx$, at $(1,2,3)$.
    Calculate the gradient vector

$$\nabla f = (y + z, x + z, y + x) = (5, 4, 3), \quad \text{at } (1,2,3).$$

The gradient in the direction of the **unit** vector $\mathbf{u} = (2/3, -2/3, 1/3)$ is the directional derivative

$$D_{\mathbf{u}}f = \tfrac{2}{3} \times 5 - \tfrac{2}{3} \times 4 + \tfrac{1}{3} \times 3 = \tfrac{5}{3}.$$

The direction of steepest ascent is that of ∇f, i.e., $(5,4,3)$. The associated unit vector is

$$\mathbf{u} = \tfrac{1}{5\sqrt{2}}(5, 4, 3).$$

                                                                                     ∎

Ex 7.5 Find the **gradient vector** for $z = 3x^2 - 2xy + 4y^2$. Evaluate it at $(1,1)$. Hence find the directional derivative of z in the direction $(0.6, -0.8)$. In what direction does z increase at the fastest rate at $(1,1)$?

Ex 7.6 Find the **gradient vector** for $f(x, y, z) = x^2 + \frac{7}{2}y^2 + 4z^2$. Evaluate this at $(3,1,1)$. In what direction does f increase at the fastest rate at $(3,1,1)$?

7.4 Higher Derivatives

In one variable differentiation we often find second or higher order derivatives useful for analysing the behaviour of functions, e.g., deciding between maximum and minimum, not to mention their direct use in modelling concepts such as acceleration. The situation is no different in the multivariable case.

It is fairly obvious how to proceed. $\frac{d^2y}{dx^2}$ is found by differentiating $\frac{dy}{dx}$ with respect to x. Hence we could try defining $\frac{\partial^2 z}{\partial x^2}$ as the derivative of $\frac{\partial z}{\partial x}$ with respect to x, **treating y as a constant**:

$$\frac{\partial^2 z}{\partial x^2} = \frac{\partial}{\partial x}\left[\frac{\partial z}{\partial x}\right].$$

There is a similar definition for $\frac{\partial^2 z}{\partial y^2}$, as well as the **mixed derivatives**

$$\frac{\partial^2 z}{\partial x \partial y} = \frac{\partial}{\partial x}\left[\frac{\partial z}{\partial y}\right], \qquad \frac{\partial^2 z}{\partial y \partial x} = \frac{\partial}{\partial y}\left[\frac{\partial z}{\partial x}\right].$$

Notation

This is another case where we need to read in reverse order, just like the situation in function composition. The derivative $\frac{\partial^2 z}{\partial x \partial y}$ involves y differentiation followed by x differentiation. The right-hand variable gets first shot. Fortunately, as we now see, this is rarely of much significance.

Example 7.13 Consider $f(x, y) = x^3 y^2$.

We have

$$\frac{\partial f}{\partial x} = 3x^2 y^2, \qquad \frac{\partial^2 f}{\partial x^2} = \frac{\partial}{\partial x}\left[3x^2 y^2\right] = 6xy^2, \qquad \frac{\partial^3 f}{\partial x^3} = \frac{\partial}{\partial x}\left[6xy^2\right] = 6y^2,$$

$$\frac{\partial f}{\partial y} = 2x^3 y, \qquad \frac{\partial^2 f}{\partial y^2} = \frac{\partial}{\partial y}\left[2x^3 y\right] = 2x^3.$$

For the mixed derivatives we have

$$\frac{\partial^2 f}{\partial y \partial x} = \frac{\partial}{\partial y}\left[\frac{\partial f}{\partial x}\right] = \frac{\partial}{\partial y}\left[3x^2 y^2\right] = 6x^2 y,$$

$$\frac{\partial^2 f}{\partial x \partial y} = \frac{\partial}{\partial x}\left[\frac{\partial f}{\partial y}\right] = \frac{\partial}{\partial x}\left[2x^3 y\right] = 6x^2 y.$$

The results are exactly the same. ■

This phenomenon is true **for any well-behaved function**, and persists for higher derivatives and for any number of variables. We have, not only

$$\frac{\partial^2 f}{\partial y \partial x} = \frac{\partial^2 f}{\partial x \partial y},$$

but also

$$\frac{\partial^4 f}{\partial x \partial y \partial z \partial x} = \frac{\partial^4 f}{\partial y \partial x^2 \partial z} = \frac{\partial^4 f}{\partial z \partial y \partial x^2} = \text{etc.,}$$

the result being the same whenever we perform **two** x differentiations, **one** y one and **one** z one, no matter what order is used.

Notation

There are some other notations for these higher derivatives but we shall not pursue them further here. The most popular is the extension of f_x. There is no problem with f_{xx}, but mixed derivatives cause potential confusion, since

$$\frac{\partial^2 f}{\partial x \partial y} = f_{yx}.$$

This looks unusual, but is perfectly logical. In each case y is nearer to f and so is the first variable to be used in the differentiation.

The previous example is not a very convincing illustration of the equality of mixed derivatives, since x and y have no real interaction with each other in $x^3 y^2$. The next example has a more complicated relationship and not only illustrates the equality, but shows that sometimes one order is easier to use than the other.

Example 7.14   Find the second-order mixed derivatives for $f(x, y) = x e^{xy}$.

The details are as follows. Note that the first calculation requires the **Product Rule** twice, but the second one only once.

$$\frac{\partial f}{\partial x} = xy e^{xy} + e^{xy}$$

$$\frac{\partial^2 f}{\partial y \partial x} = x^2 y e^{xy} + x e^{xy} + x e^{xy} = x^2 y e^{xy} + 2x e^{xy},$$

$$\frac{\partial f}{\partial y} = x^2 e^{xy}$$

$$\frac{\partial^2 f}{\partial x \partial y} = x^2 y e^{xy} + 2x e^{xy}.$$

The results are identical, but the second calculation was shorter.   ■

Ex 7.7 Calculate $\dfrac{\partial^2 f}{\partial x^2}, \dfrac{\partial^2 f}{\partial y \partial x}, \dfrac{\partial^2 f}{\partial x \partial y}, \dfrac{\partial^2 f}{\partial y^2}$ for each of the following functions:

$$x^2 + 3xy + 4y^2, \qquad x e^{xy} + y^2 x, \qquad x \sin(xy).$$

Verify that $\frac{\partial^2 f}{\partial y \partial x} = \frac{\partial^2 f}{\partial x \partial y}$ for each of these.

Ex 7.8 Let $f(x, y) = (x^2 + y^2)^{-1}$. Verify that $(y, -x) \cdot \nabla f = 0$ and interpret this geometrically. Evaluate $f_{xx} + f_{yy}$.

7.5   The Chain Rule

The **Chain Rule** for one variable:

$$\frac{dy}{dx} = \frac{dy}{du}\frac{du}{dx}, \quad (y \text{ a function of } u, \ u \text{ a function of } x), \qquad (7.6)$$

is arguably the most powerful of the differentiation rules. It is therefore natural to seek extensions to two or more variables.

Think about it like this

The Chain Rule has three principal uses:

1. It allows us to change variable. If we have a function $f(u)$ and prefer to have x as independent variable, with $u = g(x)$, then $f'(g(x)) = f'(u)g'(x)$ provides the required derivative.

2. It helps us simplify problems by breaking them up into simpler components. This is, to some extent, the reverse of 1: we can break $f(g(x))$ into $f(u)$ and $g(x)$.

3. Related to 2, we can sometimes break a differentiation problem into two parts, one of which can be carried out and the other left for a different treatment, e.g., an experimental measurement. Without the Chain Rule, the problem may be entirely intractable.

There are several versions of the Chain Rule for functions of more than one variable, depending on the context. There is, however, a common idea. We **multiply** the derivatives, just as we multiply rates of change when the output of one process is passed on as the input of another. The only new idea is that we may have more than one variable involved and hence a need to **add** these contributions.

Notation

In what follows, there will be a mix of 'd' and '∂', sometimes even for the same pair of variables. the key is to think of the context before choosing the symbol: if z is being treated as a function of one variable, use d, otherwise use ∂.

7.5.1   One variable to two variables

Suppose that z is a function of **one** variable u, which is a function of **two** variables x and y. We calculate partial derivatives as follows.

Frame 7.4   *Chain Rule for one variable to two variables*

$$\frac{\partial z}{\partial x} = \frac{dz}{du}\frac{\partial u}{\partial x}, \qquad \frac{\partial z}{\partial y} = \frac{dz}{du}\frac{\partial u}{\partial y} \qquad (7.7)$$

If we recall that, in differentiating w.r.t. x we are holding y constant, then this is simply an application of (7.6), ignoring the occurrence of y. Indeed, we have already used it, in Example 7.14, and the next example confirms it using (7.7).

Example 7.15   Differentiate e^{xy} w.r.t. x.

Here we have $z = e^u$, $u = xy$, so

$$\frac{\partial z}{\partial x} = \frac{d}{du}\left[e^u\right]\frac{\partial}{\partial x}\left[xy\right] = e^u y = ye^{xy}.$$

∎

Example 7.16   Differentiate $w = \sin(x^2 + y^2 + z^2)$ w.r.t. z.

Here we have $w = \sin u$, $u = x^2 + y^2 + z^2$, so $\frac{dw}{du} = \cos u$, $\frac{\partial u}{\partial z} = 2z$, and

$$\frac{\partial w}{\partial z} = 2z \cos u = 2z \cos(x^2 + y^2 + z^2).$$

Note that w, as a function of u, has one variable and we use d, but as a function of x, y, z, it has three variables and we use ∂.   ∎

7.5.2   Two variables to one variable

This is the key version as far as this chapter is concerned. Suppose that z is a function of **two** variables x and y, each of which is a function of **one** variable t.

The simple Chain Rule (7.6) can be applied to z as a function of t, via x, **OR** as a function of t, via y. To obtain the full story we must **add** the contributions.

Frame 7.5   *Chain Rule for two variables to one variable*

$$\frac{dz}{dt} = \frac{\partial z}{\partial x}\frac{dx}{dt} + \frac{\partial z}{\partial y}\frac{dy}{dt} \qquad (7.8)$$

Example 7.17   Find $\frac{dz}{dt}$, where $z = e^{-xy}$, $x = t$, $y = t^2$.

Calculate the four derivatives readily available from these equations. Two use a similar calculation to Example 7.15, using the earlier Chain Rule.

$$\frac{\partial z}{\partial x} = -ye^{-xy}, \qquad \frac{\partial z}{\partial y} = -xe^{-xy},$$

$$\frac{dx}{dt} = 1, \qquad \frac{dy}{dt} = 2t.$$

Now use (7.8):

$$\frac{dz}{dt} = -ye^{-xy} \times 1 - xe^{-xy} \times 2t = -e^{-xy}(y + 2xt).$$

If desired, we could express this result in t alone. Substitute $x = t$, $y = t^2$:

$$\frac{dz}{dt} = -e^{-t^3}3t^2,$$

consistent with $z = e^{-t^3}$ and the normal Chain Rule.   ∎

Whether or not to convert the answer to t is unclear and it may be better to leave a mix of x, y and t, unless told otherwise.

Think about it like this

It may be that the new Chain Rule has been specifically chosen for a purpose. For example, we may not know the precise definitions for x and y, intending to measure them and their rates of change. In such circumstances, only (7.8) can be used and it does advance the calculation.

We now look at an application of this Chain Rule that provides a simple interpretation.

Example 7.18   A person goes for a walk in such a way that, on a map, the position at time t is $(x(t), y(t))$. Suppose the height above sea-level is given by a function $h(x, y)$, deduced from the contours, say. We require to find the (time) rate at which the walker is climbing at time t.

Note that h is effectively a function of t only, since the walker is at a known height at each time: t fixes x and y, which together fix h. The answer is a simple application of the Chain Rule, version (7.8):

$$\frac{dh}{dt} = \frac{\partial h}{\partial x}\frac{dx}{dt} + \frac{\partial h}{\partial y}\frac{dy}{dt}.$$

The first term has calculated how quickly the walker climbs due to the gradient in the x-direction, using the walker's speed in that direction. The second calculates the same for the y-direction and the desired answer is the total.

Suppose that we are on the 'hill' in Example 7.2: $h = 4 - x^2 - y^2$ and the walker proceeds in a straight line: $x = t$, $y = 1 - t$. Then we can calculate $\frac{dx}{dt} = 1$ and $\frac{dy}{dt} = -1$ and conclude

$$\frac{dh}{dt} = (-2x) \times 1 + (-2y) \times (-1) = 2y - 2x$$

$$\textit{or } = 2(1 - t) - 2t = 2 - 4t.$$

Thus, the walker's height increases for t in $[0, 1/2]$, then decreases.

Suppose the walker goes round the circle: $x = \cos t$, $y = \sin t$. Then

$$\frac{dh}{dt} = -2x(-\sin t) - 2y(\cos t) = 2\cos t \sin t - 2\sin t \cos t = 0,$$

so the path never goes up or down. The walker stays on a contour, as we could have concluded from Example 7.2.

Finally, a path such as $x = t$, $y = t^2$, as in Example 7.17, is a parabolic one; the above method would easily produce the rate of change of height. ■

Think about it like this

In this case the Chain Rule gives us an **ordinary** derivative, $\frac{dz}{dt}$, in spite of there being partial derivatives involved. This is due to **extra** information, namely the expressions for x and y as functions of t, which ties them down. This is similar to the situation in §7.3, where we obtained a **directional** derivative by means of constraining our view to a given direction, i.e., moving in a direction $\mathbf{u} = (u_1, u_2)$, say. We now revisit this.

Consider the case of the directional derivative at (x_0, y_0), in the direction of the unit vector $\mathbf{u} = (u_1, u_2)$. Looking for the gradient is equivalent to moving on the path

$$x = x_0 + tu_1, \qquad y = y_0 + tu_2.$$

Hence we have

$$D_{\mathbf{u}}f(x_0, y_0) = \frac{df}{dt}(x_0, y_0) = \frac{\partial f}{\partial x}\frac{dx}{dt} + \frac{\partial f}{\partial y}\frac{dy}{dt}$$

$$= u_1\frac{\partial f}{\partial x} + u_2\frac{\partial f}{\partial y} = \mathbf{u} \bullet \nabla f(x_0, y_0),$$

as we stated in §7.3.

7.5.3   Implicit Functions

One application of this Chain Rule is to the problem of calculating derivatives for a function defined **implicitly**, as considered in §6.1.

Suppose we have

$$f(x, y) = C.$$

Differentiate each side w.r.t. x, bearing in mind that we expect y to be a function of x and x is also the simple function of x: $x = x$. Use (7.8):

$$\frac{\partial f}{\partial x}\frac{dx}{dx} + \frac{\partial f}{\partial y}\frac{dy}{dx} = \frac{d}{dx}[C] = 0.$$

Since $\frac{dx}{dx} = 1$, we can solve to find the derivative we seek.

Frame 7.6   *Differentiating an implicit function*

$$\frac{dy}{dx} = -\frac{\partial f}{\partial x}\bigg/\frac{\partial f}{\partial y} \quad or \quad -\frac{f_x}{f_y} \qquad\qquad (7.9)$$

Example 7.19   Find $\frac{dy}{dx}$ when $e^{-y} - y\sin x - 4 = 0$.
   We have

$$f_x = 0 - y\cos x - 0, \qquad f_y = -e^{-y} - \sin x - 0,$$

and hence

$$\frac{dy}{dx} = -\frac{-y\cos x}{-e^{-y} - \sin x} = -\frac{y\cos x}{e^{-y} + \sin x}.$$

This formula involves both x and y, but this is not a concern: one reason for the usefulness of implicit functions is their even-handed treatment of the variables. ∎

Think about it like this

The formula in Frame 7.6 may appear strange, in that gradients, and hence derivatives, usually have a y quantity divided by an x quantity. The following explains why it is a 'natural' formula.

It is not f that is being differentiated. The nearest we have to an f derivative is ∇f, which is a vector (f_x, f_y). The gradient for the implicit function is associated with a vector in the direction $(1, -f_x/f_y)$, parallel to $(-f_y, f_x)$. These two vectors are **orthogonal**, which makes sense. The function increases fastest perpendicular to the **contours** and our implicit function's graph is a contour.

Example 7.20   Find the gradient of $x^2 - xy + 2y^2 - 4 = 0$ at $(2, 1)$.

Find the partial derivatives: $f_x = 2x - y$, $f_y = -x + 4y$. Evaluate at $(2, 1)$ and use (7.9):

$$\frac{dy}{dx}\bigg|_{(2,1)} = -\frac{2 \times 2 - 1}{-2 + 4 \times 1} = -\frac{3}{2}.$$

As mentioned above, this curve is a **contour** for

$$f(x, y) = x^2 - xy + 2y^2,$$

treated in Example 7.10. In that example we found $\nabla f = (3, 2)$, with slope $2/3$. Since $2/3 \times (-3/2) = -1$, we again confirm that the gradient and contour directions are orthogonal. ∎

We shall return to this differentiation in §8.4, when a method will be revealed that avoids the need to memorise (7.9).

7.5.4   Total Derivative

We have referred to the derivative $\frac{dz}{dt}$ in Frame 7.5 as an *ordinary* derivative, which is accurate, when we think of z being effectively a function of t alone, once x and y have been eliminated. But it has other names. The one that defines its mathematical role is the **total derivative**. This reveals that it tells the full story, in taking account of both x and y, and has an obvious link with the word **partial**, which tells only 'part' of the story.

Now, let us complicate matters a little further: suppose that we have a quantity Q that depends directly on t, as well as indirectly through x and y. Thus we regard it as a function $Q(x, y, t)$ of **three** variables. The result in Frame 7.5 extends easily:

$$\frac{dQ}{dt} = \frac{\partial Q}{\partial x}\frac{dx}{dt} + \frac{\partial Q}{\partial y}\frac{dy}{dt} + \frac{\partial Q}{\partial t}\frac{dt}{dt},$$

where the last term simplifies since $\frac{dt}{dt} = 1$. This leads to a more general formula for the total derivative; in this context it is often called the **convective derivative** and the process is called **differentiation following the motion**.

Frame 7.7   *The convective derivative (differentiation following the motion)*

$$\frac{dQ}{dt} = \frac{\partial Q}{\partial x}\frac{dx}{dt} + \frac{\partial Q}{\partial y}\frac{dy}{dt} + \frac{\partial Q}{\partial t} \qquad (7.10)$$

This formula is heavily used in modelling and the new names reflect the context: when we calculate this total derivative for a quantity, we reflect the experience of an observer moving through space. It is applied in fluid flow, for example, when we fix attention on a small element in the fluid.

Think about it like this

The result in Frame 7.7 may appear puzzling in that it contains both $\frac{dQ}{dt}$ and $\frac{\partial Q}{\partial t}$. In fact it helps us understand the difference.

Consider the walker in Example 7.18. Suppose the person is carrying a thermometer and measures the temperature, Q say. Then the rate at which the temperature changes in time is given by (7.10). This takes account of the various ways in which the temperature can change, e.g., it will vary with time, as the sun gets hotter throughout the day, and it will vary with x and y, decreasing as the walker climbs a hill, say. The total rate of change is $\frac{dQ}{dt}$.

What of $\frac{\partial Q}{\partial t}$? It is defined as the derivative when x and y are held constant. That means the walker does not move and the measured rate of change is only that due to the variation throughout the day. In this case $\frac{dx}{dt} = \frac{dy}{dt} = 0$, and (7.10) gives $\frac{dQ}{dt} = \frac{\partial Q}{\partial t}$, consistent with the definition of the partial derivative.

The following example illustrates this, with just one space dimension.

Example 7.21   Suppose we measure the temperature Q using a probe fired straight up in the air, with coordinate z. Suppose that, in some time unit, $Q(z,t) = e^{-z}\sin t$, and the probe's trajectory in time is given by $z(t) = 100t - t^2$. (It rises to a maximum height 2500, then falls back to earth at $t = 100$.)

Use (7.10) with x replaced by z and with y removed:

$$\begin{aligned}
\frac{dQ}{dt} &= \frac{\partial Q}{\partial z}\frac{dz}{dt} + \frac{\partial Q}{\partial t} \\
&= -e^{-z}\sin t \times (100 - 2t) + e^{-z}\cos t \\
&= e^{-z}\left[\cos t - (100 - 2t)\sin t\right].
\end{aligned}$$

∎

Frame 7.7 extends to more variables in an obvious way.

Example 7.22   Let Q have formula $\exp\left(-x^2 - y^2 - z^2 - \lambda t\right)$, where λ is constant.

Then the extended Chain Rule (7.10) gives

$$\frac{\partial Q}{\partial x} = -2x\exp\left(-x^2 - y^2 - z^2 - \lambda t\right) = -2xQ,$$

substituting Q for convenience, with similar expressions for $\frac{\partial Q}{\partial y}$ and $\frac{\partial Q}{\partial z}$. Also, $\frac{\partial Q}{\partial t} = -\lambda Q$.

Suppose that the point (x, y, z) moves in a straight line:

$$x = t, \qquad y = 2t, \qquad z = 3t.$$

The total derivative is

$$\frac{dQ}{dt} = -2xQ \times 1 - 2yQ \times 2 - 2zQ \times 3 - \lambda Q$$
$$= -(2x + 4y + 6z + \lambda)Q.$$

∎

Finally, the Chain Rule extends to the case of two sets of two variables: z is a function of **two** variables x and y, each of which is a function of **two** variables s and t:

$$\frac{\partial z}{\partial s} = \frac{\partial z}{\partial x}\frac{\partial x}{\partial s} + \frac{\partial z}{\partial y}\frac{\partial y}{\partial s}, \tag{7.11}$$

$$\frac{\partial z}{\partial t} = \frac{\partial z}{\partial x}\frac{\partial x}{\partial t} + \frac{\partial z}{\partial y}\frac{\partial y}{\partial t}. \tag{7.12}$$

This context is of great importance in modelling, although we shall not pursue it here. One common case is where x and y are cartesian coordinates, while s and t are polar coordinates, where we would use variables r and θ. Then $x = r\cos\theta$, $y = r\sin\theta$ is the link used in (7.11) and (7.12).

Ex 7.9 Find $\dfrac{\partial z}{\partial x}$ and $\dfrac{\partial z}{\partial y}$, where $z = f(r)$ and $r = \sqrt{x^2 + y^2}$.

Ex 7.10 Let $Q = x^2 yt$, where $x = \cos t$, $y = \sin t$. Use the Chain Rule to find $\dfrac{dQ}{dt}$.

Ex 7.11 A charged particle is moving in the straight line $x = t$, $y = t$ through a 2-dimensional electric field (t is time). It experiences a force at position (x, y) and time t: $F(x, y, t) = \dfrac{E\sin t}{x^2 + y^2}$. Calculate $\dfrac{\partial F}{\partial t}$ and $\dfrac{dF}{dt}$ and explain why they are different.

Ex 7.12

(a) Find $\dfrac{dy}{dx}$ for the (implicit) curve with equation $2y^2 - 3x^2 + 4xy = 3$.

(b) Find $\dfrac{dy}{dx}$ at $x = \frac{\pi}{2}$ given that $2y^2 \sin 2x - 2y^3 = \cos 2x$.

(c) Find the equation of the tangent at the point $(0, 4)$ to the curve defined by $y^3 x + y + 7x^4 = 4$.

Ex 7.13 A particle moving in a magnetic field has a position given by $\mathbf{r} = (\cos\omega t, \sin\omega t, t)$, where $\omega (= qB/m)$ is a constant. Find:

(a) $\dfrac{d}{dt}(|\mathbf{r}|)$, the rate of change of magnitude of $\mathbf{r}$,

(b) $|\dot{\mathbf{r}}|$, the magnitude of the velocity.

7.6 Revision Exercises

Ex 7.14 Let

$$u(x, y) = xye^{x+y}.$$

Calculate

$$\frac{\partial u}{\partial x} \quad \text{and} \quad \frac{\partial u}{\partial y}.$$

Evaluate the maximum gradient of u at $x = 1$, $y = -1$.

Ex 7.15 Find the gradient vector for $f(x, y, z) = xyz - x - y - z$.
Hence find the directional derivative at $(1, -1, 2)$ in the direction $\left(\frac{2}{3}, \frac{2}{3}, -\frac{1}{3}\right)$.

Ex 7.16 Find the gradient vector for $f(x, y) = \sqrt{x^2 + 4y}$.
Hence find the directional derivative at $(4, 5)$ in the direction $\left(-\frac{3}{5}, \frac{4}{5}\right)$.
In what direction, at the point $(4, 5)$, does $f(x, y)$ increase at the fastest rate?

Ex 7.17 Given the function $Q = (x^2 + y)e^{-t}$, calculate the partial derivatives

$$\frac{\partial Q}{\partial x}, \quad \frac{\partial Q}{\partial y}, \quad \frac{\partial Q}{\partial t}.$$

Use the Chain Rule to find the **total** derivative $\dfrac{dQ}{dt}$ if $x = e^{2t}$, $y = t$.

Ex 7.18 Consider the function

$$Q(x, y, t) = x^2 y + e^t \sin x.$$

Calculate the **total** derivative $\dfrac{dQ}{dt}$ if $x = x(t)$, $y = y(t)$. Then evaluate the total derivative when

$$x(t) = \sin(\pi t), \quad y(t) = t^2,$$

and $t = 1$.

8 DIFFERENTIALS

It has been suggested in connection with various methods, such as the Chain Rule and solving separable differential equations, that the methods are easier to recall if we allow the **symbols** dy and dx to be separated from each other. In this chapter we consider whether any meaning, even a **value**, can be associated with these **differentials**.

There are various ways in which this can be approached.

- We can give differentials a definition that allows numerical evaluation; this is useful in bounding computational errors and in conducting sensitivity analyses: if I change x by so much, what happens to y?

- They can be regarded as fictitious quantities that allow us to build up formulae; this is useful in creating mathematical models, most particularly in **thermodynamics**.

- A mathematical framework can be constructed in which they can be embedded; this gives support to the fiction just mentioned, but it is beyond the scope of this text.

We shall start with the numerical approach.

8.1 Functions of One Variable

We define **differentials** dx and dy as quantities whose ratio is the derivative of y with respect to x.

Frame 8.1   *Definition of differentials dx and dy, where $y=f(x)$*

$$dy = \frac{dy}{dx}\,dx = f'(x)\,dx \qquad (8.1)$$

Example 8.1   Find the differential relationship for $y = f(x) = x^4$.
    Since $f'(x) = 4x^3$, we have $dy = 4x^3\,dx$.   ∎

This appears to achieve little, until we investigate what the derivative means. Suppose that we change x to $x + \Delta x$, provoking a change in y to $y + \Delta y$. Then

$$\frac{\Delta y}{\Delta x} \to f'(x) \text{ as } \Delta x \to 0,$$

so that

$$\Delta y \simeq f'(x)\,\Delta x \text{ for small } \Delta x.$$

If we now **choose** $dx = \Delta x$, we find $\Delta y \simeq dy$, so the differential dy is an estimate of the change in y.

Example 8.2   Suppose $y = \sin x$ and we make a change $\Delta x = 0.1$ in $x = \pi/3$.

The differential relationship is $dy = \cos x\, dx$. Let $dx = 0.1$. Then

$$dy = \cos \pi/3 \times 0.1 = 0.05,$$

which should be a reasonable estimate of

$$\Delta y = \sin\left(\pi/3 + 0.1\right) - \sin \pi/3 = 0.0456.$$

For $\Delta x = dx = 0.001$, we find $dy = 0.0005$, $\Delta y = 0.000\,499\,6$. Note that the quality improves as dx gets smaller.   ■

Think about it like this

The calculation seem unnecessary, since we could simply have computed Δy. But there are several countering arguments:

- The calculation of dy is easier.
- The calculation of Δy can have a large rounding error when Δx is small.
- The differential method applies in symbolic (non-numerical) contexts.
- We can easily swap the roles of x and y, as we now see.

The method works in reverse, effectively doing the same type of calculation on the **inverse function**, *without actually having to find it*.

Example 8.3   Let $y = e^{-x}$ and estimate what change in x, at $x = 2$, will lead to a change $\Delta y = 0.001$.

We have $dy = -e^{-x}\, dx$. Let $dy = 0.001$, so

$$0.001 = -e^{-2}\, dx \quad \Rightarrow \quad \Delta x \simeq dx = \frac{0.001}{-e^{-2}} = -0.0074.$$

Note that this is negative, so we must **decrease** x.   ■

Think about it like this

This definition does not actually specify a meaning for a single dx item; rather it allows us to introduce two of them into an equation, with the understanding that their **ratio** is a well-defined derivative. Once we choose one of dx or dy the other is fixed by the link to $\frac{dy}{dx}$. Choosing dx and finding dy is the usual approach, consistent with the status of x as the default independent variable. We could, however, choose dy and then find dx; that would be consistent with the idea of the inverse function, since $\frac{dx}{dy} = 1/\frac{dy}{dx}$ from the **inverse-function rule** and hence $dx = \frac{dx}{dy}\, dy$.

Ex 8.1 Find an expression linking the differentials dx and dy when $y = \ln(1+x)$. What is dy at $x = 4$, if $dx = -0.001$? What is dx at $x = 9$, if $dy = 0.01$?

8.2 Newton-Raphson Method (Optional)

An immediate application of this idea is to derive a powerful method for estimating the **root** of an equation, especially if it cannot be determined by exact calculations.

Suppose that we wish to find a root α of $f(x) = 0$. The first step is to find some initial approximation $x_0 \simeq \alpha$, which can be done using a graph, a table, or trial and error.

We then seek to improve x_0. One way would be to calculate $dx = x_0 - \alpha$ from which we could easily find α. This is related to dy, where

$$dy = f'(x_0)\, dx \simeq \Delta y = f(x_0) - f(\alpha) = f(x_0),$$

since α is a root of the equation and so $f(\alpha) = 0$.

We can solve this to find

$$\alpha \simeq x_0 - \frac{f(x_0)}{f'(x_0)}.$$

The next step is a typical one in numerical methods. We replace the $\simeq$ by $=$, but change α to x_1, since the computed value is not **exactly** α.

We now have a formula that takes us from an approximation x_0 to a new one x_1, which we hope is better. The notation used here is typical of a **recurrence relation** or **iteration**. Replacing 0 by n and 1 by $n + 1$, we find one of the most commonly used numerical methods.

Frame 8.2   *Newton-Raphson method*

$$x_{n+1} = x_n - \frac{f(x_n)}{f'(x_n)} \qquad (8.2)$$

Example 8.4   Find a root of $\sin x = 0.5x$, near $x_0 = 1.9$.

Write the equation in the form $f(x) = \sin x - 0.5x = 0$; then $f'(x) = \cos x - 0.5$. The iteration is

$$x_{n+1} = x_n - \frac{\sin x_n - 0.5x_n}{\cos x_n - 0.5}, \quad x_0 = 1.9.$$

A calculator (*set to radians*) gives, to 6 dp,

$$x_1 = 1.895\,506, \qquad x_2 = 1.895\,494 = x_3,$$

and we can trust the last value to be correct to all dp shown. Equations of this type can occur in solving partial differential equations. ∎

When this method **converges** to the root α, it does so with very great speed, which is the reason for its popularity. It can, however, be rather dangerous, since it may decide to seek a root other than the one intended.

We finish with an example whose formula is implemented in many calculator and computer routines for finding square roots.

Example 8.5   Apply the Newton-Raphson method to $x^2 - a = 0$ and hence find $\sqrt{10}$ correct to 6 dp.

Let $f(x) = x^2 - a$, so there is a root at $x = \sqrt{a}$. Also, $f'(x) = 2x$, so the iteration is

$$x_{n+1} = x_n - \frac{x_n^2 - a}{2x_n} = \frac{1}{2}\left(x_n + \frac{a}{x_n}\right).$$

Choosing $x_0 = 3.1$ as an approximation to $\sqrt{10}$, we find $x_1 = 3.162\,903$ and $x_2 = 3.162\,278$, correct to 6 dp.

It is instructive to examine how this works. If x_n is slightly less than $\sqrt{a}$, then a/x_n will be slightly larger; hence the formula takes an average of an underestimate and an overestimate. ■

Ex 8.2   The equation $\sin x = x^2$ has a root near to $x = 0.9$. Use the Newton-Raphson method to find that root correct to 5 dp.

Ex 8.3   Apply the Newton-Raphson method to $x^3 - a = 0$ to find an iterative method for calculating cube roots.

Use this to find $\sqrt[3]{25}$ correct to 6 dp.

8.3   Functions of More Variables

Suppose, now, that we have a function of two variables, $z = f(x, y)$. One question we could ask is how to estimate Δz, where

$$z + \Delta z = f(x + \Delta x, y + \Delta y) - f(x, y),$$

i.e., what is the change in z caused by changing x and y **simultaneously**?

We answered this in §8.1 for a function of one variable, using differentials. If we keep y constant and change x, say, we have

$$\Delta z \simeq \frac{\partial z}{\partial x}\,\Delta x.$$

Here it is entirely correct to use the partial derivative because of the phrase *"keep y constant"*. There is a similar expression for the case where x is held constant.

The natural conclusion, which can be justified, is that we can add these estimates, to cover the situation when neither x nor y is constant. This is formally related to differentials through the following.

> *Frame 8.3*   *Differentials for a function of two variables*
>
> $$dz = \frac{\partial z}{\partial x}\,dx + \frac{\partial z}{\partial y}\,dy \qquad\qquad (8.3)$$

Think about it like this

This equation follows directly from the Chain Rule in Frame 7.5 if we 'multiply' through by dt.

Also, we see it is consistent with the work in §8.1 as follows. Suppose we hold y constant. Then $dy = 0$ since there is no change in its value. This gives $dz = \frac{\partial z}{\partial x} dx$, which is the sort of result we had before.

The extension to more variables is obvious; for $u = f(x, y, z)$,

$$du = \frac{\partial u}{\partial x} dx + \frac{\partial u}{\partial y} dy + \frac{\partial u}{\partial z} dz. \tag{8.4}$$

These differential relationships have far-reaching applications in calculus, but here we consider their use to estimate **changes** and **errors**. These follow from Frame 8.3 by using $dx = \Delta x$, $dy = \Delta y$, so $dz \simeq \Delta z$.

Example 8.6   Power in an electric circuit is given by $P = V^2/R$, where V is the voltage and R the resistance. Suppose that V is decreased from 240 to 230 (volts) and R is decreased from 100 to 90 (ohms). What is the resulting change in the power?

Taking partial derivatives of $P = \frac{V^2}{R}$ and using Frame 8.3 gives

$$\Delta P \simeq dP = \frac{\partial P}{\partial V} dV + \frac{\partial P}{\partial R} dR = \frac{2V}{R} dV - \frac{V^2}{R^2} dR.$$

Now let $dV = 230 - 240 = -10$, $dR = 90 - 100 = -10$, both being negative because the quantities decrease. Then

$$\Delta P \simeq \frac{480}{100} \times (-10) - \frac{240^2}{10^4} \times (-10) = 9.6,$$

an **increase** of approximately 9.6 watts.

Direct calculation gives $\Delta P = 11.8$, but cannot so easily answer questions such as: "What decrease in R will keep the power approximately the same, when V is decreased from 240 to 230?".

Using the same differential relationship we have

$$0 \simeq \frac{480}{100} \times (-10) - \frac{240^2}{10^4} dR \quad \Rightarrow \quad dR \simeq -8.33.$$

■

Small deliberate changes like these are not very different from small unintentional **errors**, so it should be possible to estimate the effect of, say, measurement errors on the result of using a formula.

There are, however, two differences: we will know only an upper bound on the size of the error and we are unlikely to know its sign. Hence we must proceed with some caution.

Suppose we measure x as $\bar{x}$, where $\bar{x} = x + e_x$, the error e_x being bounded **in size** by $|e_x| \leqslant \epsilon_x$. For a formula with three inputs we argue, as above,

$$e_u \simeq du = \frac{\partial u}{\partial x} e_x + \frac{\partial u}{\partial y} e_y + \frac{\partial u}{\partial z} e_z.$$

Then we can bound the error in u by

$$|e_u| \leqslant \left|\frac{\partial u}{\partial x}\right| |e_x| + \left|\frac{\partial u}{\partial y}\right| |e_y| + \left|\frac{\partial u}{\partial z}\right| |e_z|$$

$$\leqslant \left|\frac{\partial u}{\partial x}\right| \epsilon_x + \left|\frac{\partial u}{\partial y}\right| \epsilon_y + \left|\frac{\partial u}{\partial z}\right| \epsilon_z,$$

on using the **triangle inequality**. This gives the result we seek.

Frame 8.4   *Error bound for a function of three variables*

$$\epsilon_u = \left|\frac{\partial u}{\partial x}\right| \epsilon_x + \left|\frac{\partial u}{\partial y}\right| \epsilon_y + \left|\frac{\partial u}{\partial z}\right| \epsilon_z \qquad (8.5)$$

Think about it like this

The absolute value signs, and use of the triangle inequality, are essential here. Each error can be positive or negative. If e_x is negative and $\frac{\partial u}{\partial x} < 0$, then the resulting contribution to the overall error will be positive, in spite of an apparent minus sign in the formula. This will be seen in the examples that follow: we must anticipate the worst possible scenario.

Example 8.7   A triangle with sides a and b and included angle C has area $A = \frac{1}{2}ab\sin C$. Suppose we measure these values, with error bounds:

$$a = 4.0 \pm 0.1, \quad b = 2.0 \pm 0.1, \quad C = \tfrac{3\pi}{4} \pm 0.01 \ (RADIANS).$$

What is the maximum error in the calculated value of A?

We start with the differential relationship

$$dA = \frac{\partial A}{\partial a} da + \frac{\partial A}{\partial b} db + \frac{\partial A}{\partial C} dC$$

$$= \left(\tfrac{1}{2}b\sin C\right) da + \left(\tfrac{1}{2}a\sin C\right) db + \left(\tfrac{1}{2}ab\cos C\right) dC.$$

Let $da = db = 0.1$ and $dC = 0.01$. Then

$$|dA| \leqslant \frac{1}{2} \cdot 2 \cdot \frac{1}{\sqrt{2}} \cdot 0.1 + \frac{1}{2} \cdot 4 \cdot \frac{1}{\sqrt{2}} \cdot 0.1 + \frac{1}{2} \cdot 2 \cdot 4 \cdot \frac{1}{\sqrt{2}} \cdot 0.01$$

$$= \frac{34}{\sqrt{2}} \times 0.01 = 0.24,$$

which is the required error bound.

Note that $\cos\frac{3\pi}{4} = -\frac{1}{\sqrt{2}}$, but the final term must be turned positive, since we could have $dC < 0$. ∎

Errors are often expressed as **percentages**, and in some cases the error bounding becomes simpler. The following example shows this.

Example 8.8   The force on a car of mass m as it turns a bend of radius r at speed v is $F = mv^2/r$. Suppose that we measure m to within 1%, v

to within 2% and r to within 1%. What is the resulting uncertainty in the calculated value of F.

Note that we are not given any values for these parameters. This is of no consequence since percentage error bounds are give. (This is because only powers are involved in the formula; trigonometric and exponential terms are not as straightforward.)

We start with the differential relationship

$$dF = \frac{\partial F}{\partial m} dm + \frac{\partial F}{\partial v} dv + \frac{\partial F}{\partial r} dr$$
$$= \frac{v^2}{r} dm + \frac{2mv}{r} dv - \frac{mv^2}{r^2} dr.$$

Divide on the left by F and on the right by the equivalent mv^2/r:

$$\frac{dF}{F} = \frac{dm}{m} + 2\frac{dv}{v} - \frac{dr}{r}.$$

Since we know $\left|\frac{dm}{m}\right| \leqslant 1\%$, etc., we have

$$\left|\frac{dF}{F}\right| \leqslant 1\% + 2 \times 2\% + 1\% = 6\%,$$

where the minus sign in the last term is reversed, to ensure we cover the worst possible scenario. ∎

Ex 8.4 If $z = x^2y^2 - 2xy$, find Δz and dz when $x = 2$, $y = 1$ and $\Delta x = 0.1$, $\Delta y = -0.2$.

Ex 8.5 Find the differential of u, where $u = xy + yz + zx$.

(a) Use du to estimate the change in u at $(1,1,1)$, when x and z each increase by 0.1, while y decreases by 0.1. Compare this with the actual change.

(b) Suppose that each of x, y and z is measured as 1.0, with the error in each bounded by 0.1. Use du to estimate an error bound for u.

Ex 8.6 The area of a triangle ABC is given by the formulae

$$S = \frac{1}{2}bc\sin A = \frac{1}{2}ca\sin B = \frac{1}{2}ab\sin C.$$

If b and c are measured to within 0.1% and A to within 1%, estimate the maximum percentage error in the calculated area when $A = \pi/6$.

8.4   Implicit Functions

Differentials provide a way to find the derivative of an **implicit function**, as given in Frame 7.6, without a need to memorise that formula.

Suppose we have an implicit function $f(x, y) = C$ (constant). Define $u = f(x, y)$ and write down its differential:

$$du = \frac{\partial f}{\partial x}\, dx + \frac{\partial f}{\partial y}\, dy = f_x\, dx + f_y\, dy. \tag{8.6}$$

Now if x and y satisfy the implicit function equation, we have $u = C$ and hence $du = 0$. (8.6) becomes

$$0 = f_x\, dx + f_y\, dy \quad \Rightarrow \quad \frac{dy}{dx} = -\frac{f_x}{f_y},$$

exactly as in Frame 7.6.

Example 8.9   Find $\frac{dy}{dx}$ when $x^2 - 2xy + 5y^2 = 8$.

Let this expression be u:

$$du = (2x - 2y)\, dx + (-2x + 10y)\, dy. \tag{8.7}$$

Since $u = 8$ (constant), $du = 0$ and

$$\frac{dy}{dx} = -\frac{2x - 2y}{-2x + 10y} = \frac{x - y}{x - 5y}.$$

To find the tangent at the point $(1, -1)$, set $x = 1$, $y = -1$ in (8.7):

$$0 = 4\, dx - 12\, dy \quad \Rightarrow \quad \left.\frac{dy}{dx}\right|_{(1,-1)} = \frac{4}{12} = \frac{1}{3},$$

and the tangent is

$$(y + 1) = \frac{1}{3}(x - 1) \quad \Rightarrow \quad y = \frac{1}{3}x - \frac{4}{3}.$$

∎

Ex 8.7   Find du for $u = x^2 y + y^2 x$. Hence find $\frac{dy}{dx}$, when $x^2 y + y^2 x = 3$.

8.5   Thermodynamics

A major area where partial derivatives occur is **thermodynamics**. This subject abounds with variables and it is common practice to change them frequently. Also, different contexts can throw up different rates of change involving the same quantities. Common processes are **isothermal**, where the temperature is constant, and **adiabatic**, where heat energy is constant. The associated formulae are different.

We must therefore take great care to notate exactly which variables are treated as constant in any partial derivative. There is an addition to the normal notation to help with this.

We write

$$\left(\frac{\partial u}{\partial x}\right)_{\langle\text{List}\rangle},$$

where $\langle\text{List}\rangle$ quotes those variables assumed to be constant when computing the derivative. Thus, if u is being treated as a function of x and y, we write

$$\left(\frac{\partial u}{\partial x}\right)_{y},$$

and if it is being treated as a function of x, y and z, we write

$$\left(\frac{\partial u}{\partial x}\right)_{y,z}.$$

Notation

Strictly speaking, this isn't always needed, and is used merely to underline the chosen context. For example, if u is a function of x and y only, then $\frac{\partial u}{\partial x}$ automatically means that y is held constant, so it is unnecessary to write $\left(\frac{\partial u}{\partial x}\right)_{y}$. But there *are* contexts where it is essential, e.g., when there are other variables involved and they are not explicitly used in the formulae.

Example 8.10   The **ideal gas law** states $pv = RT$, where p is pressure, v is volume and T is temperature; R is a constant. This is an **implicit** function, which we can solve for any of the three variables, then calculate derivatives.

For example:

$$v = \frac{RT}{p}, \qquad \left(\frac{\partial v}{\partial p}\right)_{T} = -\frac{RT}{p^2},$$

$$T = \frac{1}{R}pv, \qquad \left(\frac{\partial T}{\partial v}\right)_{p} = \frac{1}{R}p.$$

∎

Since there are so many variables that can be in play, a popular technique is to use **differentials** and the type of expression in Frame 8.3. These can be manipulated algebraically, to eliminate differentials that are not required in the particular context. The power of this method is that we can reverse Frame 8.3 to derive derivatives from differentials.

Frame 8.5   *Finding derivatives from differentials*

$$du = g(x,y)\,dx + h(x,y)\,dy \quad \Rightarrow \quad \frac{\partial u}{\partial x} = g(x,y),\ \frac{\partial u}{\partial y} = h(x,y)$$

Notation

The brackets $()_y$ and $()_x$ can be used here, if wished.

Think about it like this

The result in Frame 8.5 can be justified as follows. Suppose that we hold y constant, so that $dy = 0$. Then

$$du = g(x,y)\,dx + 0 \quad \Rightarrow \quad \frac{du}{dx} = g(x,y),$$

and we obtain the result on changing to $\frac{\partial u}{\partial x}$, since y is constant.

The following example shows how this can be used and, incidentally, confirms that it works.

Example 8.11   Let $u = x^2 y$ and suppose that we wish to change the independent variables from (x,y) to (x,u), with y now dependent.

The differential relation is

$$du = 2xy\,dx + x^2\,dy.$$

Solve this (algebraically) for dy, which *is* always possible:

$$dy = \frac{1}{x^2}\,du - \frac{2y}{x}\,dx,$$

from which we *read off*

$$\frac{\partial y}{\partial u} = \frac{1}{x^2}, \qquad \frac{\partial y}{\partial x} = -\frac{2y}{x}.$$

In this case, we can solve algebraically to find $y = u/x^2$ and differentiate it directly:

$$\frac{\partial y}{\partial u} = \frac{1}{x^2}, \qquad \frac{\partial y}{\partial x} = -\frac{2u}{x^3} = -\frac{2x^2 y}{x^3} = -\frac{2y}{x},$$

verifying the earlier answers.   ■

In general, it is impossible to rework equations of this kind, to change the independent variables algebraically. Use of Frame 8.5 is often the only possible method for calculating such derivatives.

The following example illustrates the sort of procedures regularly used in thermodynamics, and derives one of an important set of equations.

Example 8.12   The first and second laws of thermodynamics produce the differential relation

$$du = T\,ds - p\,dv.$$

Here u is the internal energy and s the entropy, but there is no need to understand what these terms mean for present purposes. Using the definition of a differential, we can deduce

$$\left(\frac{\partial u}{\partial s}\right)_v = T, \qquad \left(\frac{\partial u}{\partial v}\right)_s = -p.$$

Now we know that the order of differentiation does not affect results, so

$$\frac{\partial}{\partial v}\left(\frac{\partial u}{\partial s}\right) = \frac{\partial}{\partial s}\left(\frac{\partial u}{\partial v}\right).$$

Hence we have

$$\left(\frac{\partial T}{\partial v}\right)_s = -\left(\frac{\partial p}{\partial s}\right)_v.$$

This, and three similar relations, form the **Maxwell equations**. These thermodynamical equations are not to be confused with his famous equations for electromagnetism. ∎

Ex 8.8 Let $u = 2x^3 - x^2 y$. Find du in terms of dx and dy. Solve this for dy in terms of du and dx and read off $\left(\frac{\partial y}{\partial x}\right)_u$ and $\left(\frac{\partial y}{\partial u}\right)_x$. Solve the original equation for y in terms of u and x and confirm your answers by direct differentiation.

Ex 8.9 The **van der Waals** equation of state for a gas takes into account intermolecular forces and the volume of the molecules. It has the form:

$$\left(p + \frac{a}{v^2}\right)(v - b) = RT.$$

Find an expression for dT and hence $\left(\frac{\partial v}{\partial p}\right)_T$. (Hint: set $dT = 0$.)

8.6 Application to Integration

The notation $\int_a^b f(x)\, dx$ contains a differential. We can ask if there is any reason for this, other than to indicate the variable driving the calculation.

The answer is that this notation relates to the original development of integration, where dx was regarded as a "vanishingly small" quantity.

Think about it like this

> This is a fiction, but helps construct integrals by simple means. Basically, we regard dx as non-zero for calculation purposes, but so small that functions of x can be treated as **constant** within any interval of width dx.

There are, therefore, two ways to construct an integral to solve a real problem.

(A) Use Δx (or Δt, etc.), apply $\sum$ and then take the limit as $\Delta x \to 0$.

(B) Use dx (or dt, etc.), apply $\int$ to get the answer. In a sense we treat dx as Δx, with the limit 'pre-loaded'.

One example will suffice to show how to use this quick method.

Example 8.13 Consider a triangular dam of width b and depth h, as shown in the diagram below. The objective is to calculate the total force on the face of the dam.

The force on an area A of the dam is $F = pA$, where p is the water pressure, given by

$$p = 9800x \text{ N m}^{-2}$$

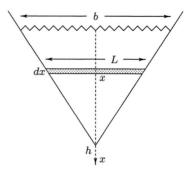

at depth x, so that it *varies* with x.

Consider the shaded element of notional width dx.

The area of this element is $L\,dx$; using similar triangles gives

$$\frac{L}{b} = \frac{h - x}{h} \quad \Rightarrow \quad L = \frac{b}{h}(h - x).$$

The force on this element is

$$dF = pA = pL\,dx = 9800x \times \frac{b}{h}(h - x)\,dx,$$

and the total force is found by *integrating* this:

$$
\begin{aligned}
F &= 9800 \int_0^h \frac{b}{h} x(h - x)\,dx \\
&= \frac{9800b}{h}\left[\frac{1}{2}hx^2 - \frac{1}{3}x^3\right]_0^h \\
&= \frac{9800b}{h} \times \frac{1}{6}h^3 = \frac{4900}{3}bh^2 \text{ (N)}.
\end{aligned}
$$

Note where the fictional idea of dx was used: the element does not really have zero width, yet we assume that the pressure is *constant* throughout. ∎

Think about it like this

We have seen several uses of differentials and it is time to mention a logical problem associated with them. Some applications, like the example above, use differentials in calculations that require them to be non-zero, then later assume they are zero. Indeed, Newton and Leibniz used them in this way when they invented calculus and incurred the wrath of leading philosophers at the time.

It took many years to find a satisfactory resolution of this problem. Meanwhile, applied mathematicians and scientists continued to use differentials, reassured by the fact that they encountered no contradictions and produced equations that corresponded well with physical observations. Because of this, differentials have persisted in practical mathematics and the neatness of the calculations makes them popular with many practitioners.

Perhaps the best way to think of them is as small quantities that are non-zero at the start of the calculation but **automatically** tend to zero at the appropriate time to deliver the required derivative or integral.

Ex 8.10 Consider a dam or a trough with a semi-circular end face, radius R. We wish to determine the total force on the face. The force on an area A subject to pressure p is Ap, assuming p is constant. For fresh water, $p = 9800x$ (in $\mathrm{N\,m^{-2}}$), where x is the depth below the surface, measured in metres.

Find the force dF on the element of area of thickness dx, shaded in the diagram. Integrate this to find an expression, as a definite integral, for the total force. Evaluate the integral, using the substitution $u = R^2 - x^2$.

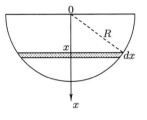

8.7 Revision Exercises

Ex 8.11 Stefan's Law states that the total rate of emission of radiant energy by an ideal radiator is given by $R = kT^4$, where k is a constant and T is the Kelvin temperature.

Write down an expression for dR in terms of dT. Hence, find an approximate expression for the percentage increase in the rate R when T increases by $p\%$.

Estimate the percentage increase in R when the temperature increases from $50°\,\mathrm{C}$ to $60°\,\mathrm{C}$. (Absolute zero is $0°\,\mathrm{K} = -273°\,\mathrm{C}$.)

Ex 8.12 Find the differential du, where $u = \cos(xy)$.

Suppose x is measured as 0.60, with maximum error size 0.01, while y is measured as 1.20, with maximum error size 0.02. Use du to estimate the largest possible error in u.

Ex 8.13 The edges of a rectangular box are measured to be $a = 12.3$ with maximum error size 0.01, $b = 17.1$ with maximum error size 0.02 and $c = 18.5$ with maximum error size 0.01. What is the maximum error made in the calculation of the volume of the box?

Ex 8.14 The function $y(x)$ is determined implicitly by the equation of the curve

$$x^2 + 2xy + xe^y = 0.$$

Determine the tangent to the curve at the point $(-1, 0)$.

Ex 8.15 Find the differential dz, where $z = (x + y)^2 + x\sin(xy)$.

Hence find an expression for $\dfrac{dy}{dx}$, where $(x + y)^2 + x\sin(xy) = 0$.

9   LIMITS and CONTINUITY

Many mathematical methods become unreliable if some function involved behaves badly, even at just one point.

Example 9.1   A popular method for locating a **root** of $f(x) = 0$ is to find a and b such that $f(a)$ and $f(b)$ have opposite signs. Apply this to

$$\text{(a) } x^2 - \frac{1}{2} = 0, \qquad \text{(b) } \frac{1}{2x - 1} = 0.$$

(a) $f(0) = \frac{1}{2}$, $f(1) = -\frac{1}{2}$. Indeed there is a root between 0 and 1, at $x = 1/\sqrt{2} \simeq 0.7071$.

(b) $f(0) = -1$, $f(1) = 1$. But the numerator of this function is never zero, so there can be no root. What has happened here is that the function is badly behaved at $x = \frac{1}{2}$, shooting to $-\infty$ on the left and $+\infty$ on the right of that point.

■

The method illustrated in this example is a good one, provided we add the stipulation that the function must be **continuous**, which is a mathematical representation of the everyday idea of continuity: the graph is joined up, without any gaps.

Think about it like this

Typical language is to say that someone is "in continuous employment", having no "gap in their employment record", when they are never out of a job.

The formal definition of continuity involves the idea of a **limit**, which hitherto we have treated informally. That approach will still suffice, but there are some aspects of limits that need further investigation, in part because we will need them in the final chapter.

9.1   Continuity

The formal definition of continuity is :

$f(x)$ is continuous at $x = a$ if $f(a)$ is defined and $f(x) \to f(a)$ as $x \to a$.

What this means is that if we ignore the value at $x = a$ and try to guess it using the trend of values around (*and on both sides of*) $x = a$, our guess would be the value itself.

A function is **continuous** in $[a, b]$ if it is continuous at every point in that interval. There is no need to grasp the formal definition to understand what that implies. We must be able to draw the graph of the function, starting at a and moving rightwards to finish at b, without lifting pen from paper, i.e., the graph has no gaps or jumps. (This statement rules out moving vertically, which would not be consistent with the single-valued nature of a function.)

Think about it like this

When we draw a graph we link together values of the function at adjacent points. If the function has a jump or a gap at $x = a$ then the information we are getting from adjacent points, which we use for the **limit**, must be at odds with the value at $x = a$.

A point where a function fails to be continuous is a **discontinuity** or **singularity**. There are three principal situations in which singularities arise.

(A) $\lim_{x \to a} f(x)$ exists, with value L say, but $f(a) \neq L$ or $f(a)$ is not defined. This is a **removable singularity** since we can fix it by (re)defining $f(a)$ as L.

Example 9.2 Consider $f(x) = \dfrac{\sin x}{x}$. This is well-defined everywhere except at $x = 0$, where it has no value. (The term $0/0$ is indeterminate; it is the main topic for the next section.)

A graph of this function can be obtained by joining up sample points.

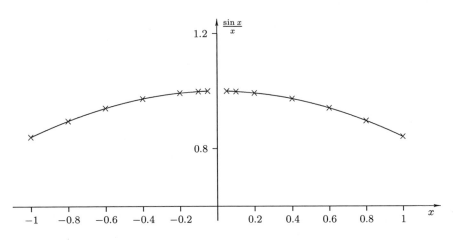

We see that there is good reason to conjecture that $\lim_{x \to 0} f(x) = 1$. If we define $f(0) = 1$, then we 'remove' the singularity and achieve a **continuous** function.

This function is an important one in Physics and Electrical Engineering, and is usually notated as $\mathrm{sinc}(x)$. ∎

(B) The limit at $x = a$ exists, but is infinite. The function has an **essential singularity**. There is no value that can be given to $f(a)$ to fix this.

Example 9.3 The function $f(x) = \dfrac{1}{x^2}$ has an essential singularity at $x = 0$. Its graph is shown below.

The function tends to $+\infty$ on both sides of 0. Hence it is **discontinuous** at 0, in spite of the fact that its behaviour is sufficiently consistent for the limit to be defined.

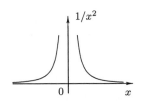

■

(C) The limit at $x = a$ is undefined. This means there is no information on which to base a consistent value for $f(a)$, so this is again an **essential singularity**. The most common situation in which this occurs is when the information around $x = a$ is conflicting; this will be explored in §9.3, but an immediate example is the **sign** function $\operatorname{sgn} x$ at $x = 0$. The information at the left of 0 is that all values are -1, while on the right it is that all values are $+1$. This gap is to great to be bridged by any defined value at $x = 0$.

Think about it like this

Using the everyday idea of continuity, the following analogy explains the difference between singularities. Suppose you are on a train journey travelling from Aberdeen to London, via Edinburgh. There are three situations that could occur at Edinburgh.

1. The train stops at Edinburgh for a few minutes, then carries on. Your journey is **continuous**.

2. The train stops at Edinburgh; you leave it to buy a newspaper, then join it again before it continues to London. Your journey has a discontinuity, but it is **removable**. You could have bought a newspaper at Aberdeen and had a continuous journey.

3. The train stops at one platform at Edinburgh and terminates; you must leave the train and pick up one going to London from a different platform. Your journey has a discontinuity, which is **essential**.

9.2   The Problem of 0/0

Sometimes a formula reduces to $\frac{0}{0}$ when the independent variable is given a specific value, $x = a$ say. This expression is **indeterminate**: it is impossible to give it any value without generating a contradiction. The only way to deal with this is to find the **limit** as $x \to a$. Indeed, this was precisely the difficulty that forced us to use limits in differentiation.

We have already seen this: in Example 9.2 the function $f(x) = \sin x/x$ produced the value $\frac{0}{0}$ at $x = 0$ (although this value should have been explicitly banned from being in the domain). It was fixed by using the limit, which happened to have a well-defined value.

There are other situations in which this appears and in which we need to identify a suitable value. It would be useful to find a methodical approach. There are, in fact, three common methods:

- algebraic manipulation, as used in some cases of "differentiation from first principles", where a factor causing the zeroes can be found and cancelled;

- the use of power series, which is effectively a more organised way of cancelling the troublesome factor;

- a method known as **L'Hôpital's rule**, which we now consider.

Suppose that we are interested in finding

$$\lim_{x \to a} \frac{f(x)}{g(x)}, \qquad \text{where } f(a) = g(a) = 0.$$

This means that the simple approach of setting $x = a$ breaks down.

This is another suitable place to use **differentials**. To explore what is happening near $x = a$ we set $x = a + dx$. If $y = f(x)$ we have $dy = f'(a)\,dx$ and so $y = f(x) \simeq f(a) + dy = 0 + f'(a)\,dx$. The situation with $g(x)$ is similar, so we find

$$\frac{f(x)}{g(x)} \simeq \frac{f'(a)\,dx}{g'(a)\,dx} = \frac{f'(a)}{g'(a)}.$$

We take this last value to be the desired limit.

Frame 9.1   *L'Hôpital's rule*

$$\text{If } f(a) = g(a) = 0, \quad \lim_{x \to a} \frac{f(x)}{g(x)} = \frac{f'(a)}{g'(a)},$$

assuming at least one of $f'(a)$, $g'(a)$ is non-zero

Example 9.4   Find $\displaystyle\lim_{x \to 0} \frac{e^x - 1}{\sin 3x}$.

Define $f(x)$ and $g(x)$ and use Frame 9.1:

$$f(x) = e^x - 1, \qquad g(x) = \sin 3x.$$

Note that $f(0) = g(0) = 0$. Then

$$\begin{aligned} f'(x) &= e^x, & g'(x) &= 3\cos 3x, \\ f'(0) &= 1, & g'(0) &= 3. \end{aligned}$$

Since at least one of these is non-zero we can deduce the limit: $\frac{f'(0)}{g'(0)} = \frac{1}{3}$. ∎

In the case where $f'(a) \neq 0$, $g'(a) = 0$ the limit is infinite or may not exist (with clashing infinities on each side of a). Such cases should be explored graphically.

If $f'(a) = g'(a) = 0$, the initial problem persists, but there is a simple solution. We repeat the method, using the second derivative, and so on, until we find at least one derivative that is non-zero. The following example illustrates this.

Example 9.5   Find $\displaystyle\lim_{x \to 0} \frac{1 - \cos x}{x^2}$.

Define $f(x)$ and $g(x)$ and use Frame 9.1:

$$f(x) = 1 - \cos x, \qquad g(x) = x^2.$$

Note that $f(0) = g(0) = 0$. Then

$$f'(x) = \sin x, \qquad g'(x) = 2x,$$
$$f'(0) = 0, \qquad g'(0) = 0.$$

Since both are zero, differentiate again:

$$f''(x) = \cos x, \qquad g''(x) = 2,$$
$$f''(0) = 1, \qquad g''(0) = 2.$$

Since at least one of these is non-zero we can deduce the limit: $\frac{f''(0)}{g''(0)} = \frac{1}{2}$. ∎

Ex 9.1 Use L'Hôpital's rule to evaluate:

(a) $\displaystyle\lim_{x \to 1} \frac{x^2 - 1}{x^3 - 1}$,   (b) $\displaystyle\lim_{x \to 2} \frac{x^3 - 2x^2 - 4x + 8}{(x^2 - 4)^2}$,   (c) $\displaystyle\lim_{x \to \pi} \frac{\sin 2x}{\sin x}$.

9.3   One-sided Limits

A normal limit involves examining the values of the function on **both** sides of the point. But this may not be possible or it may be too demanding.

Thus, there are situations where we are unable to evaluate the function on both sides of a particular point, due to a domain restriction. What we can do is to look only on the side at which it is possible, looking for a trend in the values and reporting a **one-sided limit**. The intuitive approach still works; the only significant difference is in the notation. We write for the **right limit** $x \to a+$; here we approach a from above (+), i.e., using values greater than a, which lie to the right on a graph. Similarly we write for the **left limit** $x \to a-$, approaching from below (−).

Example 9.6   What is the limit of $\sqrt{x}$ at $x = 0$?

This function is not defined for $x < 0$, so we can only look at values to the right of 0. These give information consistent with a value 0 at $x = 0$, which is, of course, the function's value. We write

$$\lim_{x \to 0+} \sqrt{x} = 0.$$

∎

This is one of the types of limit we will require in the next chapter. But there are other applications: they help us investigate **essential singularities** where there is no limit. In many cases, like $\operatorname{sgn} x$ mentioned in §9.1, this is because the information on each side conflicts: *we have well-defined left and right limits, but they do not agree.*

Two examples will suffice.

Example 9.7   Investigate the limits at $x = 0$ for (a) $H(x)$, (b) $1/x$.

(a) This is the **Heaviside function**, which models a 'switch'. Its graph is shown below.

On the left the values are all zero, so the left limit is 0; on the right we have values 1, so the right limit is 1. These do not agree so we have an essential singularity.

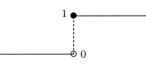

$$\lim_{x \to 0-} H(x) = 0, \qquad \lim_{x \to 0+} H(x) = 1.$$

(b) This time the limits are both infinite and fail to agree. Hence this function has an essential discontinuity on both counts: clash and infinite value.

$$\lim_{x \to 0-} \frac{1}{x} = -\infty,$$

$$\lim_{x \to 0+} \frac{1}{x} = +\infty.$$

■

Think about it like this

These *one-sided* limits may appear strange, but are no different from ordinary limits, except that we look only on one side of the point in question. You can think of 'riding along' the graph from the side in question, heading for the point in question, while trying to spot the height you will be at when you finally arrive at that point.

Ex 9.2   Consider the function

$$f(x) = \begin{cases} 4x + 7, & \text{if } -2 \leqslant x < -1; \\ ax + b, & \text{if } -1 \leqslant x < 3; \\ 10 - 3x, & \text{if } 3 \leqslant x \leqslant 4. \end{cases}$$

Here a and b are constants whose values are to be chosen to ensure $f(x)$ is continuous on $[-2, 4]$.

The right and left limits must match at $x = -1$ and at $x = 3$. First, set $x = -1$ in each of the first two pieces and stipulate that the values agree. This should give you an equation linking a and b. Repeat this for $x = 3$ and the last two pieces.

Solve the resulting equations and hence complete the specification of $f(x)$.

Ex 9.3   Consider the function $f(x) = x^{3/2}$. Explain why this function can have domain no bigger than $x \geqslant 0$. This means it cannot have a derivative at $x = 0$ since the definition of a derivative involves a full limit, using values on both sides of the point in question. Draw a graph of $f(x)$ for $0 \leqslant x \leqslant 4$ and discuss whether it has a well-defined tangent at $x = 0$.

Find the derivative $f'(x)$ for $x > 0$. Show that it has a limit, in fact a natural 'gradient' value, as $x \to 0+$, i.e., using values to the right only of $x = 0$. This limit is the *right derivative*. (A function can also have a *left derivative*; if it has both and they are equal, it has a full derivative.)

9.4   Relative Growth and Decay

Some limits, as $x \to \infty$ or $x \to 0$, appear to lead to meaningless quantities, such as $0/0$, but also $0 \times \infty$ or ∞/∞. There may, however, be a perfectly well-defined limit, since one of the competing components, 0 or ∞, may be stronger than the other.

We start with an example, before setting out some simple rules.

Example 9.8   What is the limit of $\dfrac{x^2}{e^x}$ as $x \to \infty$?

We know that x^2 and e^x both tend to ∞ as x increases, so this appears to produce an answer of ∞/∞. The graph on the right shows a maximum at $x = 2$ and a clear limit:

$$\lim_{x \to \infty} \frac{x^2}{e^x} = 0.$$

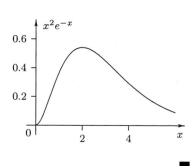

∎

The simplest rules for common functions are that, in any competition as $x \to \infty$,

exponentials e^{kx} $(k > 0)$ tend to ∞

faster than

powers x^r $(r > 0)$ tend to ∞

faster than

logarithms $\log_a x$ tend to ∞.

(Polynomials are classed as powers, whatever their degree.)

Example 9.9 $\dfrac{\ln x}{\sqrt{x}} \to 0$, $\dfrac{e^{0.1x}}{x^{100}} \to \infty$ as $x \to \infty$.   ∎

Similar rules hold as $x \to 0+$:

powers x^r $(r < 0)$ tend to ∞

faster than

logarithms $\log_a x$ tend to $-\infty$.

Think about it like this

Note the use of $0+$. It is needed because $\ln x$ is not defined for $x < 0$. The same problem occurs with x^r for some r, e.g., $r = -\frac{1}{2}$, when $x^r = 1/\sqrt{x}$.

Example 9.10   Consider what happens to $x^r \ln x$ as $x \to 0+$, when $r > 0$. We can rewrite the function as $\dfrac{\ln x}{x^{-r}}$. Both components tend to ∞ in size (since $-r < 0$), but the power term does so more quickly, 'winning' the battle. Hence the limit is 0.   ∎

The most useful deductions from these rules are summed up in the Frame below, which we shall need to use in the next chapter.

Frame 9.2   *Examples of competing limits*

$$\lim_{x\to\infty} \frac{e^x}{x^r} = \infty, \qquad \lim_{x\to\infty} x^r e^{-x} = 0,$$

$$\lim_{x\to\infty} \frac{\ln x}{x^r} = 0, \qquad \lim_{x\to 0+} x^r \ln x = 0;$$

in all of these limits, we assume $r > 0$

Ex 9.4   Give values for the following limits, with brief explanations:

$$\lim_{x\to\infty} \frac{x^{10}}{e^{0.1x}}, \quad \lim_{x\to\infty} \frac{\ln x}{x^{0.1}}, \quad \lim_{x\to\infty} \frac{x}{\ln x}, \quad \lim_{x\to 0+} \sqrt{x}\,\ln x, \quad \lim_{x\to 0} \frac{e^{-x}}{x^2}, \quad \lim_{x\to 0+} x\ln\frac{1}{x}.$$

9.5   Revision Exercises

Ex 9.5   Consider the following function definition:

$$f(x) = \frac{\sqrt{1+x} - \sqrt{1-x}}{x}.$$

Explain why this formula cannot be used for $|x| > 1$.

There is no limiting idea that can extend the definition into the region $|x| > 1$, and so the best we could hope for is to obtain a continuous function on the interval $[-1, 1]$. This requires us to identify a suitable value for $f(0)$, consistent with the limit of $f(x)$ as $x \to 0$. Hence we must find that limit.

Use L'Hôpital's Rule to evaluate $\lim f(x)$ as $x \to 0$.

Verify the answer by multiplying $f(x)$ 'above and below' by a suitable expression, involving square roots, followed by some algebraic simplification.

What value for $f(0)$ gives a continuous function for x in $[-1, 1]$?

Ex 9.6   Find the following limits, if they exist:

$$\text{(a)} \ \lim_{x\to 0} \frac{\sinh(2x)}{\sin(3x)}, \qquad \text{(b)} \ \lim_{x\to 0} \frac{e^x - 1}{x^2}.$$

10   ADVANCED INTEGRATION

This chapter is devoted to two topics in integration. The first concerns the integration of **discontinuous functions**, particularly those with **essential singularities**, as investigated in the previous chapter. Also covered under that heading are integrals where the range of integration is infinite. These are not really discontinuous, but their inverse functions are.

The second is an extension of the scope of **substitution**. Until now we have restricted our attention to substitutions that can be viewed as a reversal of the Chain Rule. We shall look at other implementations and can now take advantage of **differentials**. In particular, we shall look at the use of the inverse function, as a substitution.

10.1   Non-infinite Singularities

Removable singularities cause no difficulty in integration. These are situations where the function behaves consistently, and well, on both sides of a point, but behaves inconsistently or is not defined at that point. Since an isolated point has zero area below it, this can have no effect on the integral, which we evaluate simply by 'ignoring' the discontinuity.

Similarly, 'jump' discontinuities, where the value of the function at some point jumps by a finite amount, cause no difficulty in integration, provided there is only a finite number of them. We merely divide the range of integration into subranges, at the jump points, then integrate each separately and add the answers, relying on the integration rule:

$$\int_a^b f(x)\,dx = \int_a^c f(x)\,dx + \int_c^b f(x)\,dx. \qquad (10.1)$$

Think about it like this

> This rule effectively ignores what happens at c, which is acceptable, as long as the function is not infinite there. That case will be examined in the next section.

A removable singularity is illustrated in the next example.

Example 10.1   Evaluate $\displaystyle\int_0^2 f(x)\,dx$ where $\quad f(x) = \begin{cases} 1, & \text{if } 0 \leqslant x < 1, \\ 2, & \text{if } x = 1, \\ x, & \text{if } 1 < x \leqslant 2. \end{cases}$

Using an extension of (10.1), we have

$$\int_0^2 f(x)\,dx = \int_0^1 1\,dx + \int_1^1 2\,dx + \int_1^2 x\,dx$$
$$= \Big[x\Big]_0^1 + \Big[2x\Big]_1^1 + \Big[\tfrac{1}{2}x^2\Big]_1^2$$
$$= (1 - 0) + (2 - 2) + (2 - \tfrac{1}{2}) = {}^5\!/_2.$$

This can be confirmed geometrically by area calculations. The sum of the areas shown in the graph on the right is $1 + 0 + {}^3\!/_2 = {}^5\!/_2$. The middle value is zero since there is no area under an isolated point, a fact that the usual calculation method handled automatically $(2 - 2 = 0)$.

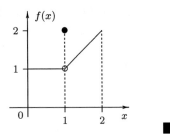

As an example of an **essential singularity**, consider the **Heaviside function**. This was previously regarded as a simple 'switch' from 0 to 1 at $x = 0$. This is somewhat restrictive, so we shall now work with a more general version. Choose any $a > 0$ and define

$$H_a(x) = \begin{cases} 0, & \text{if } x < a, \\ 1, & \text{if } x \geqslant a. \end{cases} \tag{10.2}$$

This now switches at 'time' a and hence has a 'jump' discontinuity at a.

Notation

> Recall that changing argument from x to $x - a$ shifts a graph to the right through a. Hence we could write $H_a(x) = H(x - a)$ for all x, where $H(x)$ is the original Heaviside function.

Now define:

$$F_a(x) = \int_0^x H_a(t)\, dt. \tag{10.3}$$

There are two cases to consider:

$$x < a: \quad F_a(x) = \int_0^x 0\, dt = 0,$$

$$x \geqslant a: \quad F_a(x) = \int_0^a 0\, dt + \int_a^x 1\, dt = x - a.$$

The graphs of H_a and F_a are shown below.

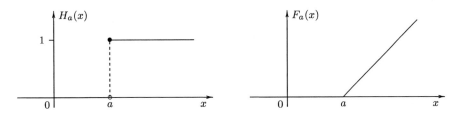

There is an important observation to be made from these two graphs. They show that the integration has 'smoothed' out the jump, producing a **continuous** function. This is generally the case; integration is a smoothing process and is often involved in instrument design, where the reading must reflect the underlying measurement and not any wobbling about it.

Think about it like this

> Recall that integration is used to measure the **mean** or **average** for a function. That concept also involves smoothing: we average data to try to remove random fluctuations. Differentiation is the opposite, e.g., differentiating the continuous function $|x|$ produces one with a jump discontinuity.

Ex 10.1 This exercise uses the *integer part* function, $\mathtt{INTPT}(x)$, which outputs the largest integer less than or equal to x. For a positive x this is just the whole number part when it is written down in decimal notation:

$$\mathtt{INTPT}(1) = \mathtt{INTPT}(1.28735) = \mathtt{INTPT}(1.5) = \mathtt{INTPT}(1.857) = 1.$$

(For negative x, however, it is not quite so natural: $\mathtt{INTPT}(-1.2) = -2$.)

We aim to evaluate $\int_0^3 x^2 \,\mathtt{INTPT}(x)\, dx$.

The integer part function is discontinuous at $x = 1$ and $x = 2$, which suggests we should break the integral up into three parts, with ranges $[0, 1)$, $[1, 2)$ and $[2, 3)$. (Whether or not the isolated point 3 is used is immaterial.)

On $[0, 1)$ we have $\mathtt{INTPT}(x) = 0$ and so that interval contributes 0 to the final answer.

On $[1, 2)$, we have $\mathtt{INTPT}(x) = 1$ and the integrand becomes x^2. Treat $[2, 3)$ similarly, then evaluate the resulting integrals and find the required answer.

10.2   Improper Integrals (Second Type)

More serious is the case where the function tends to $-\infty$ or ∞ as we approach a point. We now consider the possibility of integrating a function with an 'infinite' singularity within the range of integration, perhaps at one end.

Strictly speaking, the integral is not properly defined, since the summation definition fails in any interval containing a point where where the function has no finite value. There **may**, however, be a finite quantity of area below the graph, in spite of it appearing to stretch over an infinite distance. It is not unreasonable to try to measure that area. The only really safe method is to use a **limit** as an intermediate step, and it must be a **one-sided** limit, since we cannot dare to cross the singularity.

We start with a singularity at one end of the interval $[a, b]$. Thus, suppose that $f(x)$ has an infinite value at $x = b$, and is well-behaved elsewhere, while $g(x)$ has an infinite value at $x = a$. We use the following methods.

Frame 10.1   *Improper integrals (Second type)*

$$\int_a^b f(x)\, dx = \lim_{c \to b-} \int_a^c f(x)\, dx, \qquad \int_a^b g(x)\, dx = \lim_{c \to a+} \int_c^b g(x)\, dx$$

$$\tag{10.4}$$

Notation

As a reminder, the notation $c \to b-$ means that we look only at values less than b, i.e. on the '$-$' side of b, when finding the limit. (Values greater than b play no role in the integral.) Similarly, $c \to a+$ means that we consider only values greater than a.

Think about it like this

The reason for the name 'improper' is that, although the values we compute are valid and useful, the integrals do not satisfy all the rules that pertain to 'normal' integrals. We treat the **Second** type before the **First** because it is a natural follow-on from the finite discontinuity case.

Example 10.2 Evaluate $\displaystyle\int_0^1 \frac{1}{\sqrt{1-x^2}}\,dx.$

The application of Frame 10.1, to avoid any problem with the 'infinity' in the integrand at $x = 1$, is as follows. We must stay to the left of $x = 1$ and hence use a **left limit**.

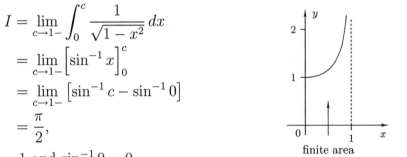

$$I = \lim_{c \to 1-} \int_0^c \frac{1}{\sqrt{1-x^2}}\,dx$$

$$= \lim_{c \to 1-} \left[\sin^{-1} x\right]_0^c$$

$$= \lim_{c \to 1-} \left[\sin^{-1} c - \sin^{-1} 0\right]$$

$$= \frac{\pi}{2},$$

since $\sin\frac{\pi}{2} = 1$ and $\sin^{-1} 0 = 0.$ ■

Think about it like this

It may seem paradoxical to have a finite area with one side infinite, but recall that in the geometric series, for example, we can sometimes add up an infinite sequence of numbers and still get a finite answer. That is similar to what is happening here. To get a finite answer the function must blow up slowly. (In the next section it must die away quickly.)

Example 10.3 Evaluate $\displaystyle\int_0^1 \frac{1}{\sqrt{x}}\,dx.$

This time the problem point is $x = 0$. We approach it from above, using a **right limit**.

$$I = \lim_{c \to 0+} \int_c^1 \frac{1}{\sqrt{x}}\,dx$$

$$= \lim_{c \to 0+} \left[2\sqrt{x}\right]_c^1$$

$$= \lim_{c \to 0+} \left[2 - 2\sqrt{c}\right] = 2.$$

■

Sometimes – as in the previous examples where we could have used $\sin^{-1} 1 = \frac{\pi}{2}$ or $\sqrt{0} = 0$ directly – we can safely 'ignore' the discontinuity, but there are cases where this is dangerous and Frame 10.1 must be used.

Example 10.4   Evaluate $\displaystyle\int_0^1 \ln x \, dx$.

The problem point is again $x = 0$, since $\ln x \to -\infty$ as $x \to 0+$. Replace it by c and approach from above.

$$\int_0^1 \ln x \, dx = \lim_{c \to 0+} \int_c^1 \ln x \, dx$$

$$= \lim_{c \to 0+} \left[x \ln x - x \right]_c^1 \qquad \text{(integration by parts)}$$

$$= \lim_{c \to 0+} \left[1 \ln 1 - 1 - c \ln c + c \right]$$

$$= -1 - \lim_{c \to 0+} c \ln c = -1.$$

The final limit used here is found in Frame 9.2. More simply, we can assume it is zero, because powers are stronger than logs.   ∎

It is in cases where there is a discontinuity strictly inside the range of integration that we are at greatest danger, since the point in question is not involved in the final step of evaluation at the limits of the integral, when its effect might be detected. When we spot such a discontinuity, the procedure is to break the integral into two subintegrals at that point and then apply Frame 10.1 to each. Thus, for a discontinuity at $x = p$ in $[a, b]$, we define and evaluate the improper integral by:

$$\int_a^b f(x) \, dx = \int_a^p f(x) \, dx + \int_p^b f(x) \, dx$$

$$= \lim_{c \to p-} \int_a^c f(x) \, dx + \lim_{c \to p+} \int_c^b f(x) \, dx. \qquad (10.5)$$

Example 10.5   Discuss the integral $\displaystyle\int_{-1}^1 \frac{1}{x^2} \, dx$.

Suppose we ignore the discontinuity in $\frac{1}{x^2}$ at $x = 0$:

$$\int_{-1}^1 \frac{1}{x^2} \, dx = \left[-\frac{1}{x} \right]_{-1}^1 = -2.$$

But this is clearly wrong, since $\frac{1}{x^2} > 0$ for all $x \neq 0$. Proceeding more carefully,

$$\int_{-1}^1 \frac{1}{x^2} \, dx = \lim_{b \to 0-} \int_{-1}^b \frac{1}{x^2} \, dx + \lim_{c \to 0+} \int_c^1 \frac{1}{x^2} \, dx$$

$$= \lim_{b \to 0-} \left[-\frac{1}{x} \right]_{-1}^b + \lim_{c \to 0+} \left[-\frac{1}{x} \right]_c^1$$

$$= \lim_{b \to 0-} \left(-\frac{1}{b} - 1 \right) + \lim_{c \to 0+} \left(-1 + \frac{1}{c} \right).$$

Both limits are infinite, so neither of the two subintegrals exists. This integral is not defined. ∎

Ex 10.2 Find $\int_c^2 (x-1)^{-1/2} \, dx$ and hence evaluate $\int_1^2 (x-1)^{-1/2} \, dx$.

Ex 10.3 Show the following integrals are well-defined and find their values:

$$\text{(a)} \int_0^2 \frac{dx}{\sqrt{4-x^2}}, \qquad \text{(b)} \int_0^1 x \ln x \, dx.$$

Ex 10.4 Show the following integrals are well-defined and find their values:

$$\text{(a)} \int_0^1 \frac{x^2-1}{\sqrt{x}} \, dx, \qquad \text{(b)} \int_0^1 \frac{x^3}{\sqrt{1-x^4}} \, dx, \qquad \text{(c)} \int_0^{\pi/2} \frac{\cos x}{\sqrt{\sin x}} \, dx.$$

10.3   Improper Integrals (First Type)

Although the integrals we now examine do not necessarily involve discontinuities in the integrand, they cannot be defined in the usual way. We require a technique reminiscent of that in the previous section.

Thus, we now assume the integrand is well-behaved, but that the range of integration is itself infinite in extent. The integral is again not properly defined, since we cannot split the interval of integration into a finite number of finite sized pieces, as required by the formal definition of an integral as the limit of a sum. A similar method is available; we define this **improper integral** using a limit. There are three cases.

Frame 10.2   *Improper integrals (First type)*

$$\int_a^\infty f(x) \, dx = \lim_{b \to \infty} \int_a^b f(x) \, dx, \tag{10.6}$$

$$\int_{-\infty}^b f(x) \, dx = \lim_{a \to -\infty} \int_a^b f(x) \, dx, \tag{10.7}$$

$$\int_{-\infty}^\infty f(x) \, dx = \lim_{\substack{b \to \infty \\ a \to -\infty}} \int_a^b f(x) \, dx \tag{10.8}$$

For each of these, should the limit exist as a finite quantity, we say the integral is **convergent**; otherwise it is **divergent**.

Example 10.6   Evaluate the following integrals (where possible):

$$\text{(a)} \int_1^\infty \frac{1}{x^{3/2}} \, dx, \qquad \text{(b)} \int_1^\infty \frac{1}{\sqrt{x}} \, dx.$$

(a) Replace ∞ by b and let $b \to \infty$:

$$\int_1^\infty \frac{dx}{x^{3/2}} = \lim_{b \to \infty} \int_1^b x^{-3/2}\, dx$$

$$= \lim_{b \to \infty} \left[-2x^{-1/2} \right]_1^b$$

$$= \lim_{b \to \infty} \left(-\frac{2}{\sqrt{b}} + 2 \right) = 2.$$

Since the final value is finite, this integral is well-defined: it is **convergent**.

(b) Use the same idea as in (a):

$$\int_1^\infty \frac{dx}{\sqrt{x}} = \lim_{b \to \infty} \int_1^b x^{-1/2}\, dx$$

$$= \lim_{b \to \infty} \left[2x^{1/2} \right]_1^b$$

$$= \lim_{b \to \infty} \left(2\sqrt{b} - 2 \right),$$

which is infinite. This integral is not defined: it is **divergent**.

A comparison of the graphs of these two functions is informative. The dashed graph, that of $1/\sqrt{x}$, approaches zero much more slowly than that of $1/x^{3/2}$, thereby trapping more area, in fact an infinite amount.

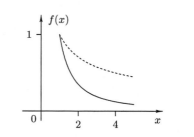

■

An important 'rule' that may be extrapolated from these results is:

$$\int_a^\infty \frac{1}{x^r}\, dx \text{ is convergent when } r > 1, \text{ but divergent when } r \leqslant 1, \ (a > 0).$$

$$(10.9)$$

The critical value here, on the border between convergence and divergence, is $r = 1$.

Example 10.7   Try to evaluate $\displaystyle \int_1^\infty \frac{1}{x}\, dx$.

The same approach as in the previous example delivers

$$I = \lim_{b \to \infty} \int_1^b \frac{1}{x}\, dx = \lim_{b \to \infty} \left[\ln b - \ln a \right],$$

which is infinite. This integral is indeed divergent.   ■

Think about it like this

> The key feature of *First type* problems is not a singularity in the integrand, although that could also occur. They are effectively the inverse of the Second type ones. Instead of having an area with an infinite side vertically – an infinite function value – we have one with an infinite side horizontally, in other words, an infinite span of x-values.

Integrals of this type are very common in practice, since they accord well with key elements in building mathematical models. For example:

$$\int_0^\infty \cdots dt : \text{'adds up' all contributions from initial time onwards,}$$

$$\int_{-\infty}^\infty \cdots dx : \text{'adds up' all contributions from one direction in space.}$$

A particularly important use is to 'anchor' quantities such as potential energy, which can have an arbitrary zero level. The points $x = \infty$ or $x = -\infty$ are often chosen as zero potential levels. Thus, for a field $E(x')$ experienced at position x', the electrostatic potential is often defined as

$$V(x) = -\int_{-\infty}^x E(x') \, dx'.$$

This represents the work required to move a unit charge from a point completely outside the field's influence $(-\infty)$ to a position x.

Example 10.8   Electrical potential due to a point charge q at the origin. Find a formula for the potential, given the field:

$$E(x') = -\frac{q}{4\pi\epsilon_0(x')^2}, \qquad \text{i.e., use} \qquad V(x) = \int_{-\infty}^x \frac{q}{4\pi\epsilon_0 u^2} \, du.$$

The dummy variable x' is commonly used in this context. Here we have replaced it by u to avoid the clumsy $(x')^2$ in the calculation.

$$\begin{aligned}
V(x) &= \lim_{b \to -\infty} \int_b^x \frac{q}{4\pi\epsilon_0 u^2} \, du \\
&= \frac{q}{4\pi\epsilon_0} \lim_{b \to -\infty} \left[-\frac{1}{u} \right]_b^x \\
&= \frac{q}{4\pi\epsilon_0} \lim_{b \to -\infty} \left(-\frac{1}{x} + \frac{1}{b} \right) \\
&= -\frac{q}{4\pi\epsilon_0} \cdot \frac{1}{x},
\end{aligned}$$

since $1/b \to 0$ as $b \to \infty$.

Note that this result is valid only if $x < 0$, since there is a discontinuity at $x = 0$, which we cannot pass. A more advanced method allows us to move off the x-axis, by-passing the origin, to find the result

$$V(x) = \frac{q}{4\pi\epsilon_0} \cdot \frac{1}{x} \qquad (x > 0).$$

Both versions are encompassed by

$$V(x) = \frac{q}{4\pi\epsilon_0} \cdot \frac{1}{|x|} \qquad (x \neq 0).$$

∎

As a further illustration, recollect the integral of the 'shifted' Heaviside function defined in (10.3). Had we defined this as

$$F_a(x) = \int_{-\infty}^{x} H_a(t)\, dt, \tag{10.10}$$

we would not have needed the restriction $a > 0$, since the lower limit $(-\infty)$ would always lie safely to the left of a.

Think about it like this

It is difficult to overstate the importance of ∞ and $-\infty$ as limits in integrals. The fact that such integrals do not satisfy the full set of integration rules is more than outweighed by practical considerations. The use of an infinite limit ensures we treat all possibilities when adding up contributions. One situation where this is especially important is probability, where we must cover all possible events. Also, as we have seen, infinity is often a useful place to 'anchor' an integral defining some quantity, since we can be sure it will not interfere with any special feature of that quantity.

We can sometimes evaluate such integrals safely without use of a limiting process. We find an indefinite integral and see if a commonsense approach to the use of the infinite value $(+\infty$ or $-\infty)$ will give a clear answer. Examples are:

$$e^{-\infty} = 0, \qquad \tan^{-1}\infty = \tfrac{\pi}{2}, \qquad \frac{1}{\infty} = 0.$$

Using these effectively skips a line in the calculation since the formally defined limit is implicit in them.

If this leads to a finite answer, the integral is likely to be convergent. If the answer is unclear, you must revert to the formal use of a limiting process.

Example 10.9   Evaluate the following integrals:

$$\text{(a)} \int_0^{\infty} \frac{1}{1+x^2}\, dx, \qquad \text{(b)} \int_0^{\infty} xe^{-x}\, dx, \qquad \text{(c)} \int_{-\infty}^{0} e^x\, dx.$$

(a) Arguing that $\tan\frac{\pi}{2} = \infty$ gives $\tan^{-1}\infty = \frac{\pi}{2}$,

$$\int_0^{\infty} \frac{dx}{1+x^2} = \left[\tan^{-1}x\right]_0^{\infty}$$

$$= \tan^{-1}\infty - \tan^{-1}0 = \frac{\pi}{2} - 0 = \frac{\pi}{2}.$$

(b) Arguing that $e^{-\infty} = 0$,

$$\int_0^{\infty} xe^{-x}\, dx = \left[-xe^{-x} - e^{-x}\right]_0^{\infty} \qquad \text{(integration by parts)}$$

$$= 0 - 0 + 0 + e^0 = 1.$$

Strictly speaking, $e^{-x} \to 0$ and $xe^{-x} \to 0$, as $x \to \infty$, using a limit result from Frame 9.2.

(c) A similar 'value' to that in (b) gives

$$\int_{-\infty}^{0} e^x \, dx = \left[e^x \right]_{-\infty}^{0} = 1 - e^{-\infty} = 1 - 0 = 1.$$

■

There is one final observation to make about such integrals. It is often the case that they appear with integrands that have no simple anti-derivatives. The only way to find a value is by a numerical method and it is sensible to ask if there is indeed such a value before trying to find it. The x^{-r} results in (10.9) are particularly helpful here, as the following example shows.

Example 10.10 Determine whether (a) $\displaystyle\int_{1}^{\infty} \frac{\cos x}{x^2} \, dx$ and (b) $\displaystyle\int_{1}^{\infty} \frac{\ln x}{x} \, dx$ are convergent.

(a) This is **convergent** because the integrand is smaller (in size) than $1/x^2$, since $|\cos x| \leqslant 1$, while the integral of $1/x^2$ converges.

(b) This is **divergent** because $|\ln x| > 1$ for large x, so the integrand is eventually greater (in size) than $1/x$, whose integral diverges.

■

Ex 10.5

(a) Find $\displaystyle\int_{0}^{b} e^{-2x} \, dx$ and hence evaluate $\displaystyle\int_{0}^{\infty} e^{-2x} \, dx$.

(b) Evaluate $\displaystyle\int_{1}^{\infty} \frac{1}{x^3} \, dx$.

Ex 10.6 Which of the following integrals would you expect to be convergent? (There is no need to try to evaluate them.)

$$\int_{1}^{\infty} \frac{dx}{x^{1.1}}, \quad \int_{1}^{\infty} \frac{dx}{x^{3/4}}, \quad \int_{1}^{\infty} \frac{dx}{x^2 \ln x}, \quad \int_{1}^{\infty} \frac{\ln x}{\sqrt{x}} \, dx, \quad \int_{1}^{\infty} \frac{\sin x}{x^{3/2}} \, dx, \quad \int_{1}^{\infty} \frac{e^{-x}}{\sqrt{x}} \, dx.$$

Ex 10.7 Show the following integrals are well-defined and find their values:

(a) $\displaystyle\int_{1}^{\infty} \frac{1}{x^{5/2}} \, dx$, (b) $\displaystyle\int_{0}^{\infty} t e^{-2t} \, dt$, (c) $\displaystyle\int_{0}^{\infty} \frac{x}{1+x^4} \, dx$, (d) $\displaystyle\int_{0}^{\infty} \frac{dx}{x^2 + 2x + 2}$.

10.4   Introduction to Substitution

The methods for evaluating improper integrals, as in all conventional integration, rely on finding an anti-derivative. It is unfortunately the case that simple anti-derivatives are quite rare. We do have classes of functions, like rational functions, where there are guaranteed methods for finding them, but there are rather few such classes. **Substitution** provides some of them.

The basic idea of substitution is to change the variable, hoping to find a simpler integral in that new variable. Because there is a need to change the differential, such as dx, this involves more than simply replacing the variable in the integrand with something else.

There are two main types of substitution. Assume the original variable is x. Then changing to u by means of $u = f(x)$ is termed **direct** or **explicit** substitution. Changing to t by means of $x = F(t)$ is termed **indirect** or **inverse** or **implicit** substitution. (As we see later, it is sometimes possible to view a substitution in both ways: if $u = f(x)$ then $x = f^{-1}(u)$, which explains why the second method is termed **inverse**.)

Notation

> Neither this distinction, nor the nomenclature, will be found in all textbooks. Those omitting it are not necessarily at fault, since a particular substitution can often be viewed in both ways. But distinguishing the structural differences – using different notation, at least initially – must surely help in identifying and implementing a substitution, since the two approaches are somewhat different.

10.4.1   Direct Substitution

Direct substitution is equivalent to reversing the Chain Rule and has been used in earlier chapters. Here we shall concentrate on indirect substitution, but we first revisit direct substitution to underline the differences.

It is implemented as follows. Choose $u = f(x)$ and replace each occurrence of $f(x)$ by u. Then argue that

$$\frac{du}{dx} = f'(x) \quad \Rightarrow \quad du = f'(x)\,dx,$$

so that we must find a part of the integrand that represents $f'(x)$ to join with dx and be replaced by du. This produces the following rule.

Frame 10.3   *Direct substitution ($u=f(x)$)*

$$\int g\bigl(f(x)\bigr) f'(x)\,dx = \int g(u)\,du \qquad\qquad (10.11)$$

Example 10.11   Integrate $x^2 \cos x^3$.

Let $u = x^3$, so $\frac{du}{dx} = 3x^2$ and $x^2\,dx = \frac{1}{3}\,du$.

$$\int x^2 \cos x^3 \, dx = \int \cos u \, \frac{1}{3} \, du = \frac{1}{3} \int \cos u \, du$$

$$= \frac{1}{3} \sin u + C = \frac{1}{3} \sin x^3 + C.$$

This result is the reverse of the Chain Rule result: $\frac{d}{dx}\left[\sin x^3\right] = 3x^2 \cos x^3$, following adjustment by a factor of 3.   ∎

Example 10.12   Evaluate $\displaystyle\int \frac{e^{\tan x}}{\cos^2 x}\,dx$.

Note that $u = \tan x$ leads to $du = \sec^2 x\,dx = \dfrac{1}{\cos^2 x}\,dx$. Hence

$$I = \int e^u \, du = e^u + C = e^{\tan x} + C.$$

∎

Once the new integral has been evaluated, we would normally – as above – replace each u in the answer by $f(x)$ to return to the original variable x. In the case of a definite integral, however, it may be preferable to change the limits from values of x to values of u, from the outset:

$$\int_a^b g\big(f(x)\big) f'(x) \, dx = \int_{f(a)}^{f(b)} g(u) \, du. \tag{10.12}$$

(See §10.4.3 for a warning about dangers lurking in this method.)

Example 10.13   Evaluate $\displaystyle\int_1^2 \frac{dx}{x(x^3 + 1)}$.

Let $u = x^3$, so $\frac{du}{dx} = 3x^2$ and $du = 3x^2\,dx$, as in Example 10.11. But this time we have to deal with, not an x^2 term, but just x. Proceed by writing $x^2 = x^3/x = u/x$:

$$du = 3\frac{u}{x}\,dx \quad \Rightarrow \quad \frac{dx}{x} = \frac{1}{3}\frac{du}{u}.$$

Also, $x = 1 \Rightarrow u = 1$ and $x = 2 \Rightarrow u = 8$. Hence

$$I = \int_1^8 \frac{1}{u+1}\frac{1}{3}\frac{du}{u} = \frac{1}{3}\int_1^8 \frac{1}{u(u+1)}\,du$$

$$= \frac{1}{3}\int_1^8 \left(\frac{1}{u} - \frac{1}{u+1}\right) du = \frac{1}{3}\left[\ln \frac{u}{u+1}\right]_1^8$$

$$= \tfrac{1}{3}\left[\ln \tfrac{8}{9} - \ln \tfrac{1}{2}\right] = \tfrac{1}{3}\ln \tfrac{16}{9} = \tfrac{2}{3}\ln \tfrac{4}{3}.$$

Note the use of **partial fractions** to deal with the rational function $\frac{1}{u(u+1)}$ generated by the substitution.   ∎

The advantages of this method are that we never have to 'invert' the function f to find x in terms of u at any stage, and the limits are easily converted to values of u. A major drawback is that it cannot be applied unless the integrand is of a rather special form, i.e., one that offers the potential to isolate a term representing $\frac{du}{dx}$.

Ex 10.8 Use the substitution $u = 4 + e^{2x}$ to evaluate $\int \dfrac{2e^{2x}}{(4 + e^{2x})^2}\, dx$.

Ex 10.9 Use the given substitutions to integrate:

(a) $\displaystyle\int_1^2 \frac{\ln x}{x}\, dx$ $(u = \ln x)$,   (b) $\displaystyle\int \frac{dx}{e^x + e^{-x}}$ $(u = e^x)$.

Ex 10.10 By using an appropriate substitution, evaluate:

(a) $\displaystyle\int_{1/2}^1 \frac{x}{\sqrt{1 - x^2}}\, dx$,   (b) $\displaystyle\int_{\pi/4}^{\pi/2} \cos x \sin^3 x\, dx$,   (c) $\displaystyle\int_1^4 \frac{e^{\sqrt{x}}}{\sqrt{x}}\, dx$.

10.4.2 Inverse Substitution

In this method we change to a new variable t using $x = f(t)$ for some function f. Hence $\frac{dx}{dt} = f'(t)$, so $dx = f'(t)\, dt$. It does not suffer from the drawback of requiring two parts to the integrand. It is termed **inverse substitution** since the new variable is not given **directly** in terms of x: if it is needed in that form we must find $t = f^{-1}(x)$. (We shall initially use t for the new variable to maintain a distinction from the u used in the direct method.)

Implementation of the method is straightforward: each manifestation of x is changed to $f(t)$, while dx is changed to $f'(t)\, dt$. An indefinite integral is immediately changed to one involving only t.

Frame 10.4   *Inverse substitution $(x=f(t))$*

$$\int g(x)\, dx = \int g\big(f(t)\big) f'(t)\, dt \qquad\qquad (10.13)$$

Example 10.14   Evaluate $\displaystyle\int \frac{1}{1 + \sqrt[3]{x}}\, dx$.

The cube root is the obvious problem here and we could try to get rid of it using $x = t^3$, so $\sqrt[3]{x} = t$. Then $dx = 3t^2\, dt$ and the integral becomes

$$\int \frac{1}{1 + t}\, 3t^2\, dt.$$

The new integral looks complicated, but the integrand is a rational function, for which there is a guaranteed method. Partial fractions come to mind, but in this case only a division to find polynomial and remainder is needed.

$$I = \int \left[3t - 3 + \frac{3}{1+t} \right] dt$$

$$= \frac{3}{2}t^2 - 3t + 3\ln|1+t| + C$$

$$= \frac{3}{2}x^{2/3} - 3\sqrt[3]{x} + 3\ln\left|1 + \sqrt[3]{x}\right| + C.$$

As in the direct case, if we have limits on the integral we can involve them without returning to x. For limits 0 to 1, we need to solve:

$$x = 0 \quad \Rightarrow \quad t = \sqrt[3]{0} = 0, \qquad x = 1 \quad \Rightarrow \quad t = \sqrt[3]{1} = 1,$$

and the integral is

$$\int_0^1 \frac{3t^2}{1+t}\, dt = \left[\frac{3}{2}t^2 - 3t + 3\ln|1+t| \right]_0^1$$

$$= \frac{3}{2} - 3 + 3\ln 2 = 3\ln 2 - \frac{3}{2}.$$

∎

Think about it like this

This ease of implementation has to be set against the fact that the integrand is potentially becoming more complicated: a *bare* x is being replaced by an *expression* involving t. There is a danger that we may end up with an integral more intractable than the original, unless we are sure that some algebraic simplification will ensue.

Ex 10.11 Use the substitution $x = e^t$ to evaluate $\displaystyle \int_1^e \frac{dx}{x(\ln x + 1)}$.

10.4.3 Comparison of Direct and Inverse Substitution

As is often the case in mathematics, methods that are inverses of each other tend to have diametrically opposed properties. The pros and cons for these substitutions are summed up in the following table.

Direct	Inverse
May not work	Always works, to give new integral
Will simplify integral if it works	May make integral more complicated
Returning to x easy	Returning to x can be difficult
Adapting limits easy	Must solve equations to adapt limits

Finally, there is danger lurking in the use of (10.12), where we change the limits rather than return to x. Many textbooks do not point this out. Direct substitution can run into difficulties if there is no inverse function for the substitution $u = f(x)$ being used, e.g., if $f(x)$ is not **one-one**.

In such a case there are **two** x values with the same u value, so the graph of $f(x)$ must turn round somewhere, as shown on the right. Hence there is an x where $f'(x) = 0$, and at that point we have a problem with $dx = \dfrac{1}{f'(x)}\, du$. The following example shows what can happen.

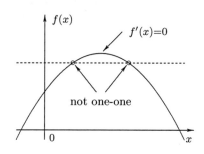

Example 10.15   Evaluate $\displaystyle\int_{-1}^{1} x^2\, dx \; (= \tfrac{2}{3})$, using the substitution $u = x^2$.

We have $du = 2x\, dx$, so the integral becomes

$$\int x^2\, dx = \int \frac{1}{2} x \cdot 2x\, dx = \int \frac{1}{2}\sqrt{u}\, du.$$

Now $x = -1$ gives $u = (-1)^2 = 1$ and $x = 1$ gives $u = 1^2 = 1$, so the integral (in u form) is

$$\int_{-1}^{1} x^2\, dx = \int_{1}^{1} \frac{1}{2}\sqrt{u}\, du = 0,$$

since the limits are equal.

This is because x^2 is not one-one in $[-1, 1]$. It can be fixed in two ways. One is to return to x, then use the limits:

$$\int \frac{1}{2}\sqrt{u}\, du = \frac{1}{3} u^{3/2} + C = \frac{1}{3}\left(x^2\right)^{3/2} + C = \frac{1}{3} x^3 + C,$$

leading to $\tfrac{1}{3}\left[1^3 - (-1)^3\right] = \tfrac{2}{3}$. The other is to use **evenness** at the outset: $\displaystyle\int_{-1}^{1} x^2\, dx = 2\int_{0}^{1} x^2\, dx$, when the substitution works; x^2 *is* one-one in the interval $[0, 1]$. ∎

10.5   Standard Substitutions

There are several classes of functions where a standard substitution is guaranteed to work, or at least to simplify the integral. Many of these are available in reference books. Some are given here, to provide a flavour of the topic.

10.5.1   Linear Substitution

The first case is very simple and very important. There are some powerful methods available for numerical integration, which work only for a standard interval, typically $[-1, 1]$ or $[0, 1]$. If our interval is not the standard one, then it should be straightforward to adapt the problem to the target interval, using a **linear** substitution. In this case we can proceed either by direct or inverse substitution since the function is simple (linear) and has an easily found inverse function.

If we need to change the interval of integration from $[a, b]$ (both ends assumed finite) to $[-1, 1]$, then we use:

$$u = \frac{2x - b - a}{b - a}, \qquad x = \tfrac{1}{2}(b + a) + \tfrac{1}{2}(b - a)u.$$

Example 10.16 Convert $\displaystyle\int_{-2}^{4} \sqrt[3]{x} \, dx$.

Here, $b = 4$, $a = -2$, so we use $x = 1 + 3u$, $dx = 3 \, du$, $u = \tfrac{1}{3}(x - 1)$, and

$$\int_{-2}^{4} \sqrt[3]{x} \, dx = 3 \int_{-1}^{1} \sqrt[3]{1 + 3u} \, du.$$

$\blacksquare$

10.5.2 Quadratic terms

Integrals involving x^2, perhaps inside a square root, are particularly common. (These could arise from a measurement of distance using the magnitude of a vector.) If there is a 'spare' x available then the direct method illustrated in §2.4 is recommended using, for example, $u = x^2$ and $du = 2x \, dx$. Otherwise, the following substitutions may help.

Frame 10.5   *Standard substitutions for quadratic terms*

'Spare' x present: $u = x^2$, $du = 2x \, dx$; otherwise:

$$a^2 - x^2 : \quad x = a \sin t, \tag{10.14}$$
$$x^2 + a^2 : \quad x = a \tan t \;\; or \;\; x = a \sinh t, \tag{10.15}$$
$$x^2 - a^2 : \quad x = a \sec t \;\; or \;\; x = a \cosh t \tag{10.16}$$

After using these, one must be prepared to identify and use:

$$\sin^2 t + \cos^2 t = 1, \quad \sec^2 t = 1 + \tan^2 t, \quad \cosh^2 t - \sinh^2 t = 1,$$

the identities on which the substitutions rely.

Example 10.17 Integrate $\sqrt{4 - x^2}$.

From (10.14), let $x = 2 \sin t$, $dx = 2 \cos t \, dt$. Then

$$\sqrt{4 - x^2} = \sqrt{4 - 4 \sin^2 t} = \sqrt{4 \cos^2 t} = 2 \cos t.$$

$$I = \int 2\cos t\, 2\cos t\, dt = 2\int (\cos 2t + 1)\, dt$$
$$= \sin 2t + 2t + C.$$

To convert back to x (if necessary):

$$I = 2\sin t \cos t + 2t + C$$
$$= \tfrac{1}{2}(2\sin t)(2\cos t) + 2t + C$$
$$= \tfrac{1}{2}x\sqrt{4 - x^2} + 2\sin^{-1}\tfrac{x}{2} + C.$$

■

Example 10.18   Integrate $\dfrac{1}{(x^2 + 1)^2}$.

From (10.15), let $x = \tan t$, $dx = \sec^2 t\, dt$. Hence

$$I = \int \frac{1}{(\tan^2 t + 1)^2}\sec^2 t\, dt = \int \frac{\sec^2 t}{\sec^4 t}\, dt$$
$$= \int \cos^2 t\, dt = \int \tfrac{1}{2}(\cos 2t + 1)\, dt$$
$$= \tfrac{1}{4}\sin 2t + \tfrac{1}{2}t + C.$$

Convert back to x using the triangle shown below. Here $x = \tan t$ has been represented by two sides x and 1, the hypotenuse calculated and then other trigonometric ratios read off:

$$\sin t = \frac{x}{\sqrt{x^2 + 1}}, \qquad \cos t = \frac{1}{\sqrt{x^2 + 1}}.$$

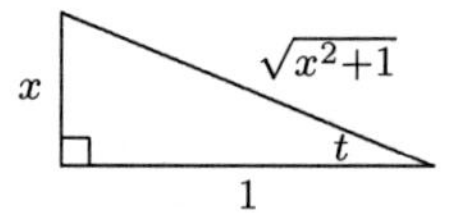

These give the required formula:

$$I = \tfrac{1}{2}\sin t \cos t + \tfrac{1}{2}t + C$$
$$= \frac{1}{2}\frac{x}{\sqrt{x^2 + 1}} \cdot \frac{1}{\sqrt{x^2 + 1}} + \frac{1}{2}\tan^{-1} x + C$$
$$= \frac{1}{2}\frac{x}{x^2 + 1} + \frac{1}{2}\tan^{-1} x + C.$$

■

Quadratics with a non-zero 'middle' term may require an initial application of **completing the square**.

Example 10.19   Integrate $\sqrt{4x - x^2}$.

Complete the square:

$$\sqrt{4x - x^2} = \sqrt{4 - (x - 2)^2},$$

then let $x - 2 = 2\sin t$, $dx = 2\cos t\, dt$. In this case it is easier to reuse the result from Example 10.17, with the linear composite rule, to find,

$$I = \frac{1}{2}(x - 2)\sqrt{4x - x^2} + 2\sin^{-1}\left(\frac{x}{2} - 1\right) + C.$$

■

Example 10.20 Evaluate $\int \dfrac{1}{x + \sqrt{9 - x^2}}\, dx$.

From (10.14), let $x = 3\sin t$, $dx = 3\cos t\, dt$, then

$$I = \int \frac{1}{3\sin t + 3\cos t}\, 3\cos t\, dt = \int \frac{\cos t}{\sin t + \cos t}\, dt.$$

This seems to be a dead-end, but there is a fairly straightforward procedure for dealing with integrands of the form $\frac{a\sin t + b\cos t}{c\sin t + d\cos t}$. For this case, we try to rewrite the top line as

$$\cos t \equiv A(\cos t - \sin t) + B(\sin t + \cos t),$$

where the first bracket contains the derivative of the bottom line and the second bracket contains the bottom line itself. The idea is to reduce the fraction to a constant plus a term of the form $f'(t)/f(t)$, with its simple integral.

Identifying the sin and cos terms in this identity leads to

$$0 = -A + B,\ 1 = A + B \quad \Rightarrow \quad A = B = \tfrac{1}{2}.$$

Hence we have

$$I = \frac{1}{2} \int \frac{\cos t - \sin t}{\sin t + \cos t}\, dt + \frac{1}{2} \int \frac{\sin t + \cos t}{\sin t + \cos t}\, dt$$

$$= \frac{1}{2} \ln |\sin t + \cos t| + \frac{1}{2} t + C.$$

In this case we shall not embark on the task of converting back to x. ∎

The final example warns against rushing to use standard methods without looking closely at the problem.

Example 10.21 Evaluate $\int \dfrac{x}{\sqrt{x^2 + 1}}\, dx$.

(10.15) would suggest we use $x = \tan t$. This will eventually lead to the answer, following yet another substitution. But it is much quicker to note the spare x here and to use $u = x^2$, $du = 2x\, dx$. Then

$$I = \int \frac{1}{\sqrt{u + 1}}\, \frac{1}{2}\, du = \sqrt{u + 1} + C = \sqrt{x^2 + 1} + C.$$

∎

10.5.3 Integrands Involving Circular Functions

Suppose that the integrand is a **rational** function of $\sin x$ and $\cos x$. (Other circular functions can easily be converted to $\sin x$ and/or $\cos x$.) Then setting

$$t = \tan \frac{x}{2} \tag{10.17}$$

will convert the integral to one whose integrand is a rational function of t, for which there is a well-known guaranteed method based on partial fractions. The equations required to implement this are given in the following Frame.

Frame 10.6   Substitution for rational function of $\sin x$ and $\cos x$

$$t = \tan \frac{x}{2}, \quad \sin x = \frac{2t}{1+t^2}, \quad \cos x = \frac{1-t^2}{1+t^2}, \quad dx = \frac{2}{1+t^2} \, dt$$

Think about it like this

Note that we set out with a **direct** substitution $t = f(x)$, but end up with an **inverse** implementation. This is because we really intend to use the inverse substitution $x = 2 \tan^{-1} t$, which is less pleasant and less easy to remember than (10.17). This type of ambiguous situation will be explored in the next section.

If the original function involves $\sin^2 x$ and $\cos^2 x$ only, then it is easier to use

$$t = \tan x, \tag{10.18}$$

with the following equations.

Frame 10.7   Substitution for rational function of $\sin^2 x$ and $\cos^2 x$

$$t = \tan x, \quad \sin^2 x = \frac{t^2}{1+t^2}, \quad \cos^2 x = \frac{1}{1+t^2}, \quad dx = \frac{1}{1+t^2} \, dt$$

Example 10.22   Use Frame 10.7 to find

$$\int \frac{1}{\sin^2 x + 4\cos^2 x} \, dx.$$

Use these equations to replace $\sin^2 x$, $\cos^2 x$ and dx in the given integral:

$$\int \frac{1}{\sin^2 x + 4\cos^2 x} \, dx = \int \frac{1}{\frac{t^2}{1+t^2} + \frac{4}{1+t^2}} \frac{dt}{1+t^2}$$

$$= \int \frac{1}{t^2 + 4} \, dt$$

$$= \tfrac{1}{2} \tan^{-1} \tfrac{t}{2} + C$$

$$= \tfrac{1}{2} \tan^{-1} \left(\tfrac{1}{2} \tan x \right) + C.$$

$\blacksquare$

Ex 10.12 Use the substitution $x = 3 \sin \theta$ to evaluate $\displaystyle\int \sqrt{9 - x^2} \, dx$.

Ex 10.13 Evaluate $\displaystyle\int_0^1 \frac{1}{(1+x^2)^2} \, dx$, using the substitution $x = \tan t$.

Ex 10.14 Use the substitution $t = \tan \frac{x}{2}$ to calculate:

$$\text{(a)} \int \frac{dx}{\sin x}, \qquad \text{(b)} \int \frac{dx}{2 + \sin x}.$$

10.6 Ambiguous Substitutions

There are two situations where the substitution seems neither direct nor indirect. In one this is because there is easy passage between $x = f(t)$ and its inverse $t = f^{-1}(x)$, as was the case in §10.5.1 (linear substitution) and §10.5.3 (circular functions). We shall explore this further under the heading of 'desperation'.

In the other situation we have a link between x and t that is doubly implicit: neither x nor t is directly available.

10.6.1 'Desperation' Substitution

This is a non-technical term describing the following tactic. If the integrand involves a nasty term, say $v(x)$, try writing $v(x) = t$. If there is no obvious way of completing the integration by that direct method, try to find the inverse function of v so $x = v^{-1}(t)$. Then replace all the x, to convert the entire integrand to one in terms of t. This is what we used in Example 10.14, to overcome the cube root term.

The following are typical 'nasty' terms:

$$t = \sqrt{x}, \quad t = \ln x, \quad t = e^x, \quad t = \frac{1}{x}, \quad t = (x-a)^n.$$

This topic is best illustrated by examples.

Example 10.23   Integrate $e^{\sqrt{x}}$.
   Let $\sqrt{x} = t$, $x = t^2$, $dx = 2t\,dt$. Then

$$I = \int e^t 2t\,dt = 2te^t - 2e^t + C,$$

using integration by parts. Hence

$$I = 2\sqrt{x}e^{\sqrt{x}} - 2e^{\sqrt{x}} + C.$$

∎

Example 10.24   Integrate $\dfrac{1}{2 + \sqrt{1+x}}$.
   Let $\sqrt{1+x} = t$, $x = t^2 - 1$, $dx = 2t\,dt$. Then

$$I = \int \frac{1}{2+t} 2t\,dt = \int \frac{2(2+t-2)}{2+t}\,dt$$

$$= 2\int \left(1 - \frac{2}{2+t}\right)\,dt = 2\big(t - 2\ln(2+t)\big) + C$$

$$= 2\sqrt{1+x} - 4\ln\left(2 + \sqrt{1+x}\right) + C.$$

∎

Example 10.25   Evaluate $\displaystyle\int \frac{1}{x^{1/2}\left(1 + x^{1/4}\right)}\, dx$.

The term $x^{1/4}$ looks frightening, so try getting rid of it with $t = x^{1/4}$. This gives $x = t^4$, $dx = 4t^3\, dt$. Then

$$
\begin{aligned}
I &= \int \frac{1}{t^2(1+t)}\, 4t^3\, dt = 4 \int \frac{t}{1+t}\, dt \\
&= 4 \int \left[1 - \frac{1}{1+t} \right] dt \\
&= 4t - 4\ln(1+t) + C \\
&= 4x^{1/4} - 4\ln\left(1 + x^{1/4}\right) + C.
\end{aligned}
$$

■

10.6.2   Fully Implicit Substitutions

These are substitutions of the form $f(x) = g(t)$, where both variables are 'implicit'. Although they appear more complicated they essentially involve no new idea. Some arise from a more inspired 'desperation' approach. Others are effectively a double substitution, involving a direct one followed by an inverse one:

$$
f(x) = u, \qquad u = g(t).
$$

The middle variable u is by-passed. Differentiating using differentials, as in §8.3, is often the key to finding how to link the differentials dx and dt.

We shall give a single example, one with a surprisingly simple outcome and which solves an important problem in gravitation (and an equivalent one in electromagnetism).

Example 10.26   The gravitational potential for a thin ring is easily found. Adding up values for a collection of rings that comprise a shell gives the potential for the shell.

Suppose the spherical shell has centre at O and radius a and that we wish to compute the potential at the point P, a constant distance r from O.

The potential for a ring on the surface at distance R from P, spanned by angles θ and $\theta + d\theta$ is known. 'Integrating' this provides the total potential, which involves the calculation of $\displaystyle\int_0^\pi \frac{\sin\theta}{R}\, d\theta$.

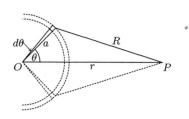

This integral is difficult because R and θ are related in a complicated way. Use a substitution to turn it into an 'R' integral and hence evaluate it.

Use the cosine rule:

$$
R^2 = r^2 + a^2 - 2ar\cos\theta,
$$

which forms an implicit link between R and θ. Remembering that a and r are constants, we can differentiate this equation to find:

$$\frac{\partial}{\partial R}\left[R^2\right]dR = -2ar\frac{\partial}{\partial \theta}\left[\cos\theta\right]d\theta,$$

which leads to the required differential link

$$\sin\theta\,d\theta = \frac{1}{ar}R\,dR.$$

The new limits depend on whether P is inside or outside the shell. First, suppose it is outside. Then

$$\theta = 0 \Rightarrow R = r - a \quad \text{and} \quad \theta = \pi \Rightarrow R = r + a.$$

We complete the integration:

$$\begin{aligned}I &= \int_{r-a}^{r+a}\frac{1}{ar}\frac{R\,dR}{R} = \frac{1}{ar}\int_{r-a}^{r+a}1\,dR\\ &= \frac{1}{ar}\left[R\right]_{r-a}^{r+a} = \frac{1}{ar}(2a) = \frac{2}{r}.\end{aligned}$$

If P is inside, the limits are $a - r$ and $a + r$, giving the answer $\frac{2}{a}$, which is *constant*. This is a well-known property in gravitation and electromagnetic theory: potential is constant inside a shell. ∎

Ex 10.15 Use the substitution $x = 2\sin^2 t$ to evaluate $\displaystyle\int_0^1\sqrt{\frac{x}{2-x}}\,dx$.

Ex 10.16 Explain why $\displaystyle\int_0^\infty\frac{dx}{\sqrt{x}(1+x)}$ is well-defined as an improper integral and find its value using an appropriate substitution.

10.7   Revision Exercises

Ex 10.17 Show that the following integral is well-defined and find its exact value:

$$\int_0^4\frac{dx}{\sqrt{16-x^2}}.$$

Ex 10.18 Show that the following integral is well-defined and find its exact value:

$$\int_0^\infty\frac{dx}{(8+x)^{4/3}}.$$

Ex 10.19 Show that the following improper integral is well-defined and find its exact value:

$$\int_{-\infty}^\infty\frac{dx}{4+x^2}.$$

Ex 10.20 Which of the following (improper) integrals have a finite value:

$$\text{(a)} \int_0^1 \frac{dx}{x^{2/3}}, \qquad \text{(b)} \int_1^\infty \frac{dx}{x^{2/3}}.$$

Calculate this value when possible.

Ex 10.21 Use the substitution $x = t^2$ to find $\displaystyle \int \frac{\sin \sqrt{x}}{\sqrt{x}}\, dx$.

Ex 10.22 Use the substitution $x = t^3$ to evaluate $\displaystyle \int_1^8 \frac{dx}{x^{2/3}\left(1 + x^{1/3}\right)}$.

Ex 10.23 Use the substitution $x = \sin t$ to evaluate $\displaystyle \int_0^{\sqrt{3}/2} \frac{dx}{\left(1 - x^2\right)^{3/2}}$.

ANSWERS TO EXERCISES

Applicable Mathematics

1.1 (a) $\frac{2}{2+x}$,
(b) $1 - y^3 - \frac{1}{2}y^6 - \frac{1}{2}y^9 - \cdots$

1.2 $r = \frac{1}{3}$, $\frac{22}{729}$

1.3 (a) $1/(1-x)^2$, (b) $1/T$

1.4 (a) $R = 2$, (b) $R = 1/\sqrt[3]{2}$ (for y)

1.5 $R = \sqrt{2}$

1.6 $1 - 2x^2 + 4x^4 - 8x^6 + \cdots$
$\left(|x| < \frac{1}{\sqrt{2}}\right)$,
$-\frac{1}{4} - \frac{1}{16}x - \frac{1}{64}x^2 - \frac{1}{256}x^3 - \cdots$
$(|x| < 4)$,
$\frac{1}{x^2} + \frac{1}{x^3} + \frac{1}{x^4} + \frac{1}{x^5} + \cdots$ $(|x| > 1)$,
$\frac{1}{x} - \frac{2}{x^2} + \frac{4}{x^3} - \frac{8}{x^4} + \cdots$ $(|x| > 2)$

1.7 $1 - x^2 + x^4 - x^6 + \cdots$,
$x - \frac{1}{3}x^3 + \frac{1}{5}x^5 - \frac{1}{7}x^7 + \cdots$,
$\frac{\pi}{4} = 1 - \frac{1}{3} + \frac{1}{5} - \frac{1}{7} + \cdots$

1.8 $x + \frac{1}{6}x^3 + \frac{3}{40}x^5 + \frac{5}{112}x^7 + \cdots$,
$R = 1$

1.9 $1 + \frac{7}{2}x + \frac{35}{8}x^2 + \frac{35}{16}x^3 + \cdots$

1.10 $3x - \frac{9}{2}x^3 + \frac{81}{40}x^5$, $1 - \frac{1}{2}x + \frac{1}{8}x^2$,
$1 - \frac{\pi^2}{2}x^2 + \frac{\pi^4}{24}x^4$

1.11 $1 - \frac{1}{3!}t^2 + \frac{1}{5!}t^5 - \cdots + \frac{(-1)^r}{(2r+1)!}t^{2r} + \cdots$,
$\mathrm{sinc}(0) = 1$

1.12 (a) $x - \frac{4}{3!}x^3 + \frac{16}{5!}x^5 - \cdots +$
$\frac{(-1)^r 2^{2r}}{(2r+1)!}x^{2r+1} + \cdots$,
(b) $c_1 = 1$, $c_3 = \frac{1}{3}$, $R = \frac{\pi}{2}$,
(c) $x - \frac{1}{2}x^2 + \frac{1}{6}x^3 - \cdots$

1.13 $-7 - 10(x - 2) - 3(x - 2)^2$

1.14 (a) $f(x) =$
$1 + \frac{1}{3}(x - 1) - \frac{1}{9}(x - 1)^2 + \cdots$,
$f(1 + h) = 1 + \frac{1}{3}h - \frac{1}{9}h^2 + \cdots$,
(b) $f(x) = 1 - \frac{1}{2}\left(x - \frac{\pi}{2}\right)^2 + \cdots$,
$f\left(\frac{\pi}{2} + h\right) = 1 - \frac{1}{2}h^2 + \cdots$, (c)
$f(x) = 1 - 2(x+1) + 4(x+1)^2 + \cdots$,
$f(-1 + h) = 1 - 2h + 4h^2 + \cdots$,

(d) $f(x) =$
$\frac{1}{a^2} - \frac{2}{a^3}(x - a) + \frac{3}{a^4}(x - a)^2 + \cdots$,
$f(a + h) = \frac{1}{a^2} - \frac{2}{a^3}h + \frac{3}{a^4}h^2 + \cdots$

1.15 (a) 0.7074,
(b) $3 + \frac{1}{6}(x - 9) - \frac{1}{216}(x - 9)^2$,
(c) 3.01667, 0.00005

1.16 $\frac{2}{\sqrt{\pi}}\left[x - \frac{1}{3 \times 1!}x^3 + \frac{1}{5 \times 2!}x^5\right.$
$\left. - \frac{1}{7 \times 3!}x^7 + \cdots\right]$

1.17 0.1, -0.01, 0.002, -0.0006,
$2.302\,585$,
$\ln 10 + 0.1(x - 10) - 0.005(x - 10)^2$
$+ 0.000\,333(x - 10)^3$
$- 0.000\,025(x - 10)^4$,
$2.397\,918$, with error estimate
$0.000\,025$

1.18 $1 - 3x + 9x^2 - 27x^3$,
$1 - \frac{1}{2}x^2 + \frac{1}{8}x^4 - \frac{1}{48}x^6$

1.19 (a) $1 + 3x^2 + 9x^4$,
$1 - \frac{1}{8}x^2 + \frac{1}{384}x^4$, (b) e^{-x^2}

1.20 $17 + 29(x - 2) + 16(x - 2)^2 +$
$3(x - 2)^3$

1.21 $2 + \frac{1}{4}x - \frac{1}{64}x^2 + \frac{1}{512}x^3$, $2.049\,375$,
$0.000\,016$

2.1 (a) $\begin{bmatrix} 1 & 2 \\ 4 & 8 \\ 9 & 18 \end{bmatrix}$, (b) $\begin{bmatrix} 1 & 1/2 & 1/3 \\ 1/2 & 1/3 & 1/4 \\ 1/3 & 1/4 & 1/5 \end{bmatrix}$,

(c) $\begin{bmatrix} +1 & -1 & +1 & -1 \\ -1 & +1 & -1 & +1 \\ +1 & -1 & +1 & -1 \\ -1 & +1 & -1 & +1 \end{bmatrix}$

2.2 All except $P + Q$ and $R - S$
exist; others:

$P^T = \begin{bmatrix} 2 & -2 \\ 1 & 0 \end{bmatrix}$, $P + R = \begin{bmatrix} 3 & 2 \\ 1 & 4 \end{bmatrix}$,

$2Q = \begin{bmatrix} -10 & 2 & 4 \\ -6 & 6 & 2 \end{bmatrix}$,

$$2R - P = \begin{bmatrix} 0 & 1 \\ 8 & 8 \end{bmatrix},$$

$$Q + S^T = \begin{bmatrix} -2 & 0 & 2 \\ -3 & 2 & 3 \end{bmatrix}$$

2.3 $\begin{bmatrix} 0 & -1 & 1 \\ 1 & 0 & -1 \\ -1 & 1 & 0 \end{bmatrix}$, (skew);

$\begin{bmatrix} i & -1 & 1-i \\ -1 & 0 & 2+i \\ 1+i & 2-i & 2 \end{bmatrix}$,

$\begin{bmatrix} -i & -1 & 1+i \\ -1 & 0 & 2-i \\ 1-i & 2+i & 2 \end{bmatrix}$, (none);

$\begin{bmatrix} 9 & 8 & 7 \\ 8 & 7 & 6 \\ 7 & 6 & 5 \end{bmatrix}$, (symm & herm);

$\begin{bmatrix} 1 & -i & -1 \\ i & 2 & 3-2i \\ -1 & 3+2i & 0 \end{bmatrix}$,

$\begin{bmatrix} 1 & i & -1 \\ -i & 2 & 3+2i \\ -1 & 3-2i & 0 \end{bmatrix}$, (herm)

2.4 (b) $\begin{bmatrix} 1 & -1 \\ -1 & 3 \end{bmatrix} + \begin{bmatrix} 0 & 3 \\ -3 & 0 \end{bmatrix}$,

$\begin{bmatrix} -1 & 3 \\ 3 & 2 \end{bmatrix} + \begin{bmatrix} 0 & 0 \\ 0 & 0 \end{bmatrix}$

2.5 $\mathrm{diag}(4, 2, -9)$

2.6 (b) Simplest answers are:

(symm) $\begin{bmatrix} 1 & 0 \\ 0 & 0 \end{bmatrix}$, $\begin{bmatrix} 0 & 1 \\ 1 & 0 \end{bmatrix}$, $\begin{bmatrix} 0 & 0 \\ 0 & 1 \end{bmatrix}$;

(diag) $\begin{bmatrix} 1 & 0 \\ 0 & 0 \end{bmatrix}$, $\begin{bmatrix} 0 & 0 \\ 0 & 1 \end{bmatrix}$; (c) 9, 6, 3,

(d) many possibilities, most elegant being I

2.7 $\begin{bmatrix} 1 & 0 & 0 & 0 \\ 0 & 1 & 0 & 0 \\ 0 & 0 & 1 & 0 \end{bmatrix}$

2.8 AB, D^2, AD are not defined; others: $BD = \begin{bmatrix} -7 \\ 10 \end{bmatrix}$,

$CB = \begin{bmatrix} 1 & 4 \\ -1 & 12 \\ -4 & 0 \end{bmatrix}$,

$B^2 = \begin{bmatrix} 17 & -12 \\ -6 & 8 \end{bmatrix}$,

AC is 2×2, CA is 3×3

2.9 Place the given data in matrices A (5×3), B (1×5) and C (3×3). Then find: CA^T, $A^T B^T$, $CA^T B^T$

2.10 (a) All are defined except CD^T:

$$A^T C^T = \begin{bmatrix} -1 & -1 & 2 \\ 6 & 12 & -6 \\ 4 & 10 & -2 \end{bmatrix},$$

$$A^T B = \begin{bmatrix} -5 & 4 \\ 6 & 0 \\ -4 & 8 \end{bmatrix},$$

$$B^T A = \begin{bmatrix} -5 & 6 & -4 \\ 4 & 0 & 8 \end{bmatrix},$$

$$B^T D = \begin{bmatrix} -11 \\ 20 \end{bmatrix},$$

$$C^T A^T B^T D = \begin{bmatrix} 149 \\ 182 \end{bmatrix},$$

(b) many possibilities, e.g.,

$\begin{bmatrix} 1 & -1 \\ -1 & 1 \end{bmatrix} \begin{bmatrix} 1 & 1 \\ 1 & 1 \end{bmatrix}$, (d)

$P_y P_x = -i P_z$ (compared with $+i P_z$), $P_z P_x = i P_y = -P_x P_z$, $P_y P_z = i P_x = -P_z P_y$

2.11 Not necessarily the same

2.12 $\begin{bmatrix} 2 & 3 & 1 \\ 5 & 6 & 4 \\ 8 & 9 & 7 \end{bmatrix}$, $\begin{bmatrix} 7 & 8 & 9 \\ 1 & 2 & 3 \\ 1 & 2 & 3 \end{bmatrix}$

2.13 $\mathrm{diag}(2, 3, 0)$, $\mathrm{diag}(2, 3, 0)$, $\mathrm{diag}(1, 1)$, $\mathrm{diag}(-1, -1)$

2.14 (a) $\begin{bmatrix} a & 0 \\ b & c \end{bmatrix}$, $\begin{bmatrix} a & 0 & 0 \\ b & c & 0 \\ d & e & f \end{bmatrix}$,

(b) $u_{ij} = 0$ when $i > j$, (c) diagonal matrices, (d) not unique

2.15 (a) 1, $\begin{bmatrix} 2 & 1 \\ 5 & 3 \end{bmatrix}$; 0, no inverse; -10,

$\begin{bmatrix} 0.1 & 0.2 \\ 0.3 & -0.4 \end{bmatrix}$; 1, $\begin{bmatrix} i & 2 \\ -1 & i \end{bmatrix}$;

(b) $a = -2, b = 1, c = 1$

2.16 (a) $\begin{bmatrix} 18 & -24 \\ -24 & 36 \end{bmatrix}$, (b) 5, 23,

(c) $\begin{bmatrix} -49 & 65 \\ -130 & 146 \end{bmatrix}$

2.17 $k = \pm 1/\sqrt{3}$, $l = \pm 1/\sqrt{2}$,
$m = \pm 1/\sqrt{6}$

2.18 (a) 5, $\begin{bmatrix} 4 & -2 \\ -2 & 1 \end{bmatrix}$; 2, $\begin{bmatrix} 1 & -i \\ i & 1 \end{bmatrix}$;
(b) YNNYYY

2.20 $2x_1^2 + 2x_1x_2 + x_2^2 + 2x_1x_2$, which
is the same as $x_1^2 + (x_1 + x_2)^2$

2.21 $\begin{bmatrix} 1 & a \\ 0 & 1 \end{bmatrix}$, $\begin{bmatrix} 1+a \\ 1 \end{bmatrix}$

2.22 $\begin{bmatrix} -\frac{1}{2} & \frac{\sqrt{3}}{2} \\ \frac{\sqrt{3}}{2} & \frac{1}{2} \end{bmatrix} \begin{bmatrix} \frac{1}{2} & \frac{\sqrt{3}}{2} \\ \frac{\sqrt{3}}{2} & -\frac{1}{2} \end{bmatrix}$
$= \begin{bmatrix} \frac{1}{2} & -\frac{\sqrt{3}}{2} \\ \frac{\sqrt{3}}{2} & \frac{1}{2} \end{bmatrix}$,
rotation through $60°$

2.23 $\begin{bmatrix} 0 & -1 & 0 \\ 1 & 0 & 0 \\ 0 & 0 & 1 \end{bmatrix} \begin{bmatrix} 1 & 0 & 1 \\ 0 & 1 & 0 \\ 0 & 0 & 1 \end{bmatrix}$
$= \begin{bmatrix} 0 & -1 & 0 \\ 1 & 0 & 1 \\ 0 & 0 & 1 \end{bmatrix}$, $(1,0) \rightarrow (0,2)$,
$(0,1) \rightarrow (-1,1)$

2.24 (a) $\begin{bmatrix} 1 & 3 & -7 \\ 3 & -2 & 0 \\ 0 & -1 & 4 \end{bmatrix} \begin{bmatrix} a \\ b \\ c \end{bmatrix} = \begin{bmatrix} 0 \\ 7 \\ -2 \end{bmatrix}$,
(b) $I_1 = -3$, $I_2 = 2$,
(c) $x = 2$, $y = 1$, $z = 2$

2.25 (a) $x = 3$, $y = -2$, $z = 2$
(b) $x = 1$, $y = -1$, $z = -2$

2.26 $z = \frac{0.01-\beta}{0.02-\alpha}$, $\frac{9}{21} \leqslant z \leqslant \frac{11}{19}$,
$0.428 < z < 0.579$

2.27 $\alpha = 9$

2.28 (a) $x = 2$, $y = 1$, (b) no solution,
(c) $x = -1$, $y = 3$,
(d) $x = 1 + \frac{k}{2}$, $y = k$ (any k)

2.29 $\begin{bmatrix} 3 & 1 \\ 2 & 1 \end{bmatrix}$

2.30 (a) $\begin{bmatrix} -1 & -1 & 1 \\ 2 & 1 & -2 \\ 1 & 0 & -2 \end{bmatrix}$, (b) i.

$\begin{bmatrix} 1 & -1 & 0 \\ -1 & 1 & 1 \\ 0 & 1 & 0 \end{bmatrix}$, ii. no inverse

2.31 $x_1 = x_2 = 0$; $x_1 = \frac{1}{2}k$, $x_2 = k$

2.32 $3Ca + 2H_3PO_4 \rightarrow Ca_3P_2O_8 + 3H_2$

2.33 $y = -31 + 25x$

2.34 $\alpha = 6260$, $\beta = -63.14$ (to 4 sf)

2.35 (a) $\begin{bmatrix} 8 & 0 & 1 \\ 5 & 5 & 0 \end{bmatrix}$, (d) $\begin{bmatrix} 8 & 2 & 1 \\ -1 & 2 & -2 \end{bmatrix}$,
(e) $\begin{bmatrix} 4 & 5 \\ -2 & 2 \\ 3 & 0 \end{bmatrix}$

2.36 (a) £87, £74, (b) 600 of P, 450
of Q and 950 of R

2.37 $\begin{bmatrix} 5 & 2 \\ 2 & 1 \end{bmatrix}$, NO, -2, $\begin{bmatrix} -1 \\ -3 \end{bmatrix}$, NO,
$\begin{bmatrix} -1 & 2 \\ 0 & 5 \end{bmatrix}$

2.38 $\begin{bmatrix} \frac{1}{\sqrt{2}} & \frac{1}{\sqrt{2}} \end{bmatrix}^T$, $\begin{bmatrix} -\frac{1}{\sqrt{2}} & \frac{1}{\sqrt{2}} \end{bmatrix}^T$,
rotation through $45°$, $\begin{bmatrix} -1 & 0 \\ 0 & -1 \end{bmatrix}$

2.39 $\begin{bmatrix} \frac{3}{2} & -\frac{1}{2} \\ -2 & 1 \end{bmatrix}$, $\begin{bmatrix} 9 & -4 \\ 6 & -2 \end{bmatrix}$

2.40 $\begin{bmatrix} -1 & -1 & 1 \\ 1 & 0 & -1 \\ 2 & 1 & -2 \end{bmatrix} \begin{bmatrix} x_1 \\ x_2 \\ x_3 \end{bmatrix} = \mathbf{0}$,
$\mathbf{y} = \begin{bmatrix} 0 & 0 & k \end{bmatrix}^T$, $\mathbf{x} = \begin{bmatrix} k & 0 & k \end{bmatrix}^T$

2.41 $\theta = -1$, $x = -1$, $y = 0$, $z = 1$

2.42 $\begin{bmatrix} 2 & -1 & 0 \\ 2 & 0 & 1 \\ 1 & 1 & 1 \end{bmatrix}$

3.1 31

3.2 (a) ac, adf, (b) Product of
diagonal elements

3.3 (a) 0, (b) $\lambda^n \det A$

3.4 -1, -1, 0

3.5 3, 12

3.6 r, $r^2 \sin \theta$

3.7 $\begin{bmatrix} -1 & -1/2 \\ 2 & 1/2 \end{bmatrix}$

3.8 $\begin{bmatrix} -1 & -1 & 1 \\ 2 & 1 & -2 \\ 1 & 0 & -2 \end{bmatrix}$, $\begin{bmatrix} 1 & -1 & 0 \\ -1 & 1 & 1 \\ 0 & 1 & 0 \end{bmatrix}$

3.9 $\alpha = -1$

3.10 $x = 2$, $y = -1$, $z = 2$; -4

4.1 $\mathbf{j} - \mathbf{k}$, $\mathbf{i}$, $-\mathbf{j}$, $-3\mathbf{i} + 5\mathbf{j} - 2\mathbf{k}$, -3, $-2\mathbf{i}$

4.2 (a) $2\mathbf{i} + \mathbf{j} - 7\mathbf{k}$, (b) $3\mathbf{k}$, $-3\mathbf{k}$, (c) $3\mathbf{k}$, (d) $\mathbf{i} - \mathbf{j} + \mathbf{k}$, $\sqrt{3}$, (e) 3, (f) -3, (g)/(h) $-7\mathbf{i} + 7\mathbf{j} - \mathbf{k}$

4.3 $(6, -3, -6) = 3(2, -1, -2)$, divide the vectors by 3, 3 and 9

4.5 (a) $(1, -1, 1)$, $(3, -7, -1)$, $\mathbf{0}$, (b) $(6, 12, 9)$

4.6 (a) $\frac{1}{2}\sqrt{2}$, sides 1, $\sqrt{2}$, $\sqrt{3}$ (right-angled), (b) $(2, 4, 1)$, $\frac{1}{2}\sqrt{21}$

4.7 1

4.8 (a) 2, (b) $\alpha = -1$

4.9 0

4.10 $\mathbf{r} = \left(\frac{11}{9}, \frac{22}{9}, \frac{22}{9} \right) + \left(-\frac{2}{9}, -\frac{4}{9}, \frac{5}{9} \right)$, these vectors being orthogonal

4.11 (a) $(1, -2, -2)$, (b) $\left(\frac{1}{3}, -\frac{2}{3}, -\frac{2}{3} \right)$, (c) -2

4.12 (a) $(1, 2, 3)$, (b) $\frac{1}{\sqrt{14}}(1, 2, 3)$, (c) $\frac{1}{2}\sqrt{14}$, (d) 7

5.1 (a) $x - 2z = -1$, (b) $x - y - z = 1$, $39.2°$

5.2 (a) $-2x + y + 5z = 17$, (b) $x + y - 3z = 5$, (c) $x + 3y - 4z = -5$

5.3 Y N N Y, $(-2, 5, 4)$

5.4 N Y N

5.5 $(1, 4, -1)$, no intersection, line is in plane

5.6 $\alpha = 5/4$, $(3/2, 3/2, 1)$

5.7 (a) $\mathbf{r} = (1, 2, 2) + t(0, 3, 1)$, (b) $\mathbf{r} = (2, 1, 4) + s(1, 2, 3)$, intersection: $(1, -1, 1)$

5.8 $\mathbf{r} = (1, -2, 0) + t(1, 3, 1)$

5.9 $56.8°$

5.10 $(2, -1, -3)$, $42.9°$

5.11 $x + y - 2z = -3$, $(1, -2, 3)$, $40.20°$

5.12 (a) $(1, 0, 1)$, (b) $(1, -2, 1)$, (c) $60°$

5.13 (a) $(-1, 2, -1)$, (b) $61.87°$, (c) $3x + y - 2z = 1$

6.1 0.504

6.2 (a) 0.08, (b) 0.98

6.3 $5/9$, $5/6$, $1/9$, $1/6$, $1/9$, $4/9$

6.4 (a) $1/2$, $2/3$, $2/7$, $2/27$, (b) 3 to 1 on, 4 to 1 against, (c) 115 to 2 against

6.5 $2/3$, $1/3$

6.6 (a) i. $5/12$, ii. $1/2$, (b) $5/6$, $2/3$, $1/6$, $1/3$

6.7 $3/5$, $6/11$

6.8 0.32, 0.68, 0.5333, 0.4667, 0.8

6.9 (a) $5/9$, (b) $1/2$

6.10 0.07831

6.11 $1/2$, $1/3$

6.12 $\frac{15}{43} = 0.3488$

6.13 (a) 0.295, (b) $\frac{49}{59} = 0.8305$

6.14 $1/6$, $5/36$, $6/36$, no, yes

6.15 (a) $\frac{19}{28}$, (b) $\frac{25}{56}$, (c) $\frac{7}{25}$

6.16 (a) $\frac{5}{18}$, (b) $\frac{4}{9}$, (c) $\frac{1}{4}$

7.1 $P(N = k) = (2k - 1)/36$

7.2 $\lambda = 1/21$

7.3 $P(X = x_k) = 1/4$, $\mu_X = 2.5$,
Var$(X) = 1.25$

7.4 $P(X = 1) = 1/3$,
$P(X = 2) = 4/15$,
$P(X = 3) = 1/5$,
$P(X = 4) = 2/15$,
$P(X = 5) = 1/15$, $E(X) = 7/3$

7.5 $P(X = k) = 1/5$, $P(X \leqslant 2) = 2/5$,
$P(X > 3) = 2/5$, $E(X) = 3$,
median $= 3$

7.6 (a) mode is 6, $E(N) = \frac{161}{36}$,
(b) $E(X) = 13/3$, Var$(X) = 20/9$,
$\sigma_X = 2\sqrt{5}/3$

7.7 $E(X) = 7/2$, Var$(X) = 35/12$

7.8 (a) 4, (b) 2

7.9 (a) $q/(1 + q)$, (b) $1/(1 + q)$

7.11 (a) i. 0.3932, ii. 0.0154,
iii. 0.6554, (b) $\frac{35}{128}$

7.12 (a) $\frac{11}{64} = 0.172$, (b) 0.9943

7.13 (a) i. 0.142, 0.264, ii. £150 000
(assuming only one breakdown
for a car), (b) 0.0176

7.14 (a) 0.135, (b) 0.238

7.15 (a) 0.3543, 0.1329, (b) 0.3566,
0.1333, Binomial

7.16 0.216

7.17 $\left(\frac{2}{3}\right)^{k-1} \frac{1}{3}$, £1.25

7.18 1, $4/3$

7.19 Binomial, 0.3744

7.20 (a) 0.0467, (b) 0.2765, (c) 0.5443

7.21 (a) 0.050, (b) 0.353

7.22 (a) 0.865, (b) 0.990

8.1 $3/4$, 0.2, $2 - \sqrt{2}$

8.2 (a) $\frac{3}{2}$, $\frac{11}{128}$, $\frac{11}{16}$, $\frac{29}{128}$, (b) $[0, 4]$,
$\frac{3}{16}\sqrt{x}$ $(0 \leqslant x \leqslant 4)$

8.3 3, $1 - x^{-3}$, 0.0880, $3/2$, $\sqrt{3}/2$, $\sqrt[3]{2}$

8.4 $\frac{1}{5}(x - 1)$ (x in $[1, 6]$), 0.6, 5.5, 3.5

8.5 Uniform, 15 min, 75 min^2

8.6 0.451, 115.13 days

8.7 0.197

8.8 0.6915, 0.0342, 0.1191, 0, 0.3174

8.9 0.6826, 0.1587

8.10 (a) 0.0668, 0.4514, 0.5328,
0.2112, 8.7564, 8.171, 0.5152,
(b) 9.75, 1.489

8.11 0.1151, 438.8 ml

8.12 1.24%

8.13 $1 - e^{-\lambda x}$, 0.393, 27.73

8.14 (a) 0.117, (b) 0.3104, (c) 7, (d) 3

8.15 (a) 0.8664, (b) 0.842, (c) 0.4649

8.16 (a) 0.3759, (b) 5.846, (c) 0.9332

9.4 (a) $Q_1 = 1$, $Q_2 = 2$, $Q_3 = 3$,
(b) $Q_1 = 6.0$, $Q_2 = 6.6$, $Q_3 = 8.0$

9.5 $[48.3, 62.2, 63.3, 64.6, 67.9]$,
$[61.5, 72.2, 74.5, 76.2, 78.4]$

9.6 (a) $\bar{x} = 6.434$, $s^2 = 33.8$,
$s = 5.81$, (b) 2.45, yes

9.7 Mean is 39.8, λ is 0.025, variance
is 34.98

9.8 (a) 3.3, 3.12, 0.56, (b) 10, $59/6$

9.9 15.87%

9.10 0.1796

9.11 0.0618

9.12 0.0036

9.13 0.9876

9.14 (a) $[1.657, 1.783]$, (b) $[7.9, 8.7]$

9.15 27.23 ± 0.10

9.16 (a) 831, 450, 1323

9.17 40.21, 39, 25.5, 54

9.18 43, 62, 44, 21, 7, 2, 1

9.19 9%

9.20 $[56.36, 57.24]$

9.21 174

Mathematical Methods

1.1 $P = 9$, $Q = 1$, yes

1.2 $\cosh 2x = 1 + 2\sinh^2 x$,
$\sinh(x + y) =$
$\sinh x \cosh y + \cosh x \sinh y$,
$\sinh 3x = 3\sinh x + 4\sinh^3 x$

1.3 (a) $5/4$, (b) $\pm 8/15$

1.4 $\cosh x = \frac{25}{24}$, $\sinh x = -\frac{7}{24}$

1.5 (a) $6\cosh 2x - 5\sinh 3x$,
(b) $4\sinh \frac{x}{4} + C$

1.6 (a) $2\operatorname{sech}^2(2x)$,
(b) $3x^2\cosh(3x) + 2x\sinh(3x)$,
(c) $\frac{2\sinh(2x)}{1+\cosh(2x)}$

1.7 (a)$\frac{1}{4}\sinh 2 - \frac{1}{2}$, (b)
$\ln|\sinh x| + C$, (c) $2\sqrt{\sinh x} + C$

1.8 $2\cosh x \cos x$, $-4\sinh x \sin x$

1.9 $f^{-1}(x) = 1 - \sqrt{x - 4}$ $(x \geqslant 4)$

1.10 (a) $\cosh x \geqslant 1$ for all x,
(b) $x = \ln 3$, $-\ln 7$

1.12 $\cosh^2 x = \frac{1}{2}(1 + \cosh 2x)$

1.13 $3\sin x \cosh 2x + 4\cos x \sinh 2x$

1.14 $\sinh x + \frac{1}{3}\sinh^3 x + C$

2.1 (a) $\frac{\pi}{6}$, $\left(\frac{\pi}{6}, \frac{5\pi}{6}\right)$, (b) 0.2014,
$(0.2014, 2.9402)$

2.3 $0, 30, 60, 90, 60, 0, -60, -90, 0$,
$90, 0, -90, 0$

2.4 (a) i. $\frac{3}{\sqrt{1-9x^2}}$, ii. $\frac{2}{4+x^2}$, (b) i.
$\frac{1}{3}\tan^{-1}\frac{x}{3} + C$, ii. $\sin^{-1}\frac{x}{\sqrt{2}} + C$

2.5 (a) $\frac{2}{1+4x^2}$, (b) $\frac{2x}{\sqrt{1-x^4}}$,
(c) $\frac{x^2}{1+x^2} + 2x\tan^{-1}x$

2.6 $\frac{\pi}{30}$

2.7 (a) $\sinh^{-1}\frac{1}{2} = 0.4812$, (b)
$\cosh^{-1}\frac{10}{3} - \cosh^{-1}\frac{5}{3} = 0.7752$,
(c) $\frac{1}{2}\sinh^{-1}\frac{2}{3} = 0.3126$, (d)
$\frac{1}{3}\cosh^{-1}6 - \frac{1}{3}\cosh^{-1}3 = 0.2384$

2.8 (a) $\sin^{-1}\left(\frac{x-3}{3}\right) + C$,
(b) $\sin^{-1}\left(\frac{x+1}{\sqrt{2}}\right) + C$,
(c) $\sin^{-1}(2x - 1) + C$, (d) $\frac{\pi}{16}$

2.9 (a) $\frac{1}{2}\ln(x^2 + 4) + \frac{1}{2}\tan^{-1}\frac{x}{2} + C$,
(b) $\sin^{-1}x + 2\sqrt{1 - x^2} + C$, (c)
$\frac{1}{8}\ln(4x^2 + 1) - \frac{1}{2}\tan^{-1}2x + C$,
(d) $-\sqrt{9 - x^2} - 3\sin^{-1}\frac{x}{3} + C$

2.10 (a) $\frac{5}{2}\ln(x^2 + 2x + 5) -$
$\tan^{-1}\left(\frac{x+1}{2}\right) + C$,
(b) $-4\sqrt{5 + 4x - x^2} +$
$9\sin^{-1}\left(\frac{x-2}{3}\right) + C$, (c) $\frac{1}{2}\ln(x^2 +$
$2x + 10) - \frac{1}{3}\tan^{-1}\left(\frac{x+1}{3}\right) + C$

2.11 (a) $-\frac{\pi}{4}$, $-\frac{3\pi}{4}$, (b) 0.8761,
-2.2655

2.12 $\frac{\pi}{20}$

2.13 $A = 3$, $B = -5$,
$3\ln(x^2 - 2x + 17) - \frac{5}{4}\tan^{-1}\frac{x-1}{4} + C$

2.14 $\sin^{-1}\frac{x}{2} + 4\sqrt{4 - x^2} + C$

3.1 $-\frac{1}{2}x\cos 2x + \frac{1}{4}\sin 2x + C$

3.2 (a) $\frac{1}{3}x^3\ln x - \frac{1}{9}x^3 + C$,
(b) $\frac{1}{2}(x^2 + 1)\tan^{-1}x - \frac{x}{2} + C$,
(c) $\frac{1}{4}(2x + 5)e^{2x} + C$

3.3 $\frac{1}{25}e^{4x}(4\sin 3x - 3\cos 3x) + C$

3.4 (a) $x\tan^{-1}x - \frac{1}{2}\ln(1 + x^2) + C$,
(b) $\pi^2/32$, (c) $e^6 - e^2$

3.5 $-\frac{1}{2}(x^2 + 1)e^{-x^2} + C$

3.6 $\frac{1}{2}x\sinh(2x) - \frac{1}{4}\cosh(2x) + C$

3.7 $-1/8$

4.1 $y = C - \frac{1}{2}e^{-x^2}$, $y = \frac{3}{2} - \frac{1}{2}e^{-x^2}$

4.2 $z = \frac{1}{3}t^3 + t + 1$

4.3 $y = \tanh x + C$

4.4 $P(t) = 1 + \frac{1}{2}\left[t^2\ln(1 + t) - \frac{1}{2}t^2 + t\right.$
$\left. - \ln(1 + t)\right]$

4.5 (a) $\frac{1}{2}kx(x - 1) + Ux$,
(b) $y = -\cos x - \sin x - \frac{2}{\pi}x + 1$

4.6 $A \exp\left(\frac{1}{3}x^3 + x\right)$

4.7 $x^2 + y^2 = 1$

4.8 $x = 1/\left(1 + Ae^{-at}\right)$

4.9 (a) $\frac{p}{r} = 1 + e\sin(\theta + \theta_0)$, where $p = \frac{mh^2}{\mu}$ and e is related to other constants; θ_0 is the constant of integration.

(b) $\frac{1}{r} = \frac{A}{\omega}\sin(\omega\theta + \epsilon)$, or $A\theta + \epsilon$, or $\frac{A}{\omega}\sinh(\omega\theta + \epsilon)$, depending on whether $\frac{\mu}{mh^2} <, =, > 1$. $A^2 = (2E)/(mh^2)$ and ω is related to $\frac{\mu}{mh^2}$; ϵ is the constant of integration.

4.10 $z = Ae^{-8t} + 4e^{-2t}$

4.11 (a) $u = Ae^{-0.1t} + 10$,
(b) $y = Ae^x - 2\cos x + \sin x$

4.12 $i = 2\left(1 - e^{-80t}\right)$

4.13 (a) $y = Ae^{-2t} + 1 - t$, $y = 1 - t$,
(b) $z = Ae^{5x} - 2e^x$,
$z = 4e^{5x} - 2e^x$

4.14 (a) $x = \frac{1}{3}t + C/t^2$,
(b) $Q = \frac{1}{8}e^{3t} + Ce^{-5t}$

4.15 (a) $y = -\frac{1}{3} + \frac{1}{2}x^3$,
(b) $Q = -\frac{1}{2} + \frac{3}{2}e^{2t}$

4.16 $y = \ln(1 + x^2) + 2$

4.17 $y = -\sqrt{5e^{x^2} - 1}$

4.18 $\frac{2\pi \tan^2 \alpha}{5k} h^{5/2}$

4.19 $x = Ae^{-2t} + \frac{1}{2} + 2e^{3t}$

4.20 $Q = 500$, $Q = 500 - 250e^{-0.002t}$

5.2 x_n: 1.22, 1.362, 1.5282, 1.72102

5.3 0.83789, $x(t) = \sin\left(t^2 + \frac{\pi}{4}\right)$,
$x(0.5) = 0.86007$

5.4 0.34431,
$x(t) = \frac{3}{4}e^{-2t} - \frac{1}{4} + \frac{1}{2}t$,
$x(0.2) = 0.35274$

5.5 0.5772, 0.5659, 0.5632

5.6 0.7436, 0.7459

5.7 0.5621, 0.5623

5.8 1.17162, 1.17158

5.9 (a) 0.75, 0.775, 0.782 794;
0.785 392, (b) as for (a), (c)
0.783 333, 0.785 392

5.10 0.877 524, $-0.000\,059$, 0.877 568,
$-0.000\,015$, ratio 0.254, 0.877 583

5.11 Extrapolated values: 1.5416,
1.5432; correct: 1.5431

5.12 $x(0.7) \simeq 1.232$

5.13 $x(1.2) \simeq 1.3214$

5.14 1.1709, 1.1714

5.15 0.6486, 0.6467

6.3 (a) ellipse, (b) spiral

6.6 $-1/t^2$, $-1/4$, $y + \frac{x}{4} = 2$

6.7 $\frac{dy}{dx} = \frac{2}{3t}$, $A = \frac{96}{5}$,
$L = \frac{1}{27}\left[13^{3/2} - 8\right]$

6.8 $(\sqrt{2}, \pi/4)$, $(2, \pi)$, $(\sqrt{5}, 1.107)$;
$(\sqrt{3}, 1)$, $(5/\sqrt{2}, -5/\sqrt{2})$,
$(-3/2, 3\sqrt{3}/2)$

6.10 centre $(1/2, 1/2)$, radius $1/\sqrt{2}$

6.11 $y = x + \frac{5}{4}$

6.12 $\frac{16}{105}$, $\frac{3}{2}$

6.13 $(0, e^{\pi/2})$

7.1 $x - 2y = C$, straight lines: plane

7.2 $6x^2 - 3y$, $-3x + 10y$, 0; yze^{xyz},
xze^{xyz}, xye^{xyz}; $\frac{x}{x+y} + \ln(x + y)$,
$\frac{x}{x+y}$, 0; $-1/(x + y + z)^2$ (all three)

7.3 $6x^2 + 6y^2 + 2z$, $12xy$, $2x + 2z$;
x/Δ, $2y/\Delta$, $3z/\Delta$
$(\Delta = \left(x^2 + 2y^2 + 3z^2\right)^{1/2})$;
$yz\Delta\cos(xyz) + \frac{x}{\Delta}\sin(xyz)$,
$xz\Delta\cos(xyz) + \frac{y}{\Delta}\sin(xyz)$,
$xy\Delta\cos(xyz)$ $(\Delta = \left(x^2 + y^2\right)^{1/2})$

7.4 ellipses $x^2 + 2y^2 = C$,
$-2x \exp\left(-x^2 - 2y^2\right)$,
$-4y \exp\left(-x^2 - 2y^2\right)$

7.5 $(6x - 2y, -2x + 8y)$, -2.4,
$(2,3)/\sqrt{13}$

7.6 $(2x, 7y, 8z)$, $(6,7,8)$,
$(6,7,8)/\sqrt{149}$

7.7 $2, 3, 3, 8$; $xy^2 e^{xy} + 2ye^{xy}$,
$x^2 y e^{xy} + 2xe^{xy} + 2y$,
$x^2 y e^{xy} + 2xe^{xy} + 2y$, $x^3 e^{xy} + 2x$;
$-xy^2 \sin(xy) + 2y \cos(xy)$,
$-x^2 y \sin(xy) + 2x \cos(xy)$,
$-x^2 y \sin(xy) + 2x \cos(xy)$,
$-x^3 \sin(xy)$

7.8 ∇f points radially outwards,
$4\left(x^2 + y^2\right)^{-2}$

7.9 $\dfrac{x}{\sqrt{x^2+y^2}} f'(r)$, $\dfrac{y}{\sqrt{x^2+y^2}} f'(r)$

7.10 $-2xyt \sin t + x^2 t \cos t + x^2 y$

7.11 $\dfrac{E \cos t}{x^2 + y^2}$,
$-\dfrac{2xE \sin t}{(x^2+y^2)^2} - \dfrac{2yE \sin t}{(x^2+y^2)^2} + \dfrac{E \cos t}{x^2+y^2}$

7.12 (a) $\dfrac{3x-2y}{2x+2y}$, (b) $-2/3$,
(c) $y = 4 - 64x$

7.13 (a) $\dfrac{t}{\sqrt{1+t^2}}$, (b) $\sqrt{\omega^2 + 1}$

7.14 $y(x+1)e^{x+y}$, $x(y+1)e^{x+y}$, 2

7.15 $(yz - 1, xz - 1, xy - 1)$, $-2/3$

7.16 $\left(x/\sqrt{x^2+4y},\, 2/\sqrt{x^2+4y}\right)$,
$-2/15$, $(2,1)/\sqrt{5}$

7.17 $2xe^{-t}$, e^{-t}, $-\left(x^2 + y\right)e^{-t}$,
$4xe^t + e^{-t} - \left(x^2 + y\right)e^{-t}$

7.18 $\left(2xy + e^t \cos x\right)\dfrac{dx}{dt} + x^2 \dfrac{dy}{dt} + e^t \sin x$,
$\pi\left(2xy + e^t \cos x\right)\cos(\pi t) + 2x^2 t + e^t \sin x$, $-e\pi$

8.1 $dy = \dfrac{1}{1+x}\, dx$, -0.0002, 0.1

8.2 0.87673

8.3 $x_{n+1} = \frac{1}{3}\left(2x_n + a/x_n^2\right)$, 2.924018

8.4 -0.5376, -0.6

8.5 $du =$
$(y+z)\, dx + (x+z)\, dy + (y+x)\, dz$,
(a) 0.2, 0.19, (b) 0.6

8.6 1.1%

8.7 $du = (2xy + y^2)\, dx + (x^2 + 2xy)\, dy$,
$\dfrac{dy}{dx} = -(2xy + y^2)/(x^2 + 2xy)$

8.8 $du = (6x^2 - 2xy)\, dx - x^2\, dy$,
$\left(\dfrac{\partial y}{\partial x}\right)_u = 6 - \dfrac{2y}{x}$, $\left(\dfrac{\partial y}{\partial u}\right)_x = -\dfrac{1}{x^2}$,
$y = 2x - \dfrac{u}{x^2}$

8.9 $R\, dT = (v - b)\, dp +$
$\left[\left(p + \frac{a}{v^2}\right) - \frac{2a}{v^3}(v - b)\right]\, dv$,
$-v^3(v - b)/(pv^3 - av + 2ab)$

8.10 $dF = 19600x\sqrt{R^2 - x^2}\, dx$,
$F = \frac{19600}{3}R^3$

8.11 $dR = 4kT^3\, dT$, $4p\%$, 12.4%

8.12 $-y\sin(xy)\, dx - x\sin(xy)\, dy$,
0.016

8.13 9.82

8.14 $y = -\frac{1}{3}x - \frac{1}{3}$

8.15 $A\, dx + B\, dy$, where $A =$
$[2(x + y) + xy\cos(xy) + \sin(xy)]$,
$B = \left[2(x + y) + x^2 \cos(xy)\right]$, $-\dfrac{A}{B}$

9.1 (a) $2/3$, (b) $1/4$, (c) -2

9.2 $-a + b = 3$, $3a + b = 1$, $a = -1/2$,
$b = 5/2$

9.3 $\frac{3}{2}x^{1/2} \to 0$ as $x \to 0+$

9.4 $0, 0, \infty, 0, \infty, 0$

9.5 1, $f(0) = 1$

9.6 $2/3$, ∞

10.1 15

10.2 $2 - 2\sqrt{c - 1}$, 2

10.3 (a) $\pi/2$, (b) $-1/4$

10.4 (a) $-8/5$, (b) $1/2$, (c) 2

10.5 (a) $-\frac{1}{2}e^{-2b} + \frac{1}{2}$, $1/2$, (b) $1/2$

10.6 c, d, c, d, c, c

10.7 (a) $2/3$, (b) $1/4$, (c) $\pi/4$, (d) $\pi/4$

10.8 $-1/\left(4 + e^{2x}\right) + C$

10.9 (a) $\frac{1}{2}(\ln 2)^2$, (b) $\tan^{-1}(e^x) + C$

10.10 (a) $\sqrt{3}/2$, (b) $3/16$, (c) $2e(e-1)$

10.11 $\ln 2$

10.12 $\frac{9}{4}\sin 2\theta + \frac{9}{2}\theta + C =$ $\frac{1}{2}x\sqrt{9-x^2} + \frac{9}{2}\sin^{-1}\frac{x}{3} + C$

10.13 $\frac{1}{4}\sin 2t + \frac{1}{2}t + C$, leading to $\frac{1}{4} + \frac{\pi}{8}$

10.14 (a) $\ln\left|\tan\frac{x}{2}\right| + C$, (b) $\frac{2}{\sqrt{3}}\tan^{-1}\left(\frac{2}{\sqrt{3}}\tan\frac{x}{2} + \frac{1}{\sqrt{3}}\right) + C$

10.15 $2t - \sin 2t + C$, leading to $\frac{\pi}{2} - 1$

10.16 π

10.17 $\pi/2$

10.18 $3/2$

10.19 $\pi/2$

10.20 (a) 3, (b) NO

10.21 $-2\cos\sqrt{x} + C$

10.22 $3\ln\frac{3}{2}$

10.23 $\sqrt{3}$

Index